Maggie Beer's many cookbooks include *Maggie's Harvest*, *Maggie's Kitchen* and *Maggie's Verjuice Cookbook*. As well as overseeing Maggie Beer Products in the Barossa Valley, SA, Maggie appears as a judge on *The Great Australian Bake-Off* and heads up the Maggie Beer Foundation committed to providing a good food life for all.

Professor Ralph Martins is Foundation Chair in Ageing and Alzheimer's Disease at Edith Cowan University, WA, and Professor of Neurobiology at Macquarie University, NSW.

Maggie's Recipe for Life

MAGGIE BEER *with*
PROFESSOR RALPH MARTINS

Photography by **Dragan Radocaj**

A JULIE GIBBS BOOK

for

SIMON & SCHUSTER
AUSTRALIA
A CBS COMPANY

Foreword

— Rosemary Stanton —

No one can give an absolute guarantee that a particular diet or way of eating will ensure long-term good health. Life's too complicated for such certainties. We do know, however, that a healthy diet decreases the risk of problems such as heart disease, type 2 diabetes and many of the most common cancers. The evidence supporting this has grown stronger over the years and now we can add Alzheimer's to the list of conditions where healthy eating may play a role.

Whether we look at heart disease, type 2 diabetes, common cancers or Alzheimer's, the evidence all points in favour of more plant foods, including many kinds and colours of vegetables (including pulses/legumes) as well as fresh fruits, whole grains, nuts and seeds. Researchers now add herbs and spices to that list.

In addition to their proteins, dietary fibre, essential fats, minerals and vitamins, plant foods contain literally thousands of components called 'phytonutrients' ('phyto' means 'plant') which not only have nutritional virtues, but are the compounds that give colour and flavour to foods. Extra virgin olive oil is a good example where its healthy fats put it on a par with many other liquid oils, but the 30 or so natural phytonutrients it contains, give it the health edge over other fats. These compounds are what gives this oil its unique flavour.

More than 50 years' experience as a nutritionist has convinced me that if we gave more thought to flavour, we'd eat a greater variety of freshly prepared foods instead of highly processed products. Foods whose flavour is dominated by a lot of salt, sugar and cheap fats, lead to many health problems.

Healthier foods offer so much more variety of flavour. As a busy mother and grandmother, I am aware that cooking from scratch takes more thought and a bit more time. My solution, where possible, is to share cooking tasks with those we live with. If you're on your own, try to find friends, family or neighbours with whom you can share at least some meals.

Healthy eating is not an all or nothing business. Less meat doesn't mean no meat. It just means giving vegetables and other plant foods more space on the dinner plate. Less butter doesn't mean you can't accommodate a small amount into a healthy diet. Less sugar doesn't mean the end of all sweet treats. It means smaller portions (sharing again) and only occasional indulgences. None of this is too hard – especially when Maggie Beer shares so many examples of wonderfully delicious and healthy meals. Enjoy!

Contents

Recipes

Introduction

—Maggie Beer—

For me, food without flavour, without pleasure in both the cooking and the eating, is unthinkable. Flavour has always driven me and delighted me and been my reason for being. Lusciousness and deliciousness are part of my life and will always be so, but balance, variety and great ingredients are just as important. My love of cooking is something I have always wanted to share. I want to show people how to make beautiful simple food that's accessible and achievable. I believe that cooking and eating this way every day makes your life richer.

This book has come about because I met Professor Ralph Martins back in 2010 when we were both in Canberra for the Australian of the Year Awards – we connected over a love of food. I learned about his work demonstrating that good food, exercise and mental stimulation can have a protective effect against dementia. I was awarded Senior Australian of the Year that year and improving the health and nutrition of older Australians became a passion of mine. As I chatted to Ralph it seemed that in our work we had come to the same conclusions about food from different directions. We decided to write a book together – Ralph explaining the science and my recipes crafting the flavour.

This is not a diet book but rather a book of beautiful, life-enhancing food – it's a way of life. Ralph and I want to share our knowledge with you about which foods to choose to give you the best chance of being in good health now and into your future. These are whole foods in season that are full of flavour and nutrients.

I thought I had a good knowledge of nutritious food yet working with Ralph has taken my knowledge to another level. I've always been driven by balance yet it was something I did naturally without thinking much about it. I've learned that eating well is about making sure we get a variety of foods during a day, a week or over a month. This variety not only keeps us interested by following the seasons with different vegetables, wholefoods and proteins but is known to have real health benefits. We need to eat a wide spectrum of food – lots of greens and brightly coloured vegetables for a good mix of vitamins, fermented foods that are good for our gut, oily fish for omega-3s and omega-6s, plus beef, lamb, poultry or game for essential amino acids, and lots of those nutritional powerhouses, nuts and seeds.

Balance is also about eating in a way that doesn't restrict any food groups. Grains are currently out of fashion but they have great nutritional value and are full of flavour, inexpensive and filling. I love bread and pasta but, although I'm

You'll find my recipes starting on page 68 but I've also sprinkled some quick ideas for lunches and snacks throughout Ralph's discussion of Alzheimer's disease and nutrition in Chapters 1–6. And if you're wondering what belongs in a well-stocked pantry, please see my suggestions on page 277.

I live in the country and am lucky to have lots of space for growing some of my own food. We have a large vegetable garden, a home orchard and some happy chooks. The garden gives me the most enormous pleasure. It's beautiful and relaxing of course, but what I really love are the flavours of my home-grown herbs, vegetables and fruit. Freshly picked food from your garden truly has a taste that is impossible to match.

I understand that not everybody has the space and time for a garden but even growing a few herbs on a balcony is so worthwhile – and it will save you money too. As a starting point for growing herbs in pots, try these six of my favourites – rosemary, lemon thyme, flat-leaf parsley, dill, French tarragon and basil. If space allows, then plant sage, coriander, chervil and mint too!

You can also grow lemon and lime trees in pots, and it's so wonderful to have the fruit to hand whenever you want a squeeze of lemon to finish a dish or a slice of lime for a gin and tonic. Let's bring back the days when every home had a lemon tree in the backyard!

not gluten intolerant, I have found as I age that I'm not as 'tolerant' to it. But nothing will stop me eating bread! I simply choose to eat bread that is special – slowly fermented sourdough, coarse-grain rye or spelt. I will keep my finest Italian egg pasta made with white flour for a dish when only that will do but the rest of the time I'll cook with spelt or wholegrain pasta because I love their flavour and texture too.

I also love the lashings of butter that I still have with bread but I don't have that every day, it's usually my weekend treat when we take time to linger over breakfast. I'll revel in the sweet fat of a pork shoulder cooked in buttermilk but keep it as a recipe to savour for special occasions. Fat has been the 'enemy' for the last 50 years but now the pendulum is swinging back the other way and we know that fats in moderation and good fats, such as my beloved olive oil, are very important for our health.

Speaking of good fats, coconut oil needs a special mention. It is high in saturated fat but it's a healthier kind of saturated fat and there are potential benefits for brain health. Ralph explains the science in detail on pages 40-41. Choosing oils is all about the best quality, the best choice for health, the best flavour for the dish we are cooking, and the temperature we are cooking at. Balance and moderation will always be a consideration as a tablespoon of oil or fat has the same number of kilojoules (calories) regardless of type. My preferred oil is extra virgin olive oil, but for a different flavour at times, I love extra virgin coconut oil too, as I do macadamia oil. The science on coconut oil is still emerging. Ralph tells me that results of studies so far show a lot of promise, but time will show just how much we can benefit from this oil.

Sugar, too, has its place in our diet sometimes. I love the occasional dessert, cake or sweet treat but for me it is just that – occasional – and as such it is special. It must be balanced and luscious and a delight. Perhaps I'm a lucky one as I don't have much of a sweet tooth – though don't leave me close to a perfect pavlova! If you do crave sweetness, you can try cooking with smaller quantities and less processed sugars, or less often.

The denial of any food, whether fat, sugar or gluten, simply leads to a fear of food and an obsessiveness that isn't healthy. My recipe for life is to have a healthy attitude to eating. It's about choosing foods that go together, that are good for us and full of flavour. I am as flawed as the next person when it comes to temptation but this is not a diet and I never feel guilty because when I'm indulgent – and believe me I am at times – I'm indulgent with beautiful food. After all, eating delicious food is one of the great joys in life and everybody needs to indulge once in a while.

I've always been lucky to possess lots of energy but there have been some changes in my life over the last few years that have had a surprising impact. These days I really do have as much energy as I had 20 years ago. I had what I now call the 'advantage' of needing surgery. It took some time to recover from and I naturally lost weight during this period. Afterwards, I found it easy to choose not to have that glass of wine from Monday to Thursday unless we have friends over or go out. Having long been a morning walker, I started going to a gym twice a week for the strength that I need and have found it clears my mind too. Without being on any diet, these changes have made a great difference to my wellbeing.

These improvements coincided with the knowledge I'd been gaining from Ralph about the foods that have more chance of protecting our brains than others. The foods that Ralph told me would do the most good are all foods I love that were already part of my diet – yet the difference is I've stepped back and reassessed the importance of my choices. I now think more deeply about how often or how much I eat of certain foods. I have always been fussy about my food but my fussiness is about the quality of the produce, the freshness, the seasonality – of course these are the very things that ensure our food is rich with nutrients! The challenge is always to think about how to cook each day with the maximum variety of nutrients without sacrificing an ounce of flavour.

I have a very busy life but always make time to cook every night from scratch. As a country cook, growing much of our own food, I am fortunate to have a good pantry, a vegetable garden and a lot of our own produce so dinner during the week could be as simple as a piece of fish, grilled or pan fried with some extra virgin olive oil, and vegetables from the garden. Or we might have a piece of my daughter Saskia's well-brought-up chook with a salad of lots of veggies and greens, or a wholewheat pasta with ricotta and olives. The weekends are when I love to go to town with food that takes more time and has a sense of celebration about it – whether it's just for Colin and myself or to share with family and friends.

Of course, I don't just make food for my family, I have a company that makes food commercially and producing natural food full of flavour has always been at the heart of that business. A member of my family was severely hyperactive as a baby and a wise young local doctor, way ahead of his time, put me in touch with the Feingold Diet. This is a diet of natural food with no preservatives and that framed our food life and my business life too. Commercial food does not have to mean processed food. Food production can be, and is for me, a very different thing.

For the 40 years we've been in business we've made the most of ingredients we have to hand. We make our products from scratch and choose to use fresh cream and free-range eggs for our pates and ice creams. If we need to protect products for shelf life, given the reach of our business, then we'll find a natural way. Ice cream, in particular, needs stabilisers to allow the longer shelf life that the retail trade demands but we use E numbers that are totally natural. Our stocks are made with fresh free-range bones, vegetables and herbs without additives, as are our sauces and jams. To our verjuice and wines, we add sulphur to give stability as is standard practice worldwide. We have always called our local Barossa 'facility' a kitchen and have worked very hard to keep our food natural and Australian. We are farmers ourselves and very proud to have great long-term relationships with our growers. We always begin with the Barossa and South Australia and then look further afield if we need to.

I love thinking about what's for dinner every day and I have never lost my excitement for cooking and learning. I know that good food is part of the reason I'm strong and healthy and able to keep working hard at the age of 72. I want to embrace whatever will help keep me so active as I have so much I want to do in my life and I want to live it to the full in every way. I know that good health at my age can't be taken for granted and I want to do everything I can to sustain both my good health and yours – with equal measures of flavour and pleasure. I hope you will join me in celebrating the joy of food every day.

If I only had a small garden then I'd be growing greens. You get the 'biggest bang for your buck' as they are quick to grow and incredibly nutritious. Try kale, chard, sprouting broccoli; cima di rapa, chicory, rocket and sorrel, and asparagus and artichokes in spring.

With a bit more space for a vegetable garden, the ones I wouldn't want to live without are waxy potatoes, sweet potatoes, pumpkins, carrots, onions, garlic, beetroots and celery. I also love to grow the vegetables of summer and autumn – heritage tomatoes, zucchinis (picked small), eggplants and capsicums. But all of these vegetables are relatively accessible and stand up well to storage and transport so that's why I say greens come first.

Good luck. There are so many things to love about growing food – whatever the size of your garden!

Introduction
—Professor Ralph Martins—

I first became interested in Alzheimer's research when my father-in-law, George, was diagnosed with the disease in his sixties. It was heartbreaking to watch as George transformed from an intellectual giant to someone totally dependent on care in just six short years. It made me determined to fight this devastating disease and thirty-three years later, I am still working towards diagnosing, preventing and effectively treating Alzheimer's.

So far, we know that the brain damage that ends up causing Alzheimer's begins developing in the brain 10–20 years before symptoms start to show, and that having type 2 diabetes, high blood pressure or heart disease increases our chances of getting Alzheimer's. We also know that once symptoms set in, there is no known cure. But the good news is that we have begun to identify the factors that can reduce a person's risk of developing Alzheimer's and some other forms of dementia, and slow its progression. What does this mean? Statistically it means that some people at age 60 for example, who would have developed full-blown dementia by the age of 80 may only have mild forgetfulness at 80, if they adopt and maintain our recommended lifestyle changes, especially a healthy diet.

In 2006 I became involved in the Australian Imaging, Biomarker and Lifestyle (AIBL) study of ageing. This research, along with many other population studies around the globe, is giving us valuable information about the specific nutritional and lifestyle factors associated with avoiding cognitive decline and staying healthy as we age. These include:

- regular aerobic exercise
- plenty of mental stimulation and social activity
- a healthy diet featuring fresh, seasonal fruits and vegetables, fish, dairy foods and healthy fats (such as those in olive oil, nuts and seeds) and whole grains.

Importantly, this book focuses on the dietary changes you can make right now – literally today. In chapters 1–6, I will give you some background on Alzheimer's disease, how it affects the brain and how various nutrients in our food can help prevent or exacerbate these effects. Later on, Maggie Beer provides delicious recipes using fresh, whole foods that will help you obtain the nutrients you need each day to ensure optimum brain health. I also talk a little bit about some of the lifestyle changes you can make, such as increasing the amount of incidental exercise you do, and staying mentally active.

Improving your diet and physical activity levels also has other bonuses, including:

- reducing your risk of developing type 2 diabetes and heart disease
- improving your concentration and focus
- enhancing your mood and energy levels
- improving the quality of your sleep
- building muscle and reducing body fat
- it might even save you money: it's cheaper to prepare your own food rather than relying on takeaways or precooked, processed or packaged food. Plus, you may reduce your expenditure on medications.

I think we all want to live a full and productive life, feeling energetic well into our old age. This is not just wishful thinking – you have the power to give yourself the very best chance of a healthy future. In this book, Maggie and I give you the information you need to make informed food choices, and encourage you to do the exercise and mentally stimulating tasks you need to do. But in the end, it is up to you to write the shopping list, buy the fresh ingredients and prepare the meals. It's up to you to take the time to go for a brisk walk, or jog or join a gym. We can't do that for you. We can only cheer you on, and tell you that we have seen the evidence – you most certainly *can* improve your health and quality of life.

Chapter 1

Dementia in Australia – a growing problem

As a scientist, I often marvel at the enormous advances in medicine that have helped us to live longer, healthier lives. Just 50 years ago, average life expectancy in Australia was 74 for women and 67 for men. It's now almost 85 for women and 81 for men. Other countries report similar improvements.

However, with this increased longevity comes a greater chance of developing what are often considered to be age-related diseases such as arthritis, type 2 diabetes, osteoporosis, heart disease and dementia. Indeed, the risk of developing Alzheimer's or another form of dementia increases dramatically after the age of 65, doubling approximately every five years until by the time you are 85, you have a 40 per cent chance of showing some signs of dementia.

Many people expect that their memory and brain processing speed may slow a little as they age, and this is normal. Alzheimer's on the other hand, involves much more. In its early stages, Alzheimer's disease usually begins with lapses in short-term memory and difficulty finding the right words for everyday objects. Other early symptoms include taking much longer than normal to do familiar tasks and finding them confusing, being unable to follow a simple sequence of instructions, losing interest in usual hobbies and social interactions and having uncharacteristic mood swings.

Unfortunately, given that many more of us are surviving into old age, we can only expect a huge rise in the number of people who develop this condition. According to the Australian Institute of Health and Welfare (AIHW), around 340,000 Australians had dementia in 2015, a number predicted to rise to 400,000 by 2020. Alzheimer's disease accounts for about 70 per cent of these cases. The remaining 30 per cent of cases include vascular dementia, Lewy body disease and frontotemporal dementia.

But it is not only those with dementia who struggle daily with the disease. Nearly one million Australians are involved in caring for family members or friends living with dementia. These family members and friends watch their loved ones deteriorate slowly and feel much loss and grief. In its advanced stages, dementia care often involves many years in a nursing home. This represents a huge economic and social cost to our community.

Risk factors for Alzheimer's and dementia

Most of us know the risk factors for certain well-known diseases. For example, if you smoke you are at high risk of developing lung, throat or mouth cancers; if you are overweight and have insulin resistance, you are at risk of developing type 2 diabetes, and if you have high LDL (bad) cholesterol levels and high blood pressure, you are at risk of developing heart disease. But what many people don't know is that the risk factors for type 2 diabetes and heart disease are also risk factors for Alzheimer's. These include:

- obesity
- insulin resistance
- high blood pressure
- high LDL (bad) and low HDL (good) blood cholesterol levels.

Our brains need a constant and plentiful supply of both glucose and oxygen to function well, and are therefore particularly sensitive to fluctuations in both. Conditions like type 2 diabetes and heart disease are believed to increase the risk of Alzheimer's because they compromise the availability of glucose and oxygen to the brain and cause chronic inflammation (a long-lasting immune response from the body, which causes tissue damage and cell death, and disturbs many metabolic processes).

If you think about the clogged blood vessels and arteries in heart disease, you can understand how the brain might be receiving less oxygen than it needs. And when you consider that obesity and insulin resistance (a precursor to type 2 diabetes, see pages 46–48) interfere with the body's ability to balance blood sugar levels, you can see how this may affect glucose supply to the brain.

Many people think that the fat around the waist and insulin resistance commonly seen in middle age are a normal part of ageing. They are not – they are mostly the consequence of poor diet and lifestyle choices (too much sugar, too many bad fats, smoking, lack of exercise and too much alcohol). We know that insulin resistance can be prevented and treated by lifestyle changes. Indeed, more and more studies are showing that exercising, maintaining a balanced and healthy diet, and watching your weight will help you prevent insulin resistance, and as a result, protect your brain as you get older.

IS IT IN MY GENES?

Some people worry about inheriting a genetic predisposition for dementia. However, even if we carry genes that increase our risk of Alzheimer's, a quality diet and healthy lifestyle can still delay the onset of cognitive decline. So while we can't alter our genes we can certainly change their expression to reduce our risk of Alzheimer's.

Roast olives with extra virgin olive oil and bay leaves, garlic and rosemary

Preheat the oven to 180°C (fan-forced). Toss the olives with finely chopped garlic, bay leaves, extra virgin olive oil, chopped rosemary and a splash of verjuice. Place in a baking dish and bake for 5–10 minutes. Cool slightly before serving.

THE ROLE OF OXIDATIVE STRESS

Back in 1986, my team and I were the first medical researchers to publish the finding that the brains of patients with Alzheimer's disease show higher than normal levels of oxidative stress. Oxidative stress occurs when there are more free radicals than the body can deal with. Normally the body deals with oxidative stress using antioxidants, or antioxidant-like mechanisms to neutralise these damaging chemicals, and restore a balance. The most common free radicals in the body are reactive oxygen species (ROS). ROS damage can change the instructions coded in a strand of DNA, for example. It can make circulating low-density lipoprotein molecules (LDL, often referred to as the bad form of cholesterol) more likely to get trapped in an artery wall. Or it can change a cell's membrane, allowing the wrong chemicals to go in or out. Experts now believe that oxidative stress may start the abnormal clumping of tangles inside neurons (see opposite). This is where antioxidants come in. Antioxidants are chemicals in the body that can neutralise the ROS, thus stopping the ROS from causing oxidative stress. There are hundreds of different chemicals that can act as antioxidants including the vitamins C and E, as well as carotenoids, phenols, flavonoids and many more. When our bodies can't make enough antioxidants (or get them from our diet), we are under oxidative stress, which leads to inflammation. This inflammation, if not resolved, becomes chronic, and you end up with a vicious cycle of oxidative stress increasing inflammation, which increases oxidative stress and so on.

Heritage tomatoes

These are beautiful eaten straight from the plant or from the farmers' market on a summer's day. Leave them on the window sill to ripen. Enjoy just as they are, or slice them thickly and drizzle with extra virgin olive oil, and sprinkle with sea salt flakes, pepper and shredded basil. Leave for an hour before eating.

What happens to the brain in Alzheimer's disease?

Alzheimer's disease develops slowly over several decades. This means that by the time a person shows symptoms, the damage is already quite extensive – many neurons have been lost, and a vast number of the connections between the remaining neurons have also been lost.

Here's what we know about the difference between a normal healthy brain and one with Alzheimer's.

SHRINKAGE

Firstly, all brains shrink to some extent with age, but a brain with Alzheimer's is much smaller than normal because many of the brain cells have died off as the disease has been developing. As the disease progresses, regions of the brain involved in memory shrink at a much greater rate than normal, a change that can be seen on MRI (magnetic resonance imaging).

LOW GLUCOSE UPTAKE

Other brain scans can also show that a brain with Alzheimer's uses less glucose than a normal brain. This is very important, since most of the time, glucose is the brain's only source of energy. (Our brain uses about 25 per cent of the body's glucose, despite being only about 2 per cent of our body's weight.) You might think that this abnormally low usage makes sense given that brain cells are dying off, but low glucose usage is evident even in the earliest stages of Alzheimer's, well before memory loss symptoms start and when cell loss would be minimal, leading many researchers to believe that this may actually be one of the causes of the disease.

FEWER NEURONS

Your brain contains 100 billion neurons and each neuron is linked to many other neurons, sometimes hundreds or thousands of them, via individual connection sites known as synapses. In Alzheimer's disease, synapses are damaged and eventually neurons die off, particularly in the areas of the brain involved in short-term memory processing (e.g. the hippocampus). As the disease progresses, it begins to affect areas in the cerebral cortex responsible for language, reasoning and social behaviour. Eventually, many other areas of the brain are damaged and the Alzheimer's patient loses the ability to recognise family and friends, to speak and to eat – at this stage the patient is completely dependent on carers.

ABETA AND AMYLOID PLAQUES

Abeta is a peptide (small protein) that is produced everywhere in the body but at very high levels in the brain. Abeta is normally broken down in the brain or else transferred to the bloodstream and sent to the liver to be broken down. In Alzheimer's disease, however, the removal of this Abeta doesn't seem to work properly, and the peptide starts to aggregate into four or eight units. These small aggregates have been shown to be toxic: they disrupt the function of synapses between neurons, interfering with brain cell signalling, and they can also cause oxidative stress and damage cell surfaces. These clumps of Abeta eventually aggregate into much larger, relatively inert clumps, known as amyloid plaques. When Dr Alois Alzheimer first described this disease in a post-mortem study, these plaques were the characteristic feature he noted in the brain. These plaques are what we look for using sophisticated technology, allowing diagnosis to be made up to 20 years before the onset of clinical symptoms.

TANGLES

The tau proteins are found mostly inside neurons and help stabilise other proteins that are involved in the transport of substances around the cell. In Alzheimer's disease, these tau filaments are modified abnormally, they also aggregate (in a different manner to Abeta), and disrupt the normal transport of proteins around neurons. When you look at them under the microscope, they look like tangled pieces of string, hence the name 'neurofibrillary tangles' – NFT or tangles for short. In Alzheimer's, the tangles are thought to result from the build-up of Abeta in the brain.

Mixed nuts

Preheat the oven to 180°C (fan-forced). Place a handful of your favourite nuts on a baking tray and warm in the oven for 5–10 minutes, then rub with a tea towel to remove the skins. Eat as is or scatter with sea salt flakes or toasted fennel and coriander seeds.

Diagnosing Alzheimer's

At present, diagnosing Alzheimer's is a fairly slow process, involving questionnaires, cognitive tests, imaging tests and various examinations by a neurologist over several weeks. Clinical studies in recent years have improved diagnostic methods: it is now possible to detect the disease a decade or more before symptoms appear with new diagnostic techniques, however, these diagnostic methods require highly specialised equipment that for the moment is only available in major cities. I am currently working with Macquarie University on a test that uses a hyperspectral camera to detect amyloid deposits in the eye. Early findings suggest that these eye amyloid deposits are detectable well before symptoms appear. Such eye tests would provide a relatively simple, non-invasive way to diagnose Alzheimer's early enough to apply potential preventative therapy as well as lifestyle and dietary changes, to help delay or prevent symptoms from appearing.

Treatments for Alzheimer's

It seems that every month we hear about some potential 'cure' for Alzheimer's disease. Recent examples include salicilate (a rheumatoid arthritis drug), montelukast (a drug which is currently used to treat allergic reactions), bexarotene (a cancer drug claimed to be a 'wonder' drug because it can break down Abeta clumps – though for the moment this has only been shown in worms), candesartan (a drug currently used to treat high blood pressure), FSJ (the codename for a herbal concoction that was found to improve memory in guinea pigs), and a drug that promotes the immune system in the brain (by blocking a protein called EP2). One or more of these discoveries may eventually prove to be useful, but for the moment, it's best to rely on what we know. It's also important to recognise that drugs effective in animal models do not necessarily translate to humans.

We know that if you already have Alzheimer's disease, it can't be reversed with current medical treatments. There are medications that may reduce symptoms for some people for up to 12 months, however they don't prevent the underlying deterioration, so eventually the damage to the brain continues.

The medications that are available can be divided into two groups. The first group includes the cholinergic drugs, and common ones in Australia include donepezil and rivastigmine. Cholinergic drugs boost the levels of the neurotransmitter acetylcholine. Neurotransmitters (as the name suggests) transmit messages between neurons, and acetylcholine is a particularly important neurotransmitter in brain function and memory. Therefore, the cholinergic drugs help brain cells to communicate with each other. The second type of medication consists of a drug called memantine. This drug blocks glutamate, which is another neurotransmitter, yet which is found in abnormally high levels in the brain in people with Alzheimer's. High levels of glutamate can cause too much calcium to move into brain cells, causing damage to the cells. Therefore, blocking glutamate helps to protect brain cells.

SO WHAT CAN WE DO?

From the clinical studies that have helped us detect Alzheimer's at such early pre-symptomatic stages, we have learned that signs of oxidative stress, abnormal metabolism of glucose and fat, and chronic inflammation are already happening at the earliest stages of Alzheimer's disease. These unhealthy changes are all now believed to increase our risk of developing the disease in the first place, as well as to accelerate the development of the disease, once the disease process has started. There is also plenty of evidence that changes in dietary habits can reduce these disease-causing problems. This is what I want to explore in the next section.

Boiled eggs with dukkah

Place a medium saucepan of water over high heat and bring to the boil. Gently place some eggs in the boiling water and cook for 6 minutes. Remove the eggs from the pan, run under cold water and peel. Cut the eggs in half and serve with dukkah (see page 275).

— Chapter 2 —

Eating for longevity and health

When we were young, our bodies healed faster after physical injuries, recovered more quickly after a late night, and we certainly didn't pull a muscle just leaning down to pick something up off the floor! The reality is that as we age, all of our bodily systems require more TLC than we gave them in our youth, and that includes our brains and nervous systems. And the most effective way to provide this TLC is to improve our diet and some key lifestyle factors. This may mean a few minor changes, or a major overhaul in dietary thinking.

Studies of various long-lived populations around the globe have tried to find out which dietary and lifestyle factors influence longevity and healthy ageing. Among the groups studied are people on the islands of Sardinia and Ikaria in the Mediterranean, the islands of Okinawa in Japan, the Nicoya Peninsula in Costa Rica, and from the Seventh Day Adventist community of Loma Linda in California. These populations report exceptionally high proportions of centenarians and seem to have the lowest rates of chronic disease in the world.

Now you might think that genetic differences among these regional populations may be just as important as dietary patterns in keeping these people alive and healthy for so long, but the statistics show that this is not the case. For example, when some of these people adopt a western diet and lifestyle, their health deteriorates and their life expectancy is pretty much the same as that of anyone else on a western diet. That said, it is clear that daily physical activity, a strong sense of being part of a community and living in a healthy environment all play protective roles.

What we have learned from the Mediterranean diet

With all the countries bordering the Mediterranean Sea, with their different cultures, food sources and cuisines, clearly there is no uniform 'Mediterranean diet'. But picture, if you will, an early summer evening at a large dinner table on a Greek island or on an Italian hillside – platters of seafood, salads and vegetable dishes, bean dishes, fresh tomatoes doused in olive oil and herbs, red wine, local cheeses, nuts, maybe some homemade pasta and fresh bread. This is pretty close to what is meant by a Mediterranean diet – a combination of the best aspects of the traditional diets of people from southern Italy, Spain and Greece (in particular the Nuoro province of Sardinia and the Greek island of Ikaria). There is very little red meat, foods high in saturated fat or sugar and rarely, if any, highly processed or packaged foods. (Flour is technically 'processed', since the grain has been milled, so I will use 'highly processed' to refer to the heat-treated, precooked packaged foods many of us are used to.)

Clockwise from top right: Ocean trout, nori sheets, soba (buckwheat) noodles, katsuobushi (bonito flakes), unpasteurised miso, kombu.

The Mediterranean diet, of course, goes beyond just the food itself. Also important is being physically active and enjoying meals with family and friends.

Key components of the Mediterranean diet

- Eating mostly plant-based foods (fruits, vegetables, whole grains, legumes and nuts).
- Eating fish or other seafood at least twice a week and poultry or eggs occasionally too.
- Having a moderate amount of cheese and yoghurt.
- Limiting red meat to no more than a few times a month.
- Using extra virgin olive oil as the main fat, instead of butter, lard or other oils.
- Using herbs and spices rather than salt for flavour.
- Drinking red wine with meals, in moderation.

The Mediterranean diet is rich in antioxidants and low in sugar and salt. It is also low in red meat and processed foods, hence also low in saturated fats and artificial trans-fats (unwanted fats, explained in the section on fats, see page 37). Thanks to the olive oil and seafood, it also provides a good balance of omega fatty acids. You may have heard of the omega-3 and omega-6 fatty acids (also explained in the section on fats, see page 38) – these are essential in our diet. The ratio of omega-6 to omega-3 fatty acids is also very important, and the Mediterranean diet provides a very good ratio. Indeed, there is now a wealth of scientific evidence showing that a Mediterranean-style diet reduces heart disease, cancer, obesity, type 2 diabetes and inflammation. Evidence is also accumulating that it reduces the risk of neurodegenerative conditions such as Alzheimer's and Parkinson's disease.

One study in collaboration with colleagues of mine, Dr Samantha Gardener and Dr Stephanie Rainey-Smith, has even shown that strong adherence to a Mediterranean-style diet can reduce the build-up of amyloid in the brain, one of the neurodegenerative changes that is specific to Alzheimer's. The three-year study found that people who ate less meat and more whole grains had less amyloid plaques, as did people who ate fish twice a week and a variety of vegetables every day.

What we have learned from the Japanese (Okinawan) diet

The southern Japanese Okinawa islands are known to have one of the greatest proportions of centenarians in the world. Compared to the US, Okinawans report less than half the rate of Alzheimer's disease, and a fifth of the rate of heart disease.

The people on these islands lead a simple life, grow many of their own vegetables, their protein is mostly from soy, fish and other seafood, and they eat plenty of whole grains, green and yellow vegetables, a lot of tofu, and kombu (a type of seaweed). Interestingly, they don't eat a lot of rice, and hardly any eggs, dairy or fruit, but their staple is a purple sweet potato, rich in flavonoids, carotenoids, vitamin E and lycopene (these are all antioxidants, described in more detail later).

Baby beets with hazelnuts and vino cotto

Scrub and trim the stems of the baby beets. Place the beets in a large saucepan of cold water and bring to the boil over high heat. Cook the beets for about 40 minutes or until soft. Drain, then remove the skins from the beets.

Preheat the oven to 180°C (fan-forced). Place some hazelnuts on a baking tray and bake for 5 minutes. Pour into a clean tea towel and rub to remove the skins while still warm.

To serve, drizzle the warm beets with vino cotto and hazelnut oil and scatter over coarsely chopped hazelnuts.

Unfortunately, people on these islands who have adopted a western-style diet have a much lower life expectancy, which provides clear evidence that the Okinawans' longevity is not genetic.

In general, the people on these islands have a low risk of atherosclerosis (build up of plaques inside arteries) and stomach cancer, and a very low risk of hormone-dependent cancers, such as breast and prostate cancer. The Okinawans also consume fewer kilojoules (calories) per day than people on a western diet, yet their diet is nutrient-rich, particularly when considering the level of antioxidants and flavonoids. Food isn't enjoyed in a vacuum, though, and the longevity of the Okinawans has also been attributed to their simple but active lifestyle, and the social support of family and friends in these strong communities.

Our healthy eating pyramid

As we saw in the previous chapter, diabetes and heart disease are among the risk factors for Alzheimer's, so foods that are healthy for your body, particularly your heart, will also be healthy for your brain.

Specifically, you can do two things: firstly, include a lot of the foods rich in the nutrients that slow or prevent the onset of Alzheimer's. Secondly, cut out or cut back on calorie-rich, nutrient-poor foods, such as sweets, soft drinks, fast foods, fried chips, many processed snack foods, low-quality white bread and white rice. Maggie has made this change so easy – tempting us with a variety of delicious recipes. There are recipes for every meal of the day, as well as some hearty snacks for special occasions, or for when a piece of fruit or handful of nuts isn't quite what you want. These foods will still give you plenty of energy, but also ensure you are getting foods to provide the vitamins, minerals, antioxidants, dietary fibre, good-quality protein and healthy fats that you need to keep your whole body, and therefore your brain, firing on all cylinders.

Turmeric chicken

Place 1 teaspoon each of honey, soy sauce, ground turmeric and Dijon mustard in a bowl, add 1 tablespoon extra virgin olive oil and mix well. Rub over a large chicken thigh and marinate for 20 minutes at room temperature. Season and cook in a frying pan with a dash of olive oil over low heat for 10–15 minutes, turning occasionally, until cooked.

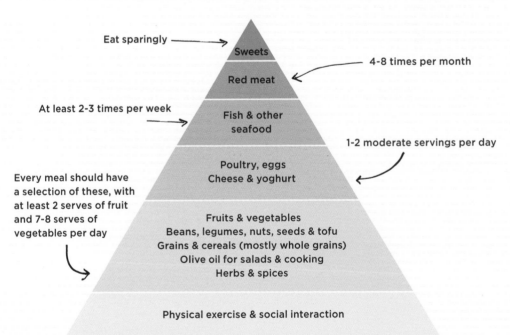

Eat sparingly ⟶ Sweets

Red meat ⟵ 4-8 times per month

At least 2-3 times per week ⟶ Fish & other seafood

1-2 moderate servings per day

Poultry, eggs
Cheese & yoghurt

Every meal should have a selection of these, with at least 2 serves of fruit and 7-8 serves of vegetables per day

Fruits & vegetables
Beans, legumes, nuts, seeds & tofu
Grains & cereals (mostly whole grains)
Olive oil for salads & cooking
Herbs & spices

Physical exercise & social interaction

At least 6 glasses of water is recommended, and red wine (optional) in moderation, with meals

— Chapter 3 —

Micronutrients for a healthy brain

In this chapter I have begun with a relatively standard list of essential vitamins and minerals, as these are needed for everybody's health. I have also included other antioxidants and nutrients that are proving to be excellent for your health. All of the above are known as micronutrients as they are only needed in very small quantities. Contrast this with the term 'macronutrients' which refers to foods we eat in much larger quantities such as protein, carbohydrates, certain fats and fibre – these are discussed in chapter 4.

We all have some level of oxidative stress in our bodies, but when we have chronic conditions such as high blood pressure (hypertension), heart disease and diabetes, this puts our bodies under extra oxidative stress, increasing the requirements for antioxidants and other micronutrients. On top of this, our digestive system may not absorb nutrients very well due to coeliac disease, irritable bowel syndrome, bowel surgery, or medications we might be taking. In such cases, dietary advice may need to be sought from appropriately qualified professionals. Either way, we are likely to benefit from a diet with a high level of the micronutrients, as described here.

In order to take in adequate amounts of these micronutrients, the National Health and Medical Research Council's dietary guidelines recommend we eat *at least* five serves of vegetables and two serves of fruit each day. As we have said earlier, our digestive system doesn't work as well as we get older, and our antioxidant defence system needs more help, too, so we suggest that the vegetable intake should be more like seven to eight serves per day. If this sounds difficult, just imagine putting together one salad with several of the ingredients below (my pick would be baby spinach leaves, sliced pear, grilled zucchini and capsicum slices, tossed in a red wine vinegar and extra virgin olive oil dressing) – it doesn't take much to increase your vegetable and fruit intake!

What is a single serve of a vegetable or fruit? Here are a few examples:

1 medium carrot

1 small cucumber or zucchini

½ medium capsicum or eggplant

½ cup cooked green or orange vegetable such as broccoli, pumpkin or spinach.

1 medium tomato or 1 small beetroot

½ cup sweet corn or sweet potato

1 cup leafy greens, snow peas or other raw salad vegetables

1 medium apple, orange or pear

1 small–medium banana

2 kiwifruit

2 apricots or 2 plums

Vitamins

Vitamins are essential for many chemical reactions in our bodies, and most need to come from what we eat. The exception is vitamin D, which we can make if our skin is exposed to sunlight. For various reasons, however, some of us may not be able to make enough (see below). Some vitamins (such as vitamins A, C and E) mostly act as antioxidants in the body.

VITAMIN A

Vitamin A (retinol) is important for healthy eyes, skin and hair, as well as our immune system. It's found in animal products such as liver, fish, fish oils, full-cream dairy products and egg yolks. Our bodies can also convert plant-based carotenoids to vitamin A. Carotenoids (such as beta-carotene and lycopene) are antioxidants found in yellow, orange and red plants such as carrots, tomatoes, pumpkin, orange sweet potato, mango, papaya and dried apricots, as well as in green leafy vegetables.

VITAMIN C

Vitamin C, also known as ascorbic acid (sodium ascorbate is the supplemental form), is a very important nutrient. We need it to make collagen – a protein needed for wound repair and for the health of your skin, tendons, blood vessels, cartilage and bones. Vitamin C also helps us absorb the type of iron found in eggs and plant foods. It is also a very important antioxidant in the body. It's found in fruits and vegetables, especially citrus fruit, blackcurrants, capsicum, kiwifruit, broccoli, Brussels sprouts, cabbage and cauliflower.

People over 50 need as much as 250 mg per day to counteract the damage caused by conditions such as type 2 diabetes, obesity and heart disease. The most important point to remember about getting your vitamin C from food is that it is a very fragile nutrient – it breaks down easily when exposed to air, light and heat. It's also water soluble, so when you need to cook vegetables, don't boil them as the vitamin C leaches out easily. It's best to steam or stir-fry them for just a short period of time (2–5 minutes), so that they still have a bit of crunch. Cooking your vegetables lightly, it is quite possible to get your daily needs of vitamin C from the vegetable and fruit intakes we have suggested on page 23.

VITAMIN D

Vitamin D is essential for the absorption of calcium, iron, magnesium, phosphorus and zinc. It controls levels of calcium and phosphorus in the blood, and is important for muscle health and immune function. Low levels of vitamin D have been linked to higher risks of multiple sclerosis, diabetes, certain cancers, autoimmune diseases, cognitive decline and heart disease. Vitamin D is also crucial for nervous system development, and many studies suggest it is important in maintaining brain function in old age and preventing Alzheimer's disease.

Vitamin D is found in oily fish and cod liver oil. Small amounts are also found in eggs and mushrooms grown under UV light. The major source of vitamin D is sunlight: UVB rays convert a cholesterol compound in our skin to an inactive form of vitamin D, which is changed to the active form in the liver and kidneys.

In the last few years, it has been claimed that a large percentage of people are deficient in vitamin

MORE IS NOT ALWAYS BETTER

Although it is far better to obtain your nutrients from fresh food, some people may need to take supplements (for example, people with certain food allergies, malabsorption problems or Crohn's disease). However, if you do take supplements, it is possible to ingest a lot more than you need of some vitamins, and it is important to remember that some vitamins can be toxic in large amounts. This is particularly relevant to the vitamins A, D, E and K, as they are fat soluble, which means they can be stored in the fat around your body. For instance, taking in too much

vitamin A can result in dry skin, eczema, dizziness, headache, nausea and loss of hair; and in the long term can cause bone and joint pain, osteoporosis and hip fracture. The other vitamins are water soluble so in general they are usually just excreted. All the same, excess amounts can be detrimental in some cases; for example, vitamin B6 has been linked with nerve damage when taken in large doses, and too much vitamin C can be hazardous. Please only take supplements under the guidance of your doctor or dietary health professional.

D, although this depends on what is regarded as an ideal level. Risk factors include having dark skin, a malabsorption problem, or simply not getting enough sun exposure. Older people are also less efficient at converting the cholesterol compound in the skin, even when they do try to get enough sun. If you think you are in one of the at-risk groups, it's a good idea to get this checked by your doctor.

VITAMIN E

Vitamin E is a fat-soluble vitamin that neutralises ROS (those unstable molecules I talked about on page 15 that can damage cells). It protects vitamin A and certain lipids (particularly polyunsaturated fatty acids) from oxidative damage and often works synergistically with water-soluble vitamin C to carry out its antioxidant functions. Vitamin E exists in eight different forms. Most supplements contain the most potent form, alpha-tocopherol, but foods contain a mixture of all eight variations.

Vitamin E is found in sunflower seeds, almonds, hazelnuts, green vegetables, legumes, peanuts and vegetable oils such as canola and olive oil. Wheatgerm is an excellent source of vitamin E, as well as several minerals, omega-3 fatty acids, B vitamins and phytosterols, so people often add a tablespoon or two of wheatgerm to their breakfast cereal for example. However, wheatgerm goes rancid rapidly, so if you choose to add this to your cereals, soups or casseroles, make sure it is fresh – buy it in small quantities and store it in the fridge.

VITAMIN B6

Vitamin B6 exists in six forms (pyridoxine in supplement form). It is important for brain health as it helps to produce chemicals that transmit messages between brain cells (neurotransmitters) such as serotonin and dopamine. Vitamin B6 is also essential for making haemoglobin (the oxygen carrier in red blood cells), for many reactions involving amino acids (the constituent parts of proteins), and for normal glucose metabolism in the brain.

Vitamin B6 is found in a wide variety of foods, including fish, chickpeas and other legumes, various meats, bananas, avocados, dried fruits and leafy green vegetables. A healthy diet can easily provide enough vitamin B6. It is rare for people to have a serious B6 deficiency, but some people can have chronically low levels, especially if they have inflammatory conditions such as rheumatoid arthritis, Crohn's disease, type 1 diabetes, or occasionally if they are taking oral contraceptives or anticonvulsants. Your doctor can arrange tests if you are concerned that you may have a deficiency.

FOLATE

Folate is essential for the production of our genetic material – DNA. It is especially important when DNA is being produced in abundance, which occurs in pregnancy and during growth. It's also needed for many of the body's chemical reactions and for healthy red blood cells.

A lack of folate in the early weeks of pregnancy can cause birth defects such as neural tube defects, which is why some women take folic acid supplements, or eat foods fortified with folic acid. Folic acid is the synthetic form of folate, and is converted to folate in the body. Of course, the ideal way to get this vitamin is from natural sources, which include leafy green vegetables (the word folate actually comes from the Latin word *folium*, which means leaf), avocados, legumes (such as black-eyed peas, chickpeas and lentils), eggs, beetroot and

COMBINING VITAMINS A, C AND E

These vitamins have been studied as a group because they appear to regenerate one another. That is, if one molecule of vitamin E has been 'used' and so has gone from an active to inactive state, a molecule of vitamin C can restore the vitamin E back to its active state. Therefore, if there is a good intake of all three vitamins, and the body needs some extra vitamin E for some reason, the other two vitamins can effectively help raise the levels of vitamin E by recycling. This may explain why studies of people who take supplements of only one vitamin usually don't find that the vitamin reduces the risk of Alzheimer's, but taking a combination of the vitamins, especially vitamins C and E, sometimes has been found to reduce the risk of Alzheimer's.

asparagus. Note that some folate is lost during cooking, so enjoy your leafy greens raw or lightly steamed.

VITAMIN B12

Vitamin B12 (also known as cobalamin, as it contains cobalt) is essential for making red blood cells and is found only in animal products (red meat, fish, poultry, eggs, milk, cheese and yoghurt). A deficiency in vitamin B12 is known as pernicious anaemia, and if left untreated can lead to neurological damage. Older people are particularly susceptible to pernicious anaemia, due to poorer absorption of vitamin B12, usually due to lower meat and dairy intake or to certain conditions or medications interfering with absorption during digestion. However, if caught early, it is easily treated.

Sufficient quantities of vitamin B12, as well as enough folate and vitamin B6, are needed for various functions in the body. These include the conversion of homocysteine to methionine – and since high homocysteine levels are very unhealthy (see below), this is a vitally important role for vitamin B12 as well as folate and vitamin B6. It also is a good example of how a group of vitamins work together to help the body function, showing that we need to maintain healthy levels of ALL the vitamins, as they tend to work in synergy to keep us healthy.

VITAMIN K

Vitamin K is a fat-soluble vitamin found mainly in green vegetables, herbs and some vegetable oils. This vitamin has long been known to be important in blood coagulation, but recently it's been found to be involved in maintaining our nervous system. It is suspected that people on a western-style diet with very low vegetable intake might suffer from a vitamin K deficiency. Not many studies have been done yet, but it has been shown in a couple of recent studies of elderly people that people not getting enough vitamin K in their diet have poorer cognitive function. Another reason to eat your greens, and remember to eat them with an oil such as olive oil, as this helps you absorb the vitamin K from the greens.

Polyphenols

As we saw in the previous section, some of the vitamins in our foods are antioxidants, which can help to reduce the oxidative stress associated with ageing and chronic conditions such as diabetes and heart disease. There are many other natural chemicals in plant foods with antioxidant properties, including polyphenols. This is an exciting field in dietary research, and new antioxidants are constantly being discovered.

Polyphenols are found in virtually all plant-based foods, including fruits, vegetables, nuts, seeds, extra

FOLATE, B12, B6 AND HOMOCYSTEINE

Amino acids are the building blocks for proteins in the body. We get protein from meat, fish and other foods, digest it down to individual amino acids (like breaking down a wall into individual bricks), then we build new proteins from these amino acids, according to what our body needs. These new proteins, in turn, are used to build or repair pretty much every tissue in the body: muscles, bones, cartilage, skin, hair and nails. Protein is also used to make blood components, hormones and enzymes (proteins used for chemical reactions).

Methionine is one of the nine essential amino acids that we must get from our diet. When our bodies use methionine, homocysteine is often produced. Low levels of homocysteine are fine, but high levels can be toxic. Homocysteine can cause damage to proteins and fats, interfere with

how cells use oxygen, and cause a build-up of free radicals, creating oxidative stress. Our bodies deal with homocysteine in two ways: converting it to cysteine (another useful amino acid), or recycling it back to methionine – and both steps require plenty of folate, vitamin B6 and vitamin B12.

High homocysteine levels can be caused by a genetic condition or by inadequate folate and B12 in our diet. High homocysteine is also linked to smoking, high alcohol intake, diabetes, rheumatoid arthritis, or poor thyroid function. Many studies have shown an association between high levels of homocysteine and an increased risk of heart disease, stroke, osteoporosis, Alzheimer's and other dementias. If your serum homocysteine levels are high, your GP will often check your levels of vitamin B12 and folate, as these are likely to be low.

virgin olive oil, herbs, spices, coffee, tea and red wine. Some of the many different polyphenols include flavonoids, curcuminoids and tannins.

For plants, polyphenols help prevent various diseases, deter insects and some herbivores, protect against UV radiation, and assist with growth. For people, polyphenols are actually responsible for a lot of the taste and smell of food – tannins, for example, give that characteristic bitterness to tea and some wines. Foods with the highest content of polyphenols per gram include spices and herbs, particularly peppermint, star anise (a key ingredient in Chinese five-spice powder) and cloves (which contain 15 per cent polyphenols).

FLAVONOIDS

These are a subset of the polyphenols, and are common in our diet. We have listed the main flavonoids in the table below, to show the variety of foods that contain them, as well as some of their beneficial effects. There are many flavonoids, as can be seen here, and the scientific evidence that many of these have health benefits is increasing. The isoflavones are somewhat controversial (see table). These are found in soy products and are known as phyto-oestrogens because

they can mimic some of the effects of oestrogen in the body. Some studies suggest that phyto-oestrogens can help improve brain function and reduce the risk of obesity, type 2 diabetes and heart disease, and one recent study found that phyto-oestrogens can help reduce Abeta accumulation in the brain, though this needs to be confirmed in clinical studies. On the other hand, phyto-oestrogens have sometimes been shown to disrupt some hormonal functions, so not all effects may be positive. Further research is required to get a better understanding of the clinical significance of phyto-oestrogens in protecting the brain against Alzheimer's.

RESVERATROL

Resveratrol is a polyphenol found in grapes (especially the skin of red varieties), red wine, blueberries, raspberries, and to a lesser extent in peanuts and cocoa. Population studies have shown that moderate consumption of red wine seems to reduce the risk of some age-related conditions such as heart disease, and some people believe resveratrol is partly responsible for this effect. Laboratory studies show resveratrol to be an effective antioxidant and to give some protection against inflammation; there is also laboratory evidence

Flavonoid group	Sources	Benefits
Anthocyanidins	Berry fruits such as blackberries, blueberries, raspberries; cherries, red cabbage, red onions, red wines	Antioxidant and anti-inflammatory effects; protect DNA; help regulate glucose levels, may protect the nervous system and improve eye function
Flavanols	Cocoa and dark chocolate, grapes, blueberries, apples, red wine, lentils, green tea, black tea	Antioxidant effects; improve vascular function and brain function
Flavonols	Green tea, broccoli, onions, apples, peas, beans, coffee, grapes, capers	Antioxidant effects; protect against oxidative stress
Flavones	Parsley, citrus peel, celery, rosemary, English spinach	Protect against inflammation; protect DNA and other cell components from oxidative stress
Flavanones	Citrus fruits, mint, parsley	Strong antioxidants; may also help regulate cholesterol; may help control inflammation
Isoflavones	Soy products, alfalfa, peanuts	Mimic some effects of oestrogen (phyto-oestrogens); may protect blood vessel function, particularly in women

that resveratrol slows the development of some cancers (such as colon cancer and skin cancer), and that it can protect against some aspects of kidney damage. This is encouraging but we must remember that what works in a laboratory doesn't always apply in real life. Other studies have shown it may also help to balance mineral levels in the brain. This is important as zinc, copper and iron are minerals that need to be carefully balanced for normal brain function: the metabolism of these minerals is known to be disturbed in Alzheimer's.

CURCUMIN

This polyphenol is found in turmeric – the bright yellow spice used in Asian and Middle Eastern cuisines. Turmeric is related to ginger, and like ginger, its root structure (rhizome) is the main part used in cooking. (Its leaf is sometimes used in India to wrap food before cooking.) Turmeric has been used in traditional medicine in India for over 2000 years to treat skin complaints such as eczema, certain allergies, and stomach and liver problems.

NUTRITIOUS NATIVE FOODS

We should mention some Australian native plants and fruits that have recently been found to be surprisingly high in vitamin C content, polyphenols and various minerals. For the moment, these are probably not stocked in your average supermarket, but are worth seeking out for their different flavours and healthy properties. Hopefully cultivation and better distribution will make them more readily available soon.

Kakadu plum

The Kakadu plum is the world's richest source of vitamin C, it contains about 50 times more vitamin C per gram of fruit than an orange. Also called the gubinge or billy goat plum, the Kakadu plum is a small, green, rather bitter-tasting fruit about the size of a large olive, which grows across the top end of Northern Australia. This fruit has long been used by Indigenous Australians for its medicinal and antiseptic properties. Apart from vitamin C, it also contains gallic and ellagic acids, giving it anti-inflammatory and anti-cancer properties. Due to its anti-inflammatory properties and high vitamin C content, adding this fruit occasionally to our diet may help protect against Alzheimer's disease. It is often used in jams and baking. See Olive oil Anzacs recipe on page 248 and Chocolate, gubinge and seed slab recipe on page 243.

Saltbush

Saltbush grows in dry or desert country inland. The leaves can be used fresh or blanched with grilled meats or vegetables, and dried saltbush flakes add a lovely salty flavour to roasts or casseroles.

Finger limes

Finger limes are unusual oval-shaped fruits containing small caviar-like capsules bursting with citrus flavour, as well as high levels of vitamin C, folate, dietary fibre and polyphenols. Their colour can range from green to light pink, and their skin looks like that of an avocado.

Quandong

The quandong, also known as a desert or native peach, is a small red fruit about the size of an apricot. It sometimes grows wild as a parasite on other plants in many states. It is also cultivated, tastes tart and tangy, and it is often sold in jams and sauces. It is high in potassium, folate and dietary fibre and is also a good source of vitamin C. See Quail with quondong and snake beans recipe on page 165.

Warrigal greens

Warrigal greens are a form of native spinach, sometimes called New Zealand spinach or Botany Bay greens. They were used by James Cook on voyages to prevent scurvy among his crew. These days they are popular with some chefs as a spinach substitute, but need to be cooked or blanched for at least 15 seconds before eating, to reduce their high levels of oxalates – chemicals that can bind to calcium and cause kidney stones. Nutritionally, warrigal greens are a good source of dietary fibre, vitamins C and K, beta-carotene and also iron and magnesium.

Clockwise from right: Finger limes, dried quandongs, saltbush, lily pillies.

The extensive use and strong belief in this compound's medicinal properties led to many population studies, which found that people who ate a lot of turmeric had a lower incidence of some cancers. This then led to many laboratory-based studies of turmeric and its active ingredient curcumin. Curcumin, or more accurately the group of antioxidants known as the curcuminoids, has now been shown to have antioxidant, anti-inflammatory, anti-cancer and anti-diabetes properties. It has even been shown to reduce the number of amyloid plaques and tau tangles in the brain in animal studies. Based on this information, my team and another research group have trialled curcumin-based tablets in elderly people with mild memory problems. In one study, the treatment was found to slow cognitive deterioration, however long-term clinical trials are needed to conclusively determine whether curcumin can help prevent Alzheimer's.

As you can see, there are plenty of good reasons to increase the amount of turmeric in your diet, though you don't have to limit your intake to curries. You can add it to scrambled eggs, use it in rice dishes, in vegetable soups, or add it to a smoothie. Fresh turmeric is now available in most supermarkets. If you haven't tried it yet, now is your chance – just note that the fresh root can be a bit bitter, so if adding it to a smoothie, experiment with a small amount first. The antioxidants in turmeric are mostly fat soluble, so including some coconut oil or other oil when cooking is necessary to help you to absorb them. Turmeric antioxidants are light- and heat-sensitive, so store the root or powder in a dark container, or in the fridge if possible, and add to dishes as late as possible when cooking to maximise the antioxidant content.

Minerals

The minerals calcium and selenium are known to be crucial for healthy ageing, though iron, zinc, copper, magnesium and manganese are also important. (At all ages, sufficient sodium, potassium, chloride, phosphorus, sulphur, chromium, iodine and molybdenum, for example, are also needed, but these are not specifically relevant to healthy ageing.)

As with vitamins, the most efficient way to take in enough of the required minerals is through a varied diet, as we tend to absorb more when they are supplied in their natural biological form, i.e. already attached to an organic molecule such as a vitamin (for example, the cobalt in vitamin B12) or a protein (for example, the iron in haem, part of haemoglobin in the blood). If you adopt the dietary principles suggested in this book, and have quality protein, a wide selection of fresh vegetables and fruit every day, and some whole grains and dairy products, you are highly unlikely to develop a deficiency in any of these minerals. However, if you have undergone gastrointestinal surgery, have other digestive problems, take iron supplements, or are taking diuretics, you should probably have your mineral levels checked by a health professional, as you may need to increase (or decrease) your intake. As with vitamin supplements, it is possible to take too many mineral supplements, leading to toxicity problems, so please consult a health professional, or reliable internet sites about dosage.

CALCIUM

We hear about calcium all the time with respect to bones and osteoporosis. It is less well known that calcium is also an essential mineral in the brain, as well as in muscles and the digestive system. In fact, it is required

OXALATES

Leafy greens, carrots and parsley contain oxalates, a chemical known to bind to calcium, making it less available in the body. High oxalate levels in the bloodstream have been linked to kidney stones which are made up of calcium oxalate crystals. However, our diet is not the only source of oxalates, and many health problems (chronic dehydration, too much calcium leaching from bones, high meat consumption) have been linked to kidney stones, so this is not a good reason to avoid oxalate-rich foods. On top of this, low serum antioxidant levels have been linked to kidney stone formation, so antioxidant-rich vegetables are actually crucial! All the same, cooking these vegetables lightly will considerably reduce their oxalate content, but as we keep mentioning, don't overcook, as many antioxidants are damaged by heat.

in all cells, and so it is important to keep up calcium levels in our diet. The requirement for people over 50 is from 1000–1300 mg per day, and this can be obtained from dairy products, tinned fish such as sardines with the bones included, almonds, tahini, unhulled sesame seeds and green leafy vegetables such as Asian greens, broccoli and kale. The calcium in spinach and silverbeet is not well absorbed, but these vegetables are excellent sources of other nutrients.

SELENIUM

While we only need trace levels of selenium in our diet, more and more studies are linking low levels of this mineral with cognitive decline and Alzheimer's disease.

Selenium is needed to make various antioxidant proteins (selenoproteins) such as glutathione peroxidase (which protects fats and other molecules against free radical damage) and selenoprotein P (which protects neurons). Recent studies have also shown that higher selenium levels can help reduce the damage caused by Abeta fibrils (the protein clumps specific to Alzheimer's disease that I mentioned on page 17). Selenium deficiency is also linked to type 2 diabetes and heart disease, both of which increase Alzheimer's risk.

The best known sources of selenium include Brazil nuts (you only need a couple a day); seafood such as oysters, mussels, prawns, scallops and fish, wholegrain breads and cereals; meat and poultry; eggs, mushrooms, cashews and sunflower seeds. Vegetables contain variable amounts, depending on the selenium levels in the soil. It is also useful to know that selenium is absorbed better from food sources than from supplements.

IRON

Iron is essential as it is part of haemoglobin – the protein in our red blood cells that transports oxygen all around the body, but it's also in hundreds of other proteins and enzymes that support energy production, help make DNA, and protect against ROS. When you're iron-deficient (anaemia), your body produces fewer red blood cells, and the cells your body does make are smaller and less efficient at delivering oxygen to your tissues and organs, which leads to fatigue, weakness and other symptoms.

Other researchers have already shown that anaemia is linked with an increased risk of cognitive decline leading to Alzheimer's, and more recently, in collaboration with my colleagues Associate Professor Kathryn Goozee and Dr Pratishtha Chatterjee, I have shown that abnormal iron metabolism can even be detected in people with preclinical Alzheimer's (before the dementia symptoms have begun).

Good food sources of iron include red meats such as beef, lamb and kangaroo; oysters, mussels, eggs, lentils and other legumes, nuts, seeds and green vegetables. Variety is key, as there is a small amount of iron in many foods. If you do not eat animal foods, do not assume you are iron-deficient. Vegetarians who have a healthy varied diet have lower iron stores, but are no more likely than meat eaters to be deficient in iron. Keep in mind that the iron in vegetables and other plant sources is absorbed better in the presence of vitamin C. Also, if you are a keen tea drinker, try not to drink your tea with meals, as drinking strong tea with your meal can interfere with iron absorption.

WHAT ABOUT SALT?

Table salt contains sodium which plays a role in maintaining blood pressure, balancing fluids and keeping our nerves and muscles working properly, but the amount we need is very small. Sodium is found naturally in many foods so it's best to keep added salt levels at a minimum.

Unless you have a problem with high blood pressure or hypertension, then adding a pinch of salt to your food now and then probably won't do any harm. The hidden source of salt in most people's diets is processed foods – levels in some processed foods can be astronomical, even in products that are supposed to be sweet, such as cakes and biscuits. The best advice is to avoid processed foods, always taste first, and only add salt occasionally. Maggie's dishes are full of flavour from the many herbs, spices, verjuice, citrus zest, garlic, ginger and other ingredients, and she has carefully considered the amount of salt included in her recipes. So many people add salt to food before tasting it, yet if salt is added at the beginning of the cooking, the flavours are balanced, less salt is used and extra salt should not be needed at the table.

ZINC

Zinc has many important roles in the body, including helping the immune system to function normally, helping cells to grow, wound healing and carbohydrate metabolism. It is also essential for the function of nerve cells, which makes it very important in protecting against cognitive decline.

Foods high in zinc include oysters, red meats, chicken, lentils, chickpeas and other legumes, cheese, nuts, oats, brown rice and green peas.

COPPER

Copper helps the body absorb iron and make red blood cells. It's also important for the health of our immune and nervous systems. Research suggests that copper and zinc play a role in the prevention of heart disease which, as we saw earlier, is a risk factor for Alzheimer's disease.

Foods high in copper include shellfish (especially oysters), organ meats, legumes such as kidney beans, mushrooms, oats, nuts and seeds, buckwheat, wild rice, tofu and tempeh, cocoa and dark chocolate, kale, fresh coconut and sunflower seeds.

MAGNESIUM

Magnesium is important for the heart, muscles and kidneys, and helps regulate levels of calcium, copper, zinc, potassium, vitamin D and other important nutrients in the body. It is also important for memory function and good sleep.

Foods high in magnesium include oats, brown rice, buckwheat, wholegrain cereals, muesli, legumes such as kidney beans, dark leafy greens such as spinach, kale and silverbeet, pumpkin and sunflower seeds, dark chocolate, tahini, Brazil nuts, almonds, cashews, linseeds (flaxseeds) and lentils.

MANGANESE

This trace mineral is important for normal brain and nerve function, and the absorption of calcium for strong bones. It is also an essential component of a protein (superoxide dismutase) that has important antioxidant properties to help prevent inflammation. Manganese is also needed for wound repair and may help prevent osteoporosis.

Foods high in manganese include whole grains, buckwheat, lentils, chickpeas, nuts and seeds, especially pine nuts, hazelnuts, pecans, walnuts and pumpkin seeds.

Vitamins	Function	Common good sources*
Vitamin A (Retinol; beta-carotene and lycopene are precursors)	An essential antioxidant. Needed for vision, also for the immune system, healthy skin and hair, and mucous membranes	Preformed vitamin A is found in liver, egg yolks, cheese, butter, fish and cod liver oil. The beta-carotenes in carrots, tomatoes, red sweet potato, pumpkin, mangoes, red capsicum, rockmelon, fresh herbs such as parsley, and spinach and other green vegetables are converted to vitamin A in the body.
Vitamin B1 (Thiamin)	Needed for many biochemical reactions in the body; deficiency leads to memory problems, peripheral nerve damage and heart problems	Whole grains and cereals such as oats; barley, brown rice; sunflower, sesame and linseeds (flaxseeds); pork; salmon, tuna and trout; Brazil nuts; peanuts; sweet corn, green peas; sweet potato; kidney, lima and pinto beans
Vitamin B2 (Riboflavin)	Needed for many biochemical reactions in the body; deficiency leads to skin rashes, itchy eyes, anaemia and foetal growth defects	Green leafy vegetables, legumes, almonds, dairy products, liver, eggs, whole grains, buckwheat and other cereals
Vitamin B3 (Niacin)	Used in the skin, digestive and nervous systems; needed for DNA repair, maintains healthier cholesterol profile, and reduces atherosclerosis	Fish (tuna, salmon), meat (chicken, beef, venison), liver and kidney, mushrooms, wholegrain products, legumes, buckwheat, peanuts, sunflower seeds, potatoes, peas and avocado
Vitamin B6 (Pyridoxal 5 phosphate = active form, pyridoxine = supplement form)	Needed in muscles, required for certain steps in the metabolism of sugars, fats, selenium, and in the making of haemoglobin and several neurotransmitters	Salmon, tuna; red meats, sunflower seeds, lentils; bananas; prunes and dried apricots; turkey, chicken and pork; chestnuts and whole grains
Folate (previously known as vitamin B9) (Synthetic form is folic acid)	Needed for growth phases, especially for DNA synthesis and repair, and for making red blood cells	Spinach, kale, silverbeet, legumes such as black-eyed peas, beetroot, beans and peas, asparagus, liver, citrus fruits, broccoli and avocado
Vitamin B12	Involved in brain function, the making of red blood cells, DNA synthesis and neurotransmitter synthesis	Meat (especially liver), fish and shellfish, poultry, milk and milk products, eggs. Note that products promoted as vegetarian sources, such as comfrey and spirulina do not contain a form of B12 that can be used by humans.
Vitamin C	An essential antioxidant to prevent build-up of free radicals. Vitamin C is also needed for wound repair, iron absorption, blood vessel, bone and skin health.	All fruits and vegetables, especially capsicums, raw green leafy vegetables, lettuce, citrus fruits, melons, parsley and other fresh herbs, strawberries, broccoli, tomatoes, papaya and Brussels sprouts NOTE: heating/cooking and long exposure to light and air destroy vitamin C.
Vitamin D	Helps your body to absorb calcium. Also thought to aid immune function, and claimed to reduce risk of Alzheimer's disease.	Fat-soluble vitamin found in fatty fish, fish liver oil
Vitamin E (Alpha-tocopherol equivalents)	Protects fats in the body from oxidation, works in synergy with vitamin C, also involved in platelet aggregation, skin health and gene expression	Fat-soluble vitamin with antioxidant properties found in sunflower seeds, almonds, hazelnuts, peanuts, wheatgerm and vegetable oils such as canola and olive oil
Vitamin K	Important for blood coagulation, also for maintaining the nervous system	Green leafy vegetables such as kale, spinach, and silverbeet; parsley, Brussels sprouts and broccoli; eggs and strawberries

*the sources are listed in no particular order

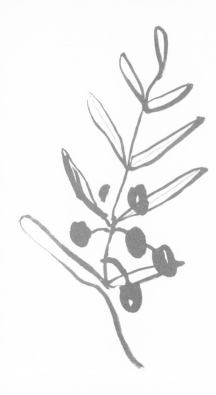

— Chapter 4 —

Macronutrients for a healthy brain

So far, we've looked at the vitamins, minerals and other micronutrients that are particularly important for brain and body health. I now want to look at how eating the right kinds of macronutrients – fats, carbohydrates and protein – can possibly prevent, or at least reduce the inflammation and abnormal sugar and fat metabolism associated with diabetes, heart disease and Alzheimer's.

Fats

Fats, oils and especially cholesterol (known collectively as lipids) in our diet have had a bad reputation for at least sixty years, even though it has long been known that some fats are essential. It has taken medical researchers and health departments nearly fifty years to change the public view from 'all fats are bad', to 'some fats are good for you'. As I have just mentioned, we know that some fats are essential, we also know other fats can be enjoyed in moderation, but there are some fats that we should limit or avoid altogether (See the diagram on page 42).

WHY WE NEED FATS, OILS AND CHOLESTEROL

Fats are important in our diet for many reasons:

- Some fatty acids are called 'essential' because the body can't make them itself (just like vitamins), and so they must be obtained from foods. The essential fatty acids belong to two groups classified as omega-3 and omega-6 fatty acids, both groups are crucial for healthy cell function.

- They are necessary for the absorption of fat-soluble nutrients including vitamins A, D, E and K, and many of the carotenoids.

- We use them to build our cells – our body is made up of many millions of cells, which are small functioning units that do the job of the tissue they are in. For example, there are liver cells which break down toxins, skin cells which provide a barrier from the outside world, and muscle cells which all contract together to help us move. Each of these cells has an outside surface: the cell membrane. Approximately 50 per cent of cell membranes consist of a variety of fats as well as cholesterol (with most of the rest being protein).

- Cholesterol is also needed to make many hormones (see page 36 for more on cholesterol), and the digestive juice bile. Cholesterol is found only in animal foods, but we don't need to eat it to get enough, because the body can easily make it.

TYPES OF FATS

The term 'fats' often refers to just the fatty acids (see below) and these can be broadly divided into three types depending on their chemical structure: saturated, monounsaturated or polyunsaturated.

Saturated fats are usually solid at room temperature. Some have a high smoke point which means they can be heated to relatively high temperatures without breaking down and becoming oxidised (rancid). Food sources rich in saturated fatty acids include butter, coconut oil, copha, cocoa butter, palm kernel oil and the fatty tissue attached to meat.

Monounsaturated fats are usually liquid at room temperature. Vegetable oils such as olive oil and canola oil have high levels, as do avocados, and most nuts (for example almonds, hazelnuts, macadamias, peanuts, pistachios, cashews and pecans).

Polyunsaturated fatty acids (PUFAs) are the major types found in seed oils (such as sunflower, corn and sesame oil) as well as in walnuts and fatty fish such as salmon, herring and sardines. There are many types of polyunsaturated fats, but they can be divided into two main groups, known as the omega-3 fatty acids and the omega-6 fatty acids. (See below for more detail on these important groups.)

Most fats and oils contain all three types of fatty acids, though in different proportions, so are grouped according to the type with the greatest proportion. For example, sesame oil contains around 15 per cent saturated, 38 per cent monounsaturated and 45 per cent polyunsaturated fatty acids, so is usually described as a polyunsaturated oil.

SHORT-, MEDIUM- AND LONG-CHAIN FATTY ACIDS

All fats and oils contain fat molecules called fatty acids, often bundled in groups of three (attached to glycerol) and so are known as triglycerides. The fatty acids are chemically composed of long chains (like a chain of beads) of carbon atoms (with hydrogen attached). Those with more than 12 carbon atoms are known as long-chain fatty acids (LCFA); those with 6–12 carbon atoms are medium-chain fatty acids (MCFA); and those with less than 6 are known as short-chain fatty acids (SCFA).

The vast majority of the fats and oils you eat – whether they are saturated or unsaturated, or come from an animal or a plant – are composed of long-chain triglycerides. These are broken down into individual fatty acids in your gut and then built back into triglycerides and packaged into bundles of fat (lipid) and protein, called lipoproteins (HDL and LDL are two types of lipoproteins). These lipoproteins are then carried by the lymphatic system into the bloodstream, where they eventually distribute their cholesterol, triglycerides and fatty acids to all the tissues of the body.

However, MCFAs (such as those in coconut oil) are treated differently – they are absorbed from our digestion but not packaged into lipoproteins, and instead go straight to the liver. In the liver, they are, for the most part, used to make ketones, an important alternative fuel for the brain. Some synthetic MCFAs, caprylic and capric acids (8 and 10 carbons respectively),

Quick baked sweet potato with bay and rosemary

Preheat the oven to 180°C (fan-forced). Slice any variety of sweet potato and toss on a baking tray with some extra virgin olive oil, bay leaves and fresh rosemary. Season with salt and pepper and roast for 15–20 minutes. Serve either on its own or as an easy side dish.

have been made synthetically into medium-chain triglycerides (MCT) and are useful in rare conditions where a person cannot break down normal fatty acids. MCT oils have also been promoted for athletes, and even for weight loss, however these claims have not been confirmed.

Cholesterol

Until recently, cholesterol was considered to be the most evil of all the fats (that label now goes to trans-fats), but as mentioned above, cholesterol is actually needed for cell membranes, to make the bile acids necessary for our digestion, and for hormone production.

Studies indicate we can make all the cholesterol we need in the liver – however we also get a lot from our diet, specifically from animal products. The liver adjusts its cholesterol production according to how much we eat, but sometimes we just get too much of it, especially if we eat a lot of red meat, deli meats and dairy foods. On top of that, the liver produces more cholesterol when we have a diet high in saturated and trans-fats, and indeed, some people have a genetic make-up that causes them to make too much cholesterol, again mainly when the diet is too high in saturated fats. On the other hand, plant foods do not contain any cholesterol. This applies even to plant foods that contain a high proportion of fats, such as avocados, nuts or seeds.

Whatever the reason for having high cholesterol levels in our blood, it is well established that there is a strong link between the amount of certain forms of cholesterol in our blood and the risk of cardiovascular disease and stroke. As we said above, cholesterol (and other fats apart from MCFAs) are carried in the blood attached to lipoproteins. These include LDL and HDL and levels can be measured using a blood test.

WHAT ARE LDL AND HDL?

Low-density lipoprotein (LDL) actually starts off from the liver as VLDL – very low density lipoprotein, and both VLDL and LDL carry fats in the form of triglycerides and cholesterol from the liver through the bloodstream to be used somewhere in the body. VLDL slowly becomes LDL as it loses its cargo of fats to various tissues for storage or energy production. LDL cholesterol is often referred to as the 'bad' cholesterol, as it can adhere to the insides of arteries and blood vessels, where it can accumulate (atherosclerosis) and cause inflammation, block blood flow and cause clots. These clots interfere with heart function, giving you serious heart problems. The clots can also travel to blood vessels in your brain, causing strokes.

Fortunately, we also have high-density lipoproteins (HDL) in our bloodstream to carry excess cholesterol *back* to the liver to be broken down. A high level of HDL is considered protective against atherosclerosis. If you are over 40, your doctor should regularly check your LDL and HDL levels, and the ratio between the two. Knowing your blood levels of these (or the ratio) is clearly very important.

When you eat a lot of fat (of any kind), and don't use it for energy, it will be packaged up for storage. This usually raises your LDL cholesterol levels, which have been linked to heart disease, high blood pressure, obesity and type 2 diabetes.

Simple brown rice and herbs

Bring 2 cups (500 ml) good-quality stock (chicken or vegetable) to the boil. Stir in 1 cup (200 g) brown rice, then reduce the heat and simmer for 25 minutes or until all the stock has been absorbed. Stir through ⅓ cup of freshly chopped herbs and ½ teaspoon sea salt flakes.

Trans-fats – the worst

Most trans-fatty acids are produced industrially, but there are a few natural trans-fats to be found in butter, meat and cheese. Synthetic trans-fats are vegetable oils that have been chemically treated ('partially hydrogenated') so that they are solid at room temperature. The polyunsaturated fats are converted to a fat known as elaidic acid, an unsaturated fatty acid whose chemical structure puts it into a class known as trans-fats. If the process is continued to full hydrogenation, the fatty acids become saturated. The process of hydrogenation was used by food manufacturers to increase the shelf life of foods such as pies, pastries, cakes and biscuits, as well as to make margarine. Partial hydrogenation became popular because technically, elaidic acid doesn't have to be declared on the food label, and its presence reduces the level of saturated fat (which does have to be labelled). Hydrogenation and then partial hydrogenation (and its trans-fat) extended shelf life, used cheap vegetable oils, and gave a crisp texture to foods that would have had a soggy texture if made with liquid oils. Partially hydrogenated oils were cheaper than animal fats, and the products were heavily promoted. Most of the fast food giants used them for decades.

Trans-fats also occur naturally in meat and dairy products, but these members of the trans-fat class do not appear to have the same deleterious effect as the elaidic acid made from vegetable oils. Elaidic acid turned out to be one of the worst fats since it not only increases LDL (the bad) cholesterol, it also lowers HDL (the good) cholesterol, and had several other undesirable effects on blood fats. This artificial fat has an odd chemical shape compared to other fats, which may interfere with normal fat metabolism.

Studies suggest a link between trans-fat consumption and cognitive problems, brain function and depression. There is also a direct link with Alzheimer's as one study has found that trans-fats increase the production of Abeta. However, the main reason for avoiding trans-fats is the large amount of evidence that its consumption is strongly linked to inflammation, high blood pressure, obesity, cardiovascular disease and an increased risk of type 2 diabetes, all of which increase the risk of Alzheimer's.

Fortunately, trans-fats are being phased out of food production globally. Countries in Europe (Denmark, Norway, Iceland, Switzerland and Austria) already have strict limits on the quantities of trans-fats in foods. In 2015, the US Food and Drug Administration set a three-year limit for the removal of trans-fats from all processed foods. In Australia, food manufacturers now make most of their margarines by a different method with minimal levels of the nasty trans-fat and this reduction in total intake has been used to claim trans-fat doesn't need to be included on food labels, except on products making a positive claim about their content of unsaturated fat.

Sliced fresh peach and fig

When in season, just wash, slice and eat. The quintessential taste of summer.

Speedy banana pancakes

Mash 1 large ripe banana in a bowl, then whisk in 1 free-range egg and 1 tablespoon coconut flour or wholemeal spelt flour. Heat a medium frying pan over low–medium heat, add 1 tablespoon extra virgin coconut oil, then pan fry tablespoons of batter until golden on both sides. Serve with natural probiotic yoghurt.

Omega-3 and omega-6 fatty acids

As mentioned earlier, there are two types of essential polyunsaturated fatty acids that we must get from our diet: the omega-3 and omega-6 fatty acids.

For instance, the omega-6 linoleic acid (LA) is converted to arachidonic acid (AA), a precursor for certain hormones such as prostaglandin and certain neurotransmitters (those chemicals that help transmit messages between brain cells). AA is needed in much larger quantities in cell membranes, especially muscle, brain and liver cells, and helps the immune system function.

Omega-3 fatty acids have been shown to have many health benefits, particularly the long-chain docosahexaenoic acid (DHA) and eicosapentaenoic acid (EPA), which are found in all fish and seafood, such as salmon, mackerel, sardines, tuna and herring. DHA has been shown to be necessary for foetal brain development during pregnancy; it also helps to maintain normal brain function in ageing, to reduce narrowing of arteries, and to reduce inflammation. EPA is needed to make hormone-like chemicals in your body which are important in cardiovascular health, inflammation and the functioning of your immune system. Another omega-3 fat often referred to as DPA (docosapentaenoic acid) is found in grass-fed meats.

Alpha-linolenic acid (ALA) is a plant-based omega-3 found in linseeds (flaxseeds), chia seeds, pumpkin seeds, walnuts, canola, tofu and some vegetables. However, ALA needs to be converted in the body to the longer chain fatty acids DHA then EPA, a process that depends on how much omega-6 we're eating. This is because omega-3s and omega-6s get converted to other necessary fatty acids by the same proteins (enzymes) in the body, so they compete for these enzymes, and if there is too much omega-6 in our diet, we're unlikely to be converting the omega-3s to other fatty acids that we need.

Nutritional anthropologists propose that our ancestors would have consumed roughly the same amount of omega-6 as omega-3 fatty acids (a ratio of 1:1). Levels vary in Australia, yet the ratio may be as high as 8:1, largely because of the amount of vegetable oil we're unknowingly eating in fried takeaway foods; shop-bought mayonnaise, margarines and other salad dressings; restaurant meals and some packaged foods. In some other western countries like the United States, the ratio has been found to range from 14:1 to 25:1.

BALANCING YOUR OMEGA-6S AND OMEGA-3S

The first step to balancing your omega fatty acids is to reduce the amount of omega-6 fats in your diet, and the easiest way to do this is to simply avoid polyunsaturated spreads and oils, fast foods (especially deep-fried ones) and some processed foods. Watch especially for products containing sunflower oil, as 70 per cent of this oil is the omega-6 fatty acid LA. Others to avoid are corn oil and cottonseed oil, due to their high omega-6 fatty acid content. The next step is to increase your intake of omega-3s.

While we can't yet recommend specific daily amounts of the omega-3 fatty acids – EPA, ALA and DHA – we do know that people who have diets high in these fatty acids, especially from fish intake, have a lower risk of heart disease, inflammation and cognitive decline. These health benefits have been seen in people who eat just two or more servings of fish per week, compared to those who rarely or never eat fish. The Mediterranean and Okinawan diets both have

Couscous and herbs

Place 1 cup (200 g) couscous in a medium bowl, pour over 1 cup (250 ml) boiling stock and cover. Leave for 5 minutes, then fluff up with a fork. Season with lots of your favourite herbs, 1 tablespoon extra virgin olive oil, sea salt flakes and pepper. Add lemon or orange zest for extra flavour.

good omega-6 to omega-3 fatty acid ratios, due to the high fish, other seafood, nut and seed consumption and lack of processed foods in the diets. For example, before 1960, the omega-6 to omega-3 ratio was about 1:1 or 2:1 in Greece, and in Japan about 20 years ago the ratio was about 4:1. Unfortunately, the adoption of a western diet has changed these ratios radically.

You could take fish oil supplements, but the processing to make the tablets may affect oil quality, and adding such tablets to an otherwise unhealthy diet is nowhere near as effective as having the fish or oils as part of your diet in the first place.

Linseed oil is particularly rich in omega-3 fatty acids, but is not often recommended, mostly because the oil goes rancid so rapidly it won't be of benefit.

Walnuts and walnut oil are good sources, with a 4:1 ratio of omega-6 to omega-3, but again they need to be fresh. If walnuts (or the oil) taste sour or rancid don't eat them!

Extra virgin olive oil

Olive oil has been studied extensively as part of the Mediterranean diet, and in our opinion it wins top prize for the healthiest fat, especially the cold-pressed extra virgin olive oil (EVOO).

Studies have shown that using EVOO as the main salad and cooking oil in your diet will significantly lower oxidative stress, increase antioxidant enzyme levels, reduce inflammation, reduce blood clotting and reduce the progression of atherosclerosis. In other words, olive oil is good for your heart. Some studies have found that adding just 10 ml of EVOO to a meal can improve levels of blood glucose, LDL cholesterol and/or blood triglyceride compared to corn oil (or no oil at all). There is also evidence that the phenolic compounds in EVOO can protect against osteoporosis. Ideally, you should use EVOO as your only oil for salads, and also as your main cooking oil (alternatively coconut oil), and do not heat it to above 180°C if possible, to maximise antioxidant content and reduce the risk of producing trans-fats.

Quality olive oil is high in antioxidant phenolic compounds (polyphenols), with more than 30 known active components, such as oleocanthal, tyrosol, hydroxytyrosol, caffeic acid and luteolin. These compounds help prevent (bad) LDL from oxidation damage and also raise the levels of (good) HDL cholesterol in your blood. The antioxidant oleocanthal, in particular, may have properties that can prevent and reduce the symptoms of Alzheimer's disease. It helps to reduce brain inflammation and has been shown to remove Abeta in experimental animal models. Oleocanthal also rivals pharmaceutical products such as ibuprofen in reducing levels of certain inflammatory compounds.

WHY QUALITY OLIVE OIL IS SO IMPORTANT

It is important to use only unrefined (cold-pressed extra virgin) olive oil, as around 80 per cent of the healthy phenolic compounds are removed in refining processes. Olive oils that are labelled 'pure olive oil' or 'light olive oil' may well be 100 per cent olive oil, but unless the words 'extra virgin' are included, are likely to have been refined, so read the labels carefully.

Dates and walnuts

Remove the seeds from fresh medjool dates and fill with a toasted walnut half.

Australian olive oils are world-renowned for their high quality and have excellent flavour. They're widely available in supermarkets and it's good to support local industry. Imported olive oils purporting to be pure extra virgin, have recently been found to be diluted with other cheaper oils, but if you must buy them, look for region of origin labels, such as 'DOP' (Denominazione di Origine Protetta) on Italian olive oil, or 'DO' (Denominación de Origen) on Spanish olive oil. When buying bottles of Australian EVOO, you can also usually make sure you are getting oil from the current harvest, as the harvest date or year of manufacture is now declared on most labels. Contrary to popular belief, tests on quality Australian extra virgin olive oil show its smoke point during cooking is almost 210°C.

PROTECTING YOUR OILS

All fats degrade in some way over time, so it's best not to buy them in bulk. Oils high in monounsaturated and polyunsaturated fatty acids are particularly susceptible to oxidation (they develop a rancid, sour taste) so it's important to store them in opaque containers in a cool dark place. In our hot Australian climate, the safest place to store walnuts, pecans, Brazil nuts, sesame seeds and other nuts and seeds, is in the fridge. The same applies to specialty oils such as sesame oil, macadamia oil, linseed oil or any other polyunsaturated oil you only use occasionally. It's best to buy small bottles of these oils and store them in the fridge. Also, make sure you throw them out by the use-by date, since any antioxidants that may have been present in the oils are likely to have been broken down by the use-by date, and the oils will have developed an acidic unpleasant flavour due to rancidity, which indicates they are no longer healthy! Extra virgin olive oil however should not be stored in the fridge as it will solidify and this will spoil the flavour and texture of it when brought back to room temperature.

Hummus and dippers

Grab your favourite vegetables and cut them into bite-sized pieces to enjoy with good-quality shop-bought hummus (look for one made with extra virgin olive oil). Baby cucumbers, radishes, carrots, celery and snow peas all have the perfect crunch factor.

Coconut oil

Coconut products have long been known to contain high levels of saturated fat and for many years we've been advised to avoid saturated fats. However, after extensive investigation and review, I suggest that coconut oil should be regarded more favourably. This is because coconut oil, unlike other fats, is high in lauric acid, a medium-chain fatty acid (MCFA).

MCFAs are unique in that, after digestion, they don't automatically become part of LDL in the bloodstream to be stored as fat, instead they are absorbed and metabolised by the liver where they can be converted to ketones – an alternative energy source for the brain if glucose is low. As we have mentioned before, glucose is the main energy source for the brain, yet glucose transport into the brain (getting across the blood–brain barrier) and then into brain cells, appears to be disturbed quite early on in Alzheimer's. The energy-producing mechanisms that use glucose also show damage very early in the disease process. In contrast, the transport into the brain of ketones doesn't change until a person has quite advanced Alzheimer's. Possibly for this reason, ketones have been found to be beneficial to people who are developing or who already have some level of memory impairment, such as in Alzheimer's disease, as it means there is fuel for this alternative energy-producing system in the brain, and brain cells do use a lot of energy. As well as this, the lauric acid in coconut oil has anti-inflammatory and anti-microbial properties.

Although some studies have shown that coconut oil raises blood cholesterol levels, it appears to raise both HDL and LDL levels, and for the moment the evidence is not clear, especially as most of the studies included coconut oil in diets intending to provide up to 30–75 per cent of total dietary energy from fat – something we would not recommend! Another problem is that the studies that have been done have used different qualities of coconut oil, and a wide variety of different people, which makes it difficult to compare results. It's also been shown that, among saturated fatty acids, lauric acid contributes the least to fat accumulation.

However, extra virgin coconut oil, which we recommend, consists of a lot more than just lauric acid, it also contains antioxidant phenolic compounds (ferulic acid and p-coumaric acid), and the coconut flesh itself is rich in dietary fibre, vitamins and minerals. Therefore, we believe good-quality unrefined coconut oil (extra virgin) has health benefits, and can be included in moderation in a healthy diet. We say 'in moderation' because although extra virgin coconut oil has many healthy properties, it is still just as high in kilojoules (calories) as other oils, and does contain about 24 per cent long-chain saturated fats too (about half that of butter).

Recent studies suggest that coconut may help in the treatment of obesity, abnormal fat metabolism, high LDL levels, insulin resistance and hypertension – all of which are risk factors for heart disease and type 2 diabetes, and therefore for Alzheimer's disease. Extra virgin coconut oil in fact appears to influence the body's fat metabolism in other ways that are beneficial to heart health. There is also evidence that the antioxidants in coconut oil can help reduce the clumping or aggregation of the Abeta peptide, which is the hallmark of Alzheimer's disease. There have been several case reports stating that coconut oil helps the memory and cognition of people who already have Alzheimer's, and my team is undertaking the world's first prevention trial for Alzheimer's disease using CocoMCT, an enriched product of coconut oil. CocoMCT is a refined oil containing no long-chain saturated fats so it has a higher percentage of lauric acid and other MCFAs, yet will have lost most of its phenolic compounds in the refining process, though this can be compensated for by eating other polyphenol-rich foods.

Cooking with coconut oil is highly recommended, as the fats don't get damaged by heating, and the oil lasts a long time on the shelf without going rancid – a major problem with vegetable oils. Coconut products add such a rich flavour to so many traditional dishes from South-East Asian countries in particular, so it is good to know that moderate quantities of this fruit also have beneficial effects. However, it should be remembered that coconut products are all energy dense (the kilojoules are still there), so you need to eat them in moderation or in balance with your overall calorie intake. The idea is not to add more fat to your diet, but to replace unhealthy fats with what we think are much more beneficial fats, and we recommend a majority being extra virgin olive oil, making sure you get your omega-3 fatty acids from a good intake of fish, nuts and seeds, with perhaps a maximum of 20 per cent of your total fat intake being extra virgin coconut oil.

Chilled pea and buttermilk soup

Chop 1 brown onion and gently fry in a little olive oil until transparent. Place the onion in a blender with 1 cup (250 ml) chicken stock, 2 cups (240 g) frozen peas, 1 cup (250 ml) buttermilk, sea salt flakes and pepper. Blend until smooth, then enjoy cool.

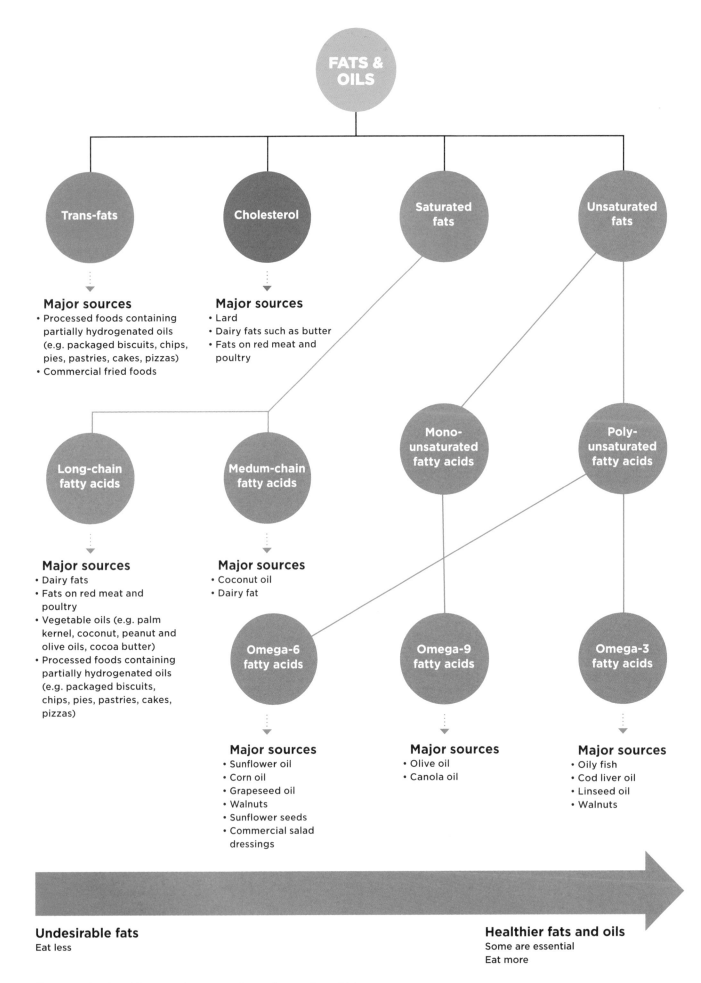

FATS & OILS

Trans-fats

Major sources
- Processed foods containing partially hydrogenated oils (e.g. packaged biscuits, chips, pies, pastries, cakes, pizzas)
- Commercial fried foods

Cholesterol

Major sources
- Lard
- Dairy fats such as butter
- Fats on red meat and poultry

Saturated fats

Unsaturated fats

Long-chain fatty acids

Major sources
- Dairy fats
- Fats on red meat and poultry
- Vegetable oils (e.g. palm kernel, coconut, peanut and olive oils, cocoa butter)
- Processed foods containing partially hydrogenated oils (e.g. packaged biscuits, chips, pies, pastries, cakes, pizzas)

Medum-chain fatty acids

Major sources
- Coconut oil
- Dairy fat

Mono-unsaturated fatty acids

Poly-unsaturated fatty acids

Omega-6 fatty acids

Major sources
- Sunflower oil
- Corn oil
- Grapeseed oil
- Walnuts
- Sunflower seeds
- Commercial salad dressings

Omega-9 fatty acids

Major sources
- Olive oil
- Canola oil

Omega-3 fatty acids

Major sources
- Oily fish
- Cod liver oil
- Linseed oil
- Walnuts

Undesirable fats
Eat less

Healthier fats and oils
Some are essential
Eat more

Note: some foods and fats are major sources of more than one type of fat, for example dairy fats are major sources of saturated fats as well as cholesterol.

A note about butter and margarine

Milk fat contains around 400 different fatty acids, making it the most complex of all the natural fats. The proportion of various fatty acids will depend on what the cows eat, though generally, butter is around 60 per cent saturated fatty acids, 35 per cent monounsaturated fatty acids and 2 per cent each polyunsaturated and natural trans-fatty acids. For the moment, studies suggest that this natural form of trans-fatty acid doesn't appear to be harmful, but it is usually ingested in small amounts, unlike the intake from fatty foods cooked in partially hydrogenated vegetable oils.

In Australia, butter is usually sourced locally or from New Zealand, where cows feed mostly on grass. This is why our butter is a brighter yellow than that available in many overseas countries (the yellow colour is due to high levels of beta-carotene). It also has higher levels of vitamin A and K.

You can safely use small amounts of butter as a spread or for cooking. However, unlike coconut oil, the fats in butter are more susceptible to being oxidised, and becoming rancid. The outside surface of butter will go a darker yellow due to exposure to air, while the inner portions remain a light yellow for much longer. If using butter, it's best to avoid the darker yellow parts of the butter, not only will you avoid the oxidised fats, the flavour will be fresher.

Modern dairy spreads often contain a proportion of vegetable oils (such as canola and olive oil) to make them easy to spread. These mixes reduce both cholesterol and saturated fat content but the energy content (kilojoules/calories) is very similar, unless water is also added to the mix. These spreadable butters may also contain antioxidants, to preserve the appearance and flavour. It is a good idea to read the list of ingredients in such butter products – choose products where the butter has been blended with oil rather than with margarine. Do not confuse spreadable butters with margarines, which are imitation butter spreads. Margarines and vegetable oil 'spreads' once contained refined and partially hydrogenated oils, which meant they were full of unhealthy trans-fats. Since food regulations in many countries (including Australia) now ban or restrict levels of trans-fats, these spreads are not as unhealthy. However, the process of making margarine typically requires refined vegetable oil, skim milk, water, maltodextrin (a synthetic starch), emulsifiers, added vitamins A and D (to make up for what is missing since it's not butter) and yellow food dyes. The ingredient list on the packet is often unclear and incomplete, making it difficult to understand what you are eating, so we don't recommend them. You also need to remember the margarine won't contain the polyphenol antioxidants of olive oil for example, even if made using a large proportion of olive oil, due to the processing required.

Toasted sourdough with 'Nicoise'

Chargrill 2 slices of sourdough. Drain a 95 g tin of tuna and combine in a bowl with 8 chopped pitted olives, ½ red onion (diced), 1 teaspoon chopped basil and 1 tablespoon natural probiotic yoghurt. Mix well, then pile on the toast. Finish with a squeeze of lemon juice.

Carbohydrates

Carbohydrates are in most of the foods we eat. When we talk about carbohydrates ('carbs'), many people think we are only referring to foods like bread, pasta, rice and biscuits. But carbs are found in vegetables, fruit, grains, nuts, seeds and even milk. The only foods that don't contain carbs are animal foods like meat, poultry, fish and eggs.

There are many forms of carbohydrates, ranging from the smallest units of carbohydrates such as glucose and fructose to the complex carbohydrates in starch and fibre. Carbohydrates are an important source of energy, providing glucose, the major source of energy for all cells, including those in the brain.

SIMPLE SUGARS

The simplest sugars include the single unit sugars (or monosaccharides) such as glucose, fructose and galactose. The brain is especially dependent on glucose, and uses about 25 per cent of the body's glucose, despite being only about 2 per cent of a person's body weight. Both fructose and glucose can be found in fruits. Sucrose, or cane sugar, the sugar we use most often in cooking, is a disaccharide, made up of glucose joined to fructose. It is rapidly broken down in our digestion to the individual units, which is why eating foods high in sugar can give us a high blood glucose level shortly after eating. Another disaccharide is lactose, made up of glucose joined to galactose. (By the way, lactose-free milk is not sugar-free, it is made by breaking the chemical bond between the glucose and galactose, so it still has the sweet flavour and the same number of kilojoules/calories as standard milk.)

COMPLEX CARBOHYDRATES AND STARCH

These are also known as polysaccharides or complex sugars, such as starch and cellulose. They are found in fruits and vegetables, nuts, seeds, legumes (beans, peas and lentils), wholegrain cereals (oats, brown rice, quinoa, buckwheat) and wholegrain flour. Because these are long chains of sugar molecules joined together, most of them take longer to break down than simple carbs, so they give us sustained energy. However, and this is very important, in foods made from refined or highly processed grains which have had the outer husk and germ removed (the bits containing the fibre and most of the protein, vitamins and minerals), the starches can be digested quickly, and so they behave more like simple sugars. We are referring here to white bread made with rapid dough risers, and also to most biscuits and cakes. This raises blood glucose much more quickly, and therefore stresses the body's glucose/insulin regulation system almost as much as sugar. On the other hand, in breads (including white bread) made with long slow fermentation, as occurs with sourdoughs, the starch forms a different structure, and is digested more slowly. Interestingly, pasta cooked *al dente* (and especially reheated pasta) is also harder to digest, and causes less of a blood glucose rise than highly processed starches.

Dietary fibre

Most dietary fibres are carbohydrates and while you can't digest them, you do need them to keep your digestive system healthy. There are three different classes of dietary fibre: insoluble, soluble and resistant starch.

Refreshing tuna bites

Drain a 95 g tin of tuna, place in a bowl with ½ diced avocado, 2 tablespoons thick natural probiotic yoghurt, a squeeze of lemon, sea salt flakes and pepper and mix until combined. Fill lettuce leaves or seeded cucumber halves and finish with slices of radish.

Insoluble fibres slow down digestion so you feel fuller for longer, which not only gives the intestines more time to absorb all the nutrients, but also helps stabilise blood glucose levels. Once these types of dietary fibre reach the large intestine, some are broken down by 'good' bacteria for food, which allows these good bacteria to multiply (see the information below on Prebiotics and Probiotics). Insoluble fibre is found in fruits and vegetables (especially the skins), wholegrain cereals, nuts and seeds. It provides bulk for your stools and some forms help to feed the friendly bacteria in the large intestine (colon).

Soluble fibre absorbs water, which not only helps you feel full, but also helps soften the contents of the colon – both of which are important for healthy bowel movements. Most importantly, when friendly bacteria in the bowel break down soluble fibres, they produce some short-chain fatty acids (SCFA) which provide energy for the cells lining the colon, keeping them healthy and more able to resist harmful bacteria.

PREBIOTICS AND PROBIOTICS

Probiotics are the 'friendly' bacteria and yeast micro-organisms that are good for you, as you need them in your digestive system. You can obtain them from certain foods like natural yoghurt and fresh sauerkraut. After being on antibiotics, which can kill off many of the friendly bacteria as well as the ones making you sick, you might be encouraged to take probiotics in supplement form, to help your digestive system get back to normal. In addition to assisting with bowel health, probiotic bacteria aid in the digestion and absorption of calcium and other minerals, influence immune function, convert starch into SCFAs, and also produce chemicals that influence the brain.

Prebiotics are the foods (such as some of the dietary fibre mentioned above) that pass undigested through the gut to feed the good (probiotic) bacteria in the colon. Prebiotics usually refer to two types of naturally obtained indigestible starches: galacto-oligosaccharides (GOS) and inulin. However, the term is also applied to dietary fibres such as pectin, beta-glucans and resistant starch, among others. Rich sources of prebiotics include members of the onion family (onions, leeks and garlic), Jerusalem artichokes, asparagus, whole wheat, barley and oats. Other sources include bananas, cocoa, legumes, almonds, linseed, seaweed, avocados, peas and apples. Raw foods contain about twice as much as cooked foods.

A diet rich in prebiotics has been linked with many health benefits. In fact, the more diverse our sources of dietary fibre, the more diverse the probiotic bacteria, which is good for our health. A lack of prebiotics, which is not unusual in a western diet, has been linked to inflammation, irritable bowel syndrome, obesity, type 2 diabetes, and even neurological problems like mood disorders, autism spectrum disorders and Alzheimer's. Also, a diet with too much fat disturbs the probiotic bacteria, as do the breakdown products from a diet that is high in red meat.

Roasted eggplant with miso

Preheat the oven to 200°C (fan-forced). Cut a large eggplant lengthways down the centre, score the flesh and place skin-side down on a baking tray. Cook for 30 minutes. Turn the oven to grill. Brush the eggplant generously with a mix of 2 tablespoons unpasteurised white (shiro) miso, 1 tablespoon tahini and 1 tablespoon hot water, and grill until golden.

Resistant starch

Resistant starch acts in a similar way to fibre. It is found in many unprocessed cereals and grains, cold cooked potato and rice, lentils, barely ripe bananas and in pasta cooked to the *al dente* stage (as well as cold or reheated pasta). This type of starch is not digested in the small intestine, yet when it reaches the colon (large bowel), it can feed good bacteria and improve bowel health.

AIM FOR MORE THAN CARBOHYDRATES

Whole grains, legumes and starchy root vegetables such as sweet potato are rich sources of carbohydrates, but they contain much more than carbs. They have 5–20 per cent protein, some healthy fatty acids, many vitamins and minerals, lots of soluble and insoluble fibre, and a variety of antioxidants. But as I mentioned earlier (and it is so important it bears repeating), in the case of grains, they must be whole, not refined.

Refined grains have had the outside bran and germ removed, which is where most of the minerals and a large proportion of the vitamins are found. Whole grains contain phenolic compounds, which have strong antioxidant properties that can help protect against cardiovascular disease and type 2 diabetes. Whole grains also contain many of the B-vitamins, and more dietary fibre, which as we saw above is important for overall digestive health, allowing us to make the most of the nutrients in our food. So aim for wholegrain cereals and breads, brown rice instead of white rice and use wholegrain couscous, quinoa, millet or buckwheat. Choose lentils, chickpeas and a variety of dried beans as they provide a rich source of nutrients and antioxidants along with their carbohydrate and protein; and with starchy vegetables like potatoes or sweet potatoes, roast them unpeeled rather than fry them as chips.

Oven-roasted chickpeas

Preheat the oven to 200°C (fan-forced). Drain and rinse 1 x 400 g tin organic chickpeas, then pat dry. Mix with 2 tablespoons extra virgin olive oil, 1 tablespoon rosemary leaves, 1 thinly sliced garlic clove, sea salt flakes and pepper. Place on a baking tray lined with baking paper and bake for 20 minutes or until golden and lightly crisp.

Sugar and obesity

When the *Australian Dietary Guidelines* were introduced over 35 years ago, they suggested limiting fats and also avoiding too much sugar. The processed food industry saw a great marketing opportunity with a range of products they could make 'low fat'. Unfortunately, when the fats were reduced, these foods just didn't taste as good (and we didn't feel as full), so manufacturers replaced fats with sugars.

When you hear the term 'sugar', you most likely think of the cane sugar (sucrose) you use in cooking, or to sweeten beverages. However, sugar comes in many forms: brown sugar, raw sugar, molasses, honey, treacle, maple syrup, golden syrup, rice malt syrup, maltose, corn syrup – it's a long list – and all of them are made up of different amounts of glucose and fructose.

When you eat carbohydrates (whether simple sugars or complex starches), the carbs are mostly broken down to glucose in your intestines and absorbed into your bloodstream, so the more glucose you absorb from your intestines, the higher your blood glucose will be.

As soon as glucose hits your bloodstream, the hormone insulin is released from special cells in the pancreas. Insulin's job is to encourage our tissues (especially our muscles and liver) to take up the glucose in our bloodstream and use it for energy, or store it as glycogen. Most of this is stored in muscles, ready for exercise. Those who exercise strenuously or for long periods use this up. Smaller amounts of glycogen are also stored in the liver, ready to replenish any drop in the blood glucose level. However, our bodies can only store enough glycogen for one active day. So once we have filled up our glycogen stores, any remaining glucose is distributed around the body and stored as fat.

In 2013, the National Health and Medical Research Council estimated that by 2025, 83 per cent of Australian men and 75 per cent of women aged 20 years and over would be overweight or obese. Such weight increases would significantly affect disease burden and health care costs, mostly due to an increased incidence of type 2 diabetes. Excess energy from any source can lead to excess body fat, but foods high in sugar and fat are very easy to overeat and, along with alcohol, are major culprits in obesity.

Sugar, insulin resistance and type 2 diabetes

If you eat a lot of refined carbs in one hit they get broken down to simple sugars very quickly, and you get a blood glucose spike. This is unhealthy, and to fix the problem a lot of insulin is released into the bloodstream to deal with this glucose. The insulin tells your muscle, fat and other tissues to absorb the glucose. When the insulin has finished its job, roughly 90 minutes after eating, you can then get a sudden drop in glucose, which in turn triggers hunger hormones (and also makes you feel a bit flat and lacking in energy). So even though you really don't *need* to eat any more food, your body is craving it. So you feel the need to reach for more sugar and the cycle continues.

For your body to work in a healthy way, your blood sugar (glucose) levels need to be pretty constant. However, if you are eating too much sugar and refined carbs, and not doing much exercise, your body struggles to control the levels of glucose and can develop what is known as insulin resistance.

Insulin resistance occurs when muscle, fat, and liver cells fail to respond normally to the hormone insulin, and glucose doesn't get used properly. As a result, the body requires higher levels of insulin to clear excess glucose in the blood. The pancreas tries to keep up with this increased demand by producing more insulin, but eventually the insulin-producing cells start to die off, and excess glucose builds up in the bloodstream. This is a major health problem because excess glucose is toxic, leading to type 2 diabetes, which in the long term can result in kidney damage, a weakened immune system, nerve damage causing loss of sensation or tingling in the extremities, poor circulation, vision loss or blindness, heart attacks and strokes, and amputation. As we have already mentioned, type 2 diabetes also increases the risk of Alzheimer's disease. This is a scary prospect, especially since this form of diabetes is increasing at an alarming rate all over the world. According to the Australian Bureau of Statistics, in 2014–2015, 4.4 per cent of the Australian population, or over 1 million people, had type 2 diabetes.

The risk of developing type 2 diabetes is greatly increased when people have high blood pressure, are obese, don't exercise, eat poorly or carry a lot of abdominal fat.

Chicken strips

Preheat the oven to 220°C (fan-forced). Cut 1 large chicken thigh fillet into 2 cm strips and mix in a bag with 1 teaspoon each of honey, soy sauce and extra virgin olive oil, and a rosemary sprig. Lay the chicken on a baking tray lined with baking paper, season and bake for 12 minutes or until golden and cooked through. Rest for 5 minutes before tucking in.

Various drugs including insulin are used to try to control type 2 diabetes, and many people fail to understand how severe a problem it is, and just get sicker as time goes on. Yet it doesn't have to be this way. In most cases, a change of diet together with exercise can reduce the dependence, or completely eliminate the need for any diabetes medication. Dietary guidelines for preventing and treating type 2 diabetes are being overhauled in many countries. The trend is to reduce the amount of sugar and to look carefully at the sources of complex carbohydrates in the diet. Whole grains and legumes give protection; refined grains do not. In fact, health experts are now suggesting that energy sources should have a greater (healthy) fat component, and less sugars of any kind. Adopting a low-sugar diet can normalise your blood sugar levels, help you lose weight, and protect against this metabolic illness.

How to cut down on sugar

If you are accustomed to a diet high in refined carbohydrates and sugar, it can be challenging to reduce your dependence on these foods. I'm talking here about taking sugar in your tea and coffee, drinking soft drinks, cordials and so-called 'energy drinks', and eating biscuits, cakes, sweet pastries, crackers made with white flour, too much white bread, rice and pasta, and all types of confectionery. These foods have little or no nutritional value, and the less you have of these, the healthier your diet will become. Think of them as 'empty kilojoules (calories)'. Cut these foods out of your diet as much as possible, and also choose brown rice instead of white and wholegrain breads rather than packaged white breads. But if you still find yourself craving sweet foods, here are some tips that may help.

Six-minute corn

Place the whole corn cob in the microwave and cook on high for 6 minutes. Allow to sit for 5 minutes before peeling back the leaves. Add a knob of butter and a pinch of sea salt flakes, and eat from the cob.

DRINK WATER

If you've had a healthy lunch with a good serve of protein, healthy fats and lots of vegetables, and a couple of hours later you think you might be hungry, try drinking a glass of water. Sometimes we can confuse hunger and thirst. If it's a hot day, add some ice.

WHAT ABOUT ARTIFICIAL SWEETENERS?

Some people believe that consuming foods or drinks that are artificially sweetened with saccharine, aspartame or sucralose will help them avoid weight gain. However, the products containing them are likely to be highly processed, and have little or no other nutritional value. Also, if the foods in question are biscuits or cakes for example, the flour and starches will still provide a considerable glucose hit, so the diabetes risk is still there. Aim for a piece of fruit, or try one of Maggie's tasty snacks which are high in nutrients and healthy fats, and designed not to give you a glucose spike.

EAT MORE GOOD FATS

Having a slightly higher intake of healthy fats as well as complete protein at main meals has been shown to make you feel fuller for longer, which helps to reduce mid-morning and mid-afternoon snacking. The *Australian Dietary Guidelines* are based on foods rather than individual nutrients, but recommend that fats can range from providing 20 to 25 per cent of the kilojoules (calories) in your diet. Good fats include extra virgin olive oil, coconut oil, and the oils in fish and other seafood, avocados, nuts and seeds.

HAVE FRESH FRUIT, NOT FRUIT JUICE

When trying to reduce sugar, don't be tempted to replace soft drink with fruit juice – it is still very high in sugar and has none of the fibre or other benefits of the fruit. Eating dried fruit is preferable to fruit juice, as it still contains the fibre, however it is also very high in sugar and may contain high levels of preservatives, so moderate consumption is key.

Some people think that even eating fruit is not a great idea, especially if they have a fructose-intolerance problem. However, for everyone else, fresh fruit contains many antioxidants and fibre, so two serves a day are recommended. Berries are some of the best fruits, being very high in antioxidants and fibre and lower in sugar than many other fruits.

DE-STRESS

This may sound odd as a tip for helping you reduce your sugar intake, but there is a close relationship between cravings for sweet foods and feeling stressed.

When you are under stress, adrenalin and cortisol are released to get your body ready to run or fight the perceived danger, whether that danger is real (someone pointing a gun at you) or imagined (worrying about your children, feeling terrified you'll lose your job). Your heart beats faster, breathing rate increases, muscles clench, and glycogen is released from the liver and muscles to give you a burst of energy. Suddenly you have a whole lot of glucose in your bloodstream again, which triggers insulin, then a drop in glucose, which in turn triggers your appetite for sweet foods. Also, if adrenalin and cortisol are elevated for long periods, your body can go into survival mode, lowering metabolic rate and storing fat around internal organs (where it is most protective, and most easily metabolised in an emergency).

Any steps you can take to reduce stress will be helpful not only to manage your intake of sugar, but also to avoid the metabolic consequences of elevated cortisol. Furthermore, chronic cortisol levels are now recognised as a big risk factor for Alzheimer's.

Leftover black lentil salad

In a bowl mix 1 cup cooked black lentils, 1 diced small avocado, ½ cup (75 g) chopped tomatoes, 2 sliced sticks celery (stalks and leaves), ½ sliced red onion, 95 g tin tuna (drained), 2 tablespoons extra virgin olive oil, a squeeze of lemon juice, sea salt flakes and pepper.

Protein

Protein is one of the major macronutrients, along with carbohydrates and fats. Protein is found in meat, fish, eggs, cheese, legumes (dried beans and peas), nuts and seeds, and also in grains. Fruits and most vegetables contain very little protein.

WHY WE NEED PROTEIN

Protein is broken down during digestion into its smallest components – amino acids. These amino acids are then used as building blocks to make up the many different proteins our bodies need. These include collagen (for muscles, bones, tendons, cartilage and skin), keratin (for hair, nails, teeth and skin), elastin (skin), various immunoglobulins (antibodies), myosin (for muscle fibres), haemoglobin (the oxygen-carrying protein in red blood cells) and enzymes (proteins that speed up chemical reactions), just to name a few.

Every cell in our bodies needs proteins to function. Once made, proteins don't last forever, and old and damaged proteins are regularly removed and replaced as part of our body's standard maintenance. Since we can't store amino acids for later use, a daily intake of protein is necessary to help make the new proteins that we need. Without an adequate protein intake, all aspects of our body functioning would suffer to some extent.

THE ESSENTIAL AMINO ACIDS

There are 20 common amino acids, nine of which must come from our diet: tryptophan, methionine, lysine, phenylalanine, histidine, isoleucine, leucine, threonine and valine. These are known as the essential amino acids because our bodies can't make them. The other eleven amino acids can either be made from the essential amino acids, or from other components of our diet.

Proteins that contain all nine essential amino acids are known as 'complete' proteins, and include all the animal-based foods (red meats, poultry, fish and other seafood, eggs, milk, cheese and yoghurt). Most proteins in plant-based foods, however, are incomplete, as they either lack one or more of the essential amino acids, or the quantities are too low for optimum health. For example, many grains are low in lysine (but high in methionine), while many beans are low in methionine (but high in lysine). However, the old idea that vegetarians and vegans need to combine foods such as beans and rice, or chickpeas and bread at any meal is not necessary as the body can use amino acids from foods at adjacent meals.

If you avoid all animal foods, or have a very low protein diet, it would be wise to consult a dietician to make sure you are getting all the essential amino acids.

FISH

As we saw in chapter 2, the consumption of fish is important for maintaining good levels of omega-3 fatty acids. Fish also provides vitamins A and D, good quality protein, selenium, zinc and iodine. However, we don't need to eat fish at every meal – just two or three times a week is fine.

Now, when I say eating fish is good for you, I don't mean fish fingers, fish burgers, or fish and chips. To get the best oils, fresh fish is what you need, and the oilier the fish, the better.

Coconut chook and sprout salad

Place 2 chicken thigh fillets in a saucepan and pour over 1 x 400 g tin coconut milk. Simmer gently for 20 minutes, then leave to cool in the liquid. Reserve the juices (for another use – lentils are delicious cooked in them), shred the meat and serve with a salad of 1 tablespoon mint leaves, 2 tablespoons flat-leaf parsley leaves, 2 tablespoons mixed sprouts, 1 tablespoon toasted pine nuts, 1 tablespoon currants and a drizzle of extra virgin olive oil and lemon juice.

Fresh fish available in Australia that are good sources of omega-3 fatty acids:

Mullet	Australian Herring
Swordfish	Australian salmon
Whitebait	Sardines
Morwong	Farmed Atlantic salmon
Mackerel	Rainbow or Ocean trout
Gemfish	Tuna

The list above is in no particular order, as the amount of oil in your fish will depend not just on the type of fish, but also on how you trim it - One tip is to keep the skin on, as this contains a lot of the fish oil, and don't trim away the edges of fillets, again these edges can be rich sources of the good oils. If you wish to choose fish based on sustainable fishing practices, see the website goodfishbadfish.com.au which has up-to-date information on sustainable oily fish, and even tips on how to prepare it. Other useful sites include heartfoundation.org.au, and frdc.com.au.

Tinned fish such as sardines, salmon and some brands of tuna can also provide omega-3 fatty acids, as well as good protein and minerals including calcium, but check the labels as some canning processes reduce the fat content, then add vegetable oils which will change the ratio of omega-6 to omega-3 fatty acids. Look for fish in olive oil or water.

To preserve the healthy fats, it is best to grill or bake rather than fry fish. If you choose to fry, use a shallow frying pan and a small amount of olive oil, and don't cook it for too long or the good fats will be damaged. And don't store your fish for more than two weeks in the freezer. Ideally, store in bags with the air removed, and eat as soon as possible, as those valuable polyunsaturated oils go rancid rather quickly.

Watermelon and lime

Dice or slice a chunk of fresh watermelon, squeeze over some lime juice and serve.

LEGUMES

Legumes (which include beans, chickpeas and lentils) are important foods to include regularly in the diet. They contain up to 20 per cent protein, and are excellent sources of many vitamins, minerals, dietary fibre and antioxidants. They are also a good source of energy. Their high fibre content makes them excellent for bowel health: the good gut bacteria love the indigestible starches in these legumes and busily break them down by fermentation (see the section on 'Prebiotics and probiotics' on page 45), producing valuable short-chain fatty acids. This fermentation process does produce some gas, but this is not a medical problem. The gas problem will be reduced if the beans are soaked, or even sprouted, as both these processes get rid of some of the indigestible starches that the gut bacteria like. The only exceptions are red lentils and split peas, which have already had the skins removed, these just need a quick rinse before cooking.

NUTS AND SEEDS

Nuts and seeds are nutritional powerhouses, being high in vitamins, minerals, protein, dietary fibre and polyunsaturated fats, as well as polyphenol antioxidants. There have been several large recent population studies which have shown that the regular consumption of nuts correlates with lower levels of mortality caused by heart disease, stroke and type 2 diabetes. This may be due to their healthy fat content, as they appear to cause changes to fat metabolism. For example, it has been shown that nut consumption can reduce levels of LDL cholesterol.

Nuts feature strongly in Maggie's recipes, due to their rich flavour and texture. All the nuts included provide good protein and polyunsaturated fatty acids, with each nut type being rich in other nutrients too. Almonds are rich in calcium and vitamin E; Brazil nuts are an excellent source of selenium; cashews are high in zinc and iron, hazelnuts are high in folate and walnuts are an excellent source of omega-3 fatty acids. (As we saw in the Fats section, the ratio of omega-6 to omega-3 in walnuts is about 4:1. We are also keen to recommend walnuts as they have been shown to reduce Abeta in the brain.)

It is important to remember, however, that nuts and seeds are calorie-dense, so again, moderation is important.

Prawns and chickpeas

Drain and rinse 1 x 400 g tin organic chickpeas. Mix with ½ sliced red onion, 1 cup (160 g) cherry tomatoes, and a few fresh basil leaves. Season with lemon juice and extra virgin olive oil, and top with a handful of peeled, deveined prawns.

WHY CUT DOWN ON RED MEAT?

Red meat is an excellent source of complete protein and iron, but it also contains high levels of saturated fat and cholesterol. Even lean cuts of beef, lamb and pork still contain about 10 per cent fat. The worst red meats, however, are processed meats such as bacon, sausages, ham and salami. A high consumption of deli meats has been strongly linked to bowel cancer and cardiovascular disease, so if you are going to cut out some red meat in your diet, these should be the first to go. Secondly, it's also important to note that red meat is rarely eaten in the healthy Mediterranean and Japanese diets linked to longevity, that I mentioned earlier (see pages 19–22). Finally, a high consumption of (unprocessed) red meat has been linked to an increased risk of diabetes.

When you buy red meat, try to buy meat from grass-fed animals, as the ratio of omega-6 to omega-3 fatty acids is around five times lower (on average) than from grain-fed animals. This change in fat quality is a side-effect of industrialising the way we raise our livestock, and it is an issue not many people may be aware of.

Yet despite recommending a reduction in red meat, I don't suggest that it should disappear altogether but rather should be eaten in moderation. We are lucky in Australia to have some of the best-quality red meats and excellent producers. Our digestive system becomes less efficient as we get older, so a small amount of good-quality red meat twice a week is a good thing, both for protein and as an excellent source of iron (and flavour). See page 31 for more on iron.

When you are buying red meat, aim for lean grass-fed beef, lamb, small quantities of liver (preferably from grass-fed animals) and kangaroo meat (it is lean, sustainable and very tasty).

10 foods to avoid

1. **Fizzy sugary drinks.** These have zero nutritional value, and are one of the best ways to develop symptoms of insulin resistance and type 2 diabetes. Artificially sweetened fizzy drinks are also nutrition-free. Opt for water, mineral water, tea or coffee (but not too much caffeine).

2. **Highly processed flour-based foods, especially packaged, baked or ready-made foods.** Sweet and savoury biscuits, cakes, slices, sweet and savoury pies, sausage rolls, pizzas and chips. Opt for a piece of fruit, dried fruit and nuts, or make one of Maggie's many tasty snacks instead.

3. **White flour.** Avoid cooking with refined white flour and buying products containing large amounts of it, such as low-quality white bread, pizza, crackers, etc. Refined flour is mostly starch and referred to as 'empty carbs'. It will lead to spikes in your blood glucose level. Opt instead for wholegrain breads and pasta, or use brown rice, oats, quinoa or buckwheat.

4. **Sweets.** Sugar, lollies and other confectionery will keep the dentist busy, and help you develop symptoms of insulin resistance and type 2 diabetes. We all love a sweet treat at times, but make it one that is full of good ingredients such as one of Maggie's desserts, or opt for a piece of fruit, dried fruit and nuts, hummus with vegetable sticks or one of Maggie's healthy snacks instead.

5. **Processed meats.** Meats like salami, bacon, sausages, corned beef, hot dogs and chorizo, and products containing them, like pizzas. These meats will contain oxidised and trans-fats, as well as preservatives such as nitrates and nitrites which have been strongly linked to bowel cancer.

6. **Deep-fried fast foods.** Hot chips or fries are especially bad, for both the starch in the white potatoes and the poor-quality oil used for frying.

7. **Sunflower, corn and peanut oil.** Minimise these vegetable oils due to their high omega-6 content (and very poor omega-3). Think extra virgin olive or coconut oil instead, or use butter, though not too much!

8. **Fruit juices.** The packaged ones are full of added sugars and when you drink juice you're not getting the benefit of the dietary fibre. Better to have a piece of fruit.

9. **Highly processed or high sugar content spreads.** Jams are usually around 50 per cent sugar, some nut spreads have a lot of added sugar and processed fats. Always check labels. It's best to eat these only occasionally.

10. **Dairy products with high sugar content.** These include commercial ice cream, flavoured yoghurt, low-fat yoghurt (which is often full of sugar), and processed cheese (which is full of highly processed non-dairy ingredients). Opt for plain, full-fat yoghurt and good-quality cheese.

20 foods to embrace

1. **Extra virgin olive oil.** See the section on olive oil for details (pages 39–40), but in a nutshell, good-quality olive oil is packed with polyphenol antioxidants, and contains mostly monounsaturated fatty acids which are less prone to damage on heating.

2. **Onions, garlic and leeks.** The onion family is high in polyphenols, such as the flavonoid quercetin. They also are good sources of manganese, copper, vitamin B6 and fibre. Red onions also contain anthocyanins: antioxidants known for their anti-inflammatory properties.

3. **Nuts.** These may be high in kilojoules (calories), but in small quantities they are excellent sources of many nutrients, including omega-3 fatty acids (walnuts), selenium (Brazil nuts), vitamin E (almonds), manganese and vitamin B1 (macadamias and pecans), quality protein and dietary fibre.

4. **Herbs.** Fresh parsley, thyme, basil, rosemary, oregano and coriander (just to name a few) are especially concentrated sources of vitamins C, A and K, flavonoids and folate; plus they're high in dietary fibre. It's also so much nicer to flavour your dishes with herbs rather than salt.

5. **Linseed (flaxseed).** These seeds are an excellent source of omega-3 fatty acids and are also rich in vitamin B1, calcium, manganese, copper, zinc and magnesium, as well as protein and dietary fibre.

6. **Dark chocolate 70% and over.** Contains magnesium, iron, copper, manganese, vitamin K and dietary fibre as well as the antioxidant flavonoids, catechins and procyanidins.

7. **Citrus fruits.** These provide vitamins C and B1, dietary fibre, folate and some are good sources of calcium (oranges for example). Citrus zest is high in polyphenol antioxidants.

8. **Red beetroots.** These are an excellent source of folate, some polyphenols and manganese; and a good source of copper and fibre. They are also particularly rich in the betalain pigments, which reduce oxidative stress and have anti-inflammatory properties. Recently it's been shown that the high nitrate content of beetroots boosts the body's nitric oxide levels, which is good for blood vessels and helps lower blood pressure.

9. **Coconut oil.** Extra virgin coconut oil is mostly saturated fat, so is excellent for cooking as it doesn't get degraded into toxic fats by heating. As it contains a high proportion of lauric acid (which is metabolised in a different way to other fats), coconut oil is less likely to upset your HDL/LDL levels (unless you are eating too much!). Plus it provides an excellent alternative energy source for your brain. See pages 40–41 for more information on coconut oil.

10. **Carrots, sweet potatoes and pumpkin.** These orange-coloured vegetables are all very rich in carotenoids (vitamin A precursors) as well as vitamins K,

C and B6 and the minerals copper and manganese. They also provide lots of dietary fibre. Make sure you eat them with a small amount of fat or oil so your body can easily absorb the carotenoids.

11. **Green leafy vegetables.** These are rich sources of vitamins A, C and K, folate, polyphenol antioxidants and dietary fibre. They are also high in manganese and magnesium; and contain iron and calcium.

12. **Broccoli and kale.** These members of the cabbage family are particularly rich in vitamins C and K; they also provide carotenoids (vitamin A precursors), polyphenol antioxidants, manganese, folate and fibre. **Red cabbage** is also good as it is high in anthocyanin antioxidants, as well as several of the above nutrients.

13. **Tomatoes.** In season, tomatoes are rich in the antioxidant lycopene and vitamin C. Tinned varieties (with no added sugar or salt) are also good as they still contain the lycopene.

14. **Turmeric and ginger.** These are related root herbs. Turmeric has strong antioxidant and anti-inflammatory properties, with its polyphenol curcumin thought to be one of the most important active components. Ginger is also known for its anti-inflammatory and antioxidant properties, with gingerol thought to be its main bioactive compound.

15. **Fish.** All fish are excellent sources of complete protein, and they vary from good to excellent sources of omega-3 fatty acids (oily fish have the highest quantity). They also provide vitamin D, and are one of the few sources of iodine.

16. **Berries.** Most berries are especially high in antioxidants, such as vitamin C (strawberries), anthocyanin antioxidants (blueberries, raspberries and blackberries) and resveratrol (blueberries). They also contain calcium, manganese, dietary fibre, vitamin K and folate.

17. **Legumes.** Chickpeas, broad beans, red kidney beans, lentils and others are all good sources of protein. Also high in dietary fibre, manganese and copper, they have no cholesterol and very little saturated fat. If mixed with whole grains or other sources legumes provide complete protein.

18. **Avocado.** This fruit provides vitamins C, E, K and B6, folate, copper, some magnesium and manganese, plenty of dietary fibre and monounsaturated fats.

19. **Whole grains and seeds.** Oats, buckwheat, millet, brown or black rice and whole wheat provide manganese, selenium, dietary fibre, folate, many B vitamins, and some protein.

20. **Eggs, cheese, whole milk and natural probiotic yoghurt.** Eggs are no longer to be avoided because of cholesterol, and they are packed with nutrition – high in easily digestible complete protein, vitamins B2, B12 and D, selenium and folate. Milk, cheese and yoghurt also provide complete protein, vitamins A, B2, B12 and D, calcium, selenium and zinc.

— Chapter 5 —

Keeping the goodness in your food

To maintain the nutrients in fresh food, it is important to store and prepare it properly. Here are some things to keep in mind.

Buy fresh and seasonal

Try to get the freshest foods for your table. Aim for locally grown produce from markets, fish markets, or just use what you get from the supermarket as soon as possible after buying.

When fruits and vegetables are in season, they are fresher as they are usually obtained locally, they taste much better, and they are often a lot cheaper. Compare the red juicy tomatoes of summer with those insipid expensive winter tomatoes that never seem to ripen. Seek out new varieties and flavours, such as heirloom tomatoes and Asian vegetables from farmers' markets, or grow some of your own if you have the time and garden space.

What about tinned or frozen food?

Tinned foods might seem okay, but the original nutrition in the food will have been reduced to some extent, depending on the food involved, by the heat required during processing. Many tinned foods have added salt and sugar as well. Having said that, tinned ingredients can be very handy when you don't have time to wait 12 hours to soak and cook your own chickpeas, or you don't have enough ripe tomatoes on hand to make fresh passata. In fact, the convenience will often mean you are more able to cook a greater variety of dishes at home. Therefore, some foods are good to have in the pantry at all times, to make this possible.

The loss of some nutrients due to processing can also apply to some frozen foods, but not all. Some fruits and vegetables, for instance, are frozen as soon as they are picked, thus retaining their goodness, often to a greater extent than those bought fresh. In Australia, this applies to frozen (Australian) peas for example.

Grow your own

If you have room for a vegetable patch and/or herb garden, grow your own. There is nothing like the satisfaction of knowing you have produced some really fresh salad or herbs, or used your own lemons or other fruits from your garden, and the flavour and goodness in the food is a great reward for your efforts. You don't even need a garden for a few herbs and leafy greens – these can be grown on a balcony in pots. See Maggie's advice on pages 10–11.

Store foods correctly

- It is important to store produce correctly to avoid damage by light, heat and oxygen.
- Leafy greens and non-root vegetables should be stored in the vegetable crisper in your fridge.
- Potatoes, onions and other root vegetables should be stored in a cool, dark place with minimum air circulation.
- Apples, oranges, lemons, bananas and whole melons should be kept at room temperature in the dark if possible (keep the bananas away from the others as they produce ethylene gas that encourages other fruits to ripen).
- Berries should be kept in the fridge.
- Oils (e.g. coconut oil and olive oil) should be kept in opaque, sealed containers in a cool, dark place.
- Butter and polyunsaturated fats (walnut oil, macadamia oil, sesame oil) should be kept in the fridge.
- Red meat, poultry and other meat products should be kept in the fridge or freezer until needed. (Preferably no longer than 3 months in the freezer.)
- Fish should be stored in the fridge and used within 24 hours of buying, or frozen for up to about 2 weeks (in the coldest section) – any longer and the flavour deteriorates, partly because the fish oils start to become rancid.

Don't peel root veggies or pumpkin

Cooking your sweet potatoes, carrots and pumpkin unpeeled helps to retain the nutrients and adds extra dietary fibre. The same applies to roasting vegetables, especially potatoes – keep the skin on wherever possible, as this is where many nutrients are found.

Avoid overcooking

Many vitamins and some antioxidants are damaged by cooking. This applies especially to vitamin C, and also to B1, B2, B6 and folate. Water-soluble vitamins and nutrients will leach out of vegetables if boiled, so if possible, eat some sources raw, or lightly steam, blanch, saute, stir-fry (in minimal oil for a short time) or microwave. If you do boil vegetables, do it for the minimum time, as the longer the vegetables are left in water, the more nutrients leach out. Microwaving and steaming are the best options, to help retain nutrients.

If cooking or frying food in olive oil, coconut oil, butter or polyunsaturated oils, make sure the oil temperature is low enough that there is no smoke – if the oil reaches the 'smoke-point' temperature (about 175°C for extra virgin coconut oil, 200°C for extra virgin olive oil, 150°C for butter), this is a clear sign of damage to the fatty acids, making the oil or fat unhealthy to eat.

On the other hand, some nutrients are more readily available for digestion after cooking. For example, orange-coloured foods such as carrots, orange sweet potatoes and tomatoes release more carotenoids such as beta-carotene and lycopene when cooked.

Red meat, poultry and eggs are easier to digest when cooked, as the protein, iron and other minerals are easier to absorb.

Avocado and mushroom sourdough

Cook slices of field mushrooms in a hot frying pan with extra virgin olive oil. Serve on grilled sourdough, topped with avocado slices, parsley, sea salt flakes and pepper.

Chapter 6

Habits for a longer life

This book focuses on the dietary changes you can make to improve your physical health and therefore reduce the risk of the cognitive decline associated with Alzheimer's. However, there are other significant lifestyle changes that will enhance the effects of a healthy diet.

Reduce alcohol

Although a low-to-moderate consumption of red wine with meals is part of the Mediterranean diet, this doesn't give us a green light to overindulge.

A glass of wine or a beer can be lovely and refreshing on social occasions, or to relax at the end of the working week – but only if your liver is healthy and you are not on medications that are affected by alcohol. (If in doubt, check with your doctor.)

More importantly, if you are struggling to maintain a healthy weight (and therefore at risk of heart disease and type 2 diabetes), then alcohol is a no-no. This is because alcohol is very high in kilojoules (calories), and also when we've had a few drinks, we tend to make unhealthy food choices.

Also, to the body, alcohol is a toxin (it's where we get the word 'intoxicated'), so the liver immediately gets to work on it to try to minimise its effects on the brain. Alcohol depresses the central nervous system, messes with cognitive function, emotion regulation, sensory perception and physical coordination; it also increases the risk of many types of cancer.

Excessive drinking (defined as more than two standard drinks a day for men or women), is known to harm the brain, liver, immune system and pancreas. Over time, excessive drinking can cause short-term memory lapses, fatty liver disease or even cirrhosis of the liver, and increases the risk of stroke and heart problems.

If you choose to drink alcohol, the healthiest option for women is to limit intake to 1 standard drink, 3–4 days a week. For men, we'd recommend no more than 1.5 standard drinks 3–4 days a week.

1 standard drink =
125 ml of white wine *
100 ml of red wine *
375 ml can of mid-strength (3.5% alcohol) beer
30 ml of spirits

One standard drink contains 10 g of alcohol, and 10 g of alcohol = 12.5 ml
* these are different because white wine usually has a lower percentage of alcohol,
here we've assumed white wine has 10% alcohol and red wine has 12.5% alcohol.

Cauliflower with tahini yoghurt dressing

Slice 2–3 cm thick sections across a cauliflower. Lay flat on a microwave-safe container with 3 tablespoons water, then cover and cook on high for 3 minutes. Place on a baking tray, drizzle with extra virgin olive oil and grill for 5 minutes or until golden. Place on a serving plate with toasted pine nuts, currants, flat-leaf parsley leaves and a dressing of 2 tablespoons natural probiotic yoghurt mixed with 2 tablespoons tahini.

Drink enough water

Water is critical for survival: our bodies need it to transport nutrients, to remove waste and toxins, to cushion our organs and joints, to regulate temperature and to hydrate our skin, for example. When we don't drink enough fluid, we can become dehydrated, which can cause fatigue, headaches, confusion and weakness. More serious complications can include heatstroke (when it's hot), urinary tract infections, kidney stones and kidney failure, seizures and low blood volume shock.

WHY WE BECOME MORE DEHYDRATED AS WE GET OLDER

As we get older, our kidneys begin to wear out, they are less able to remove toxic waste, and are less able to concentrate urine. Therefore, we tend to expel water more quickly as we age. Older people also tend to lose the sensation of being thirsty, and in many cases, choose to drink less because they fear incontinence – they don't want to have to get up to go to the toilet several times a night. Often a reduced social life, especially with elderly people living alone, leads to less drinking. Finally, medications for certain conditions (blood pressure medications, diuretics and medications for anxiety and depression) can also interfere with fluid balance by causing sweating, constipation or urinary retention.

Try the following tips to help increase your intake

- Get into the habit of drinking a glass of water as soon as you get up every day, and drink a glass of water with every meal.
- Carry a refillable water bottle with you.
- Try a variety of herbal teas, you might discover a new one you would like to have every day. Many also provide you with quite potent antioxidants, even after steeping in boiled water.
- Keep a jug of iced water in the fridge infused with some fresh mint sprigs and slices of lemon – very refreshing!

Avocado toast with vino cotto

Chargrill a piece of sourdough. Drizzle with vino cotto. Roughly chop 1 ripe avocado and pile on the toast with a final drizzle of extra virgin olive oil and some freshly ground black pepper.

What about tea and coffee?

The smell of coffee in the morning can be so uplifting, and many would claim coffee gets their brain working for the day ahead. Research supports this theory, as coffee has been shown to improve thinking skills and memory in the short term. Coffee also contains some antioxidants, and population studies suggest that coffee may protect against Parkinson's disease, type 2 diabetes and liver disease, and may decrease the risk of depression.

However, coffee can raise blood pressure, and if you have too much of it, it may also trigger the release of cortisol, which at chronic levels can contribute to abdominal fat gain. Both of these factors, in turn, may increase your risk of heart disease. On the other hand, recent studies also show that consuming moderate (1–2 cups a day) amounts of coffee protects against Alzheimer's disease. So moderation is key.

Both black and green teas contain caffeine, but around 2–4 times less caffeine than coffee (and green tea has less than black). Tea also contains many polyphenol antioxidants, particularly flavonoids such as catechins. Another chemical in tea, theanine, can cross the blood–brain barrier and also has antioxidant effects. There is some evidence theanine can reduce memory impairment in Alzheimer's disease, and reduce the amount of Abeta produced in the brain. Although clinical studies are needed to confirm these potential therapeutic effects of theanine, the polyphenol antioxidant value of tea is well documented.

Stop smoking

There are no benefits to smoking. Everybody knows it is bad for your health on multiple levels. There are many chemicals in tobacco that are toxic or carcinogenic, and they use up a significant portion of the antioxidants in your body as it desperately tries to detoxify. Smoking increases the risk of many cancers, emphysema, heart disease and stroke. When we studied 1100 older Australians in the Australian Imaging Biomarkers and Lifestyle (AIBL) study of ageing we found that the protective benefits of the Mediterranean diet on reducing brain Abeta was compromised in smokers. Smoking also increases your risk of Alzheimer's disease, particularly if you are a heavy smoker aged 50–60.

The good news is that if you give up smoking, your body eventually clears out the toxic residues, and your risk of Alzheimer's goes back down to the level of a non-smoker after a few years.

Mushrooms and pesto

Grill large field mushrooms drizzled with olive oil on the barbecue until cooked through. Finish with pesto, sea salt flakes and pepper.

Take up daily physical exercise

Your brain depends on a strong supply of glucose and oxygen from the bloodstream, and needs a healthy drainage system to clear out unwanted or damaged chemicals. This means your blood vessels and 'blood-brain barrier' need to be healthy. Aerobic exercise is most important, preferably at least 2–3 times a week, and the evidence is that the more intensive the exercise, the better. This information comes partly from Australian studies of the people enrolled in the AIBL study of ageing which have looked specifically at the benefits of different types of exercise. Those people who did the most intensive aerobic exercise had the lowest rates of cognitive decline. So get on your exercise bike, go swimming, enrol in gym sessions, start running again, whatever is appropriate considering your particular health status, age and physical ability. If you do have some physical limitations, please consult with your GP first, but there is sure to be something you can do to raise your heart rate – this will also reduce your risk of cardiovascular disease, type 2 diabetes and also improve your mood.

Stay socially connected

Humans are social beings – we thrive on contact with others. Indeed, it has been said that relationships are the key to a joyful, meaningful life. This makes sense when you consider that people who feel lonely and alienated from others are at risk of developing depression or other mental illnesses.

Most people have strong connections with family and friends. But it is also good to extend your network. Do you have a hobby you've always wanted to take up again? Or is there something you've always wanted to do but have never given yourself permission to? Maybe it was taking dancing lessons, learning to play golf or cards, joining a walking or bike-riding group, a knitting circle or a book club. The possibilities are endless, and needn't cost the earth. Social activities like these are lovely ways to meet like-minded people, and also happen to fulfil other requirements for a healthy life – exercising and using your brain.

Use your brain

Maintaining the connections between brain cells and developing new connections are equally important for the preservation of brain function – as the saying goes, 'use it or lose it'.

Any new or challenging activity will aid this, so challenge yourself to:

- learn a new language, or join conversation classes for a second language you want to improve
- learn to play a musical instrument
- enrol in a course at a college or university, or do an online course from the University of the Third Age (www.u3aonline.org.au)
- start a new hobby such as painting, pottery or another craft
- write your memoirs, a short story or even just a weekly email to someone you care about
- enjoy mentally challenging games such as bridge, chess, Sudoku, Scrabble – even online
- computer-based brain-training programs but select those that are evidence-based with appropriate proven clinical trials
- keep working, or start a new job, even casual work – all will stimulate those neurons.

Many important skills and abilities that were learned early in life are not lost until very late in the disease because they are stored in a different part of the brain. These include the ability to read, dance, play music, sing, enjoy old music, engage in crafts and hobbies, tell stories and reminisce. Capitalising on these abilities can foster success and maintain quality of life even into the moderate phase of the disease.

Slow roast onions with vino cotto

Preheat the oven to 140°C (fan-forced). Slice 3 large red onions into thin wedges. Toss with a little extra virgin olive oil and some thyme leaves in a shallow heavy-based roasting tin and roast for an hour or more until the onion takes on a deep caramel colour. Remove from the oven and drizzle with vino cotto. Return to the oven for another 10 minutes.

Serve warm or at room temperature. This makes a wonderful accompaniment to grilled steak or liver.

Conclusion

A lot of thought has gone into the recipes in this book. Taste, as always, was Maggie's first consideration. The focus of this book though, was to create recipes that are rich in a variety of nutrients for which there is considerable evidence that they help maintain good brain function, or that they reduce the risk of conditions that are known to lead to an increased risk of Alzheimer's. The seasonal variation in foods available in Australia made it easy for Maggie to put together the wide range of delicious meal choices, with every meal of the day covered. These meals and snacks will provide you with good levels of antioxidant, vitamin, mineral and healthy fat intake. The breakfasts are often protein- and energy-rich, to get you well prepared for the day, you probably won't need anything else to eat until lunchtime. The lunches and dinners are nutrient-rich and make the most of healthy colourful vegetables, quality meat, fish and other sources of protein, nuts, plenty of herbs and spices for flavour, whole grains, and healthy fats from coconut and olive oil. If you feel you need more than a piece of fruit or a handful of nuts between meals, or if you have a special occasion, Maggie has created recipes for more substantial snacks. There are also some recipe ideas for a quick nutritious fix, sprinkled throughout chapters 1-6.

We believe that including a good selection of these recipes in your everyday diet, reducing some of the bad dietary habits you might have, as well as staying physically and mentally active, will all help you maximise your chances of living a long and healthy life, free of dementia. Even if we carry genes that increase our risk of Alzheimer's to some extent, a quality diet and healthy lifestyle can still slow the disease progress, delaying the onset and slowing the rate of cognitive decline. As the diagram opposite demonstrates, the power to give yourself the very best chance of a healthy future is in your hands.

Sardines on toast

Chargrill some sourdough bread. Drain a tin of sardines and place on the sourdough toast with some thinly sliced red onion, extra virgin olive oil, flat-leaf parsley and a squeeze of lemon juice.

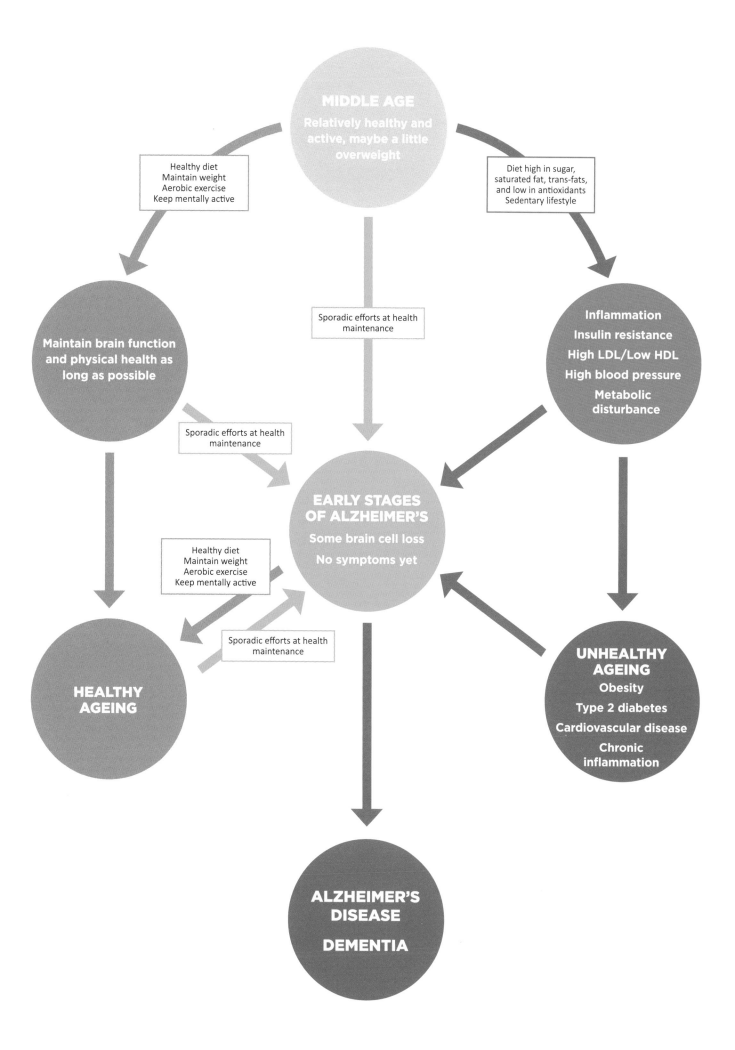

Maggie's Meal Plans

It's so important to eat seasonally, for flavour, nutrition and sustainability, so I've put together a suggested week of meals from this book for each season. You will notice that dessert only appears on these meal plans once a week. As you'll see from our healthy eating pyramid on page 22, we recommend eating sweet things sparingly.

		Spring	Summer
Day 1	**Breakfast**	Citrus, ginger, lime and coconut smoothie (page 68)	Blueberry, chia and coconut smoothie (page 78)
	Lunch	Roasted garlic mushrooms on toast with avocado (page 105)	Tomato and beetroot soup with basil (page 122)
	Dinner	Blue-eye trevalla baked in paper with bok choy, ginger, miso and soy (page 154)	Mushroom and tempeh barbecue patties (page 160)
Day 2	**Breakfast**	Scrambled eggs, asparagus and hot-smoked salmon (page 73)	Mango, lime and ginger smoothie (page 80)
	Lunch	Sweet potato fritters with smashed avocado and salmon (page 100)	Sashimi blue-eye trevalla (page 120)
	Dinner	Braised leek and lima bean ragout with mushrooms and ricotta (page 146)	Yoghurt marinated chicken with Turkish-style tabbouleh (page 163)
Day 3	**Breakfast**	Buckwheat porridge with banana and hazelnuts (page 77)	Summer bircher muesli with berries, almonds and yoghurt (page 77)
	Lunch	Verjuice carrots, barley and currant salad with Persian feta (page 106)	Tomato and beetroot soup with basil (page 122)
	Dinner	Stuffed squid and black barley (page 158)	Dukkah-crusted chicken schnitzel with heritage tomato salad (page 172)
Day 4	**Breakfast**	Homemade braised beans on whole-seed bread with avocado (page 72)	Strawberry, blueberry and coconut smoothie (page 78)
	Lunch	Dukkah-crusted chicken livers with pistou and green beans (page 110)	Tri-colour roasted beetroot salad with thyme, walnut, goat's cheese and herb salad (page 112)
	Dinner	Barbecued lemon myrtle prawns with sorrel mayonnaise (page 150)	Spelt pasta rags with tomato, olives and ricotta (page 166)
Day 5	**Breakfast**	Citrus, ginger, lime and coconut smoothie (page 68)	Almond pancakes with peaches and yoghurt (page 80)
	Lunch	Salmon ceviche with celeriac, apple, walnut and lime (page 109)	Spring onion, sweet potato and caper fish cakes with tomato and avocado salsa (page 119)
	Dinner	Soba noodles with pickled carrot and cucumber and sesame ginger sauce (page 157)	Wholewheat and yellow zucchini pasta with anchovies (page 164)
Day 6 (weekend)	**Breakfast**	Goat's cheese and spinach omelette with pepitas and cherry tomato salsa (page 74)	Roasted apricots on grilled spelt toast with ricotta (page 84)
	Lunch	Spring slaw of red cabbage, beetroot, bok choy and asparagus with walnuts (page 105)	Nori rolls with dukkah-crusted sweet potato, sprouts and oven-baked tomatoes (page 114)
	Dinner	Roast chook with broccoli tabbouleh and turmeric buttermilk dressing (page 152)	Quail with quandong and snake beans (page 165)
Day 7 (weekend)	**Breakfast**	Porridge of oats and seeds with prunes and orange (page 68)	Chickpea crepes with caponata and yoghurt (page 83)
	Lunch	Tofu with broccolini, smoked almonds and pickled ginger (page 102)	Eggplant, zucchini, caramelised onion and feta tart with brown rice and almond pastry (page 116)
	Dinner	Spring lamb rack with olive crumb on a bed of spinach and tomato sugo (page 149)	Moroccan-style baked fish (page 170)
	Dessert	Pink grapefruit jelly with segments and almonds in honey (page 211)	Coconut panna cotta with raspberries and toasted almonds (page 213)

I believe it's also healthy to indulge ourselves occasionally but for me, dessert is a 'sometimes' food, for a weekend treat or for special occasions. However, if you are watching your weight it's best to avoid these high-energy foods altogether or simply have a very small portion. To help you choose desserts or snacks that are lower in kilojoules, we've marked these recipes with a coloured star. ★

		Autumn	Winter
Day 1	Breakfast	Kale and fruit smoothie (page 88)	Orange almond winter smoothie (page 94)
	Lunch	Miso, eggplant and soba noodle salad (page 124)	Celeriac and green lentil soup (page 133)
	Dinner	Lemongrass and buttermilk poached chicken with saffron tomato ragu (page 177)	Pork shoulder slow cooked in buttermilk with cavolo nero with walnut miso dressing (page 195)
Day 2	Breakfast	Pomegranate and walnut bircher muesli (page 87)	Dried pear and rice porridge (page 93)
	Lunch	Mushroom souffle omelette (page 128)	Aromatic coconut soup with prawns and coriander (page 138)
	Dinner	Pan-fried whiting with celery and pomegranate salad (page 174)	Chicken and chickpea tagine with turmeric, sweet potato and prunes (page 198)
Day 3	Breakfast	Pear and nut muesli (page 90)	Tahini and coconut muesli (page 97)
	Lunch	Pumpkin, ginger and coconut soup (page 129)	Chicken soup with leek and barley (page 137)
	Dinner	Roasted barramundi with kale, anchovies and lemon (page 181)	Fish curry (page 190)
Day 4	Breakfast	Autumn fruit smoothie (page 88)	Coconut oil granola with macadamias and raisins (page 97)
	Lunch	Baked purple sweet potato with labneh, kale pesto and dukkah (page 130)	Spiced white sweet potato with black barley and honey turmeric walnuts (page 143)
	Dinner	Buckwheat, mushroom, bok choy and tofu (page 187)	Crispy skin salmon with winter vegetables (page 189)
Day 5	Breakfast	Poached quince, yoghurt and almond crumble (page 92)	Orange almond winter smoothie (page 94)
	Lunch	Soft poached egg, braised lettuce and capers (page 125)	Chicken soup with leek and barley (page 137)
	Dinner	Spelt pappardelle with pumpkin, sage and walnuts (page 182)	Roasted root vegetables with vino cotto, Brussels sprouts and hazelnuts (page 200)
Day 6 (weekend)	Breakfast	Porridge with pistachio and orange (page 84)	Old-fashioned oats with banana and sultanas (page 94)
	Lunch	Roasted pumpkin with salad of massaged kale, pomegranate and pepitas (page 126)	Chickpea, pumpkin and tamarind stew (page 131)
	Dinner	Turmeric, soy and ginger chicken (page 184)	Lambs fry with spinach (page 194)
Day 7 (weekend)	Breakfast	Breakfast baked eggs (page 87)	Dried pear and rice porridge (page 93)
	Lunch	Eggplant, tomato and feta salad (page 127)	Green frittata (page 140)
	Dinner	Sweet potato, ras el hanout and fennel tart with olive oil pastry (page 178)	Braised oxtail with tamarind and olives (page 192)
	Dessert	Quinces with blancmange and fennel almonds (page 227)	Baked apples (page 230)

Breakfast

Porridge of oats and seeds with prunes and orange

Fresh oats are so different from 'quick oats', which are much thinner and broken up to help them cook so quickly; and while these are a convenient time saver they don't have the flavour of traditional oats. I admit I have succumbed to making a dish of traditional oats in the microwave but my resolve is not to take this shortcut here as the relatively short cooking time on the stove top makes a world of difference to the quality of the porridge. From a flavour perspective, the prunes soaked overnight in orange juice are the icing on the cake, but if you buy really plump pitted prunes you can use them without gilding the lily at all and just add them at the last moment.

SERVES 4

250 g pitted prunes
¾ cup (180 ml) freshly squeezed orange juice
1¾ cups (155 g) organic rolled oats
2 tablespoons linseeds
1 teaspoon chia seeds
Pinch of sea salt flakes
2 tablespoons macadamia oil (see note)
2 cups (500 ml) water or milk
   (cow's milk, soy milk or nut milk)
3 tablespoons coconut cream
Toasted flaked almonds, to serve

Soak the prunes overnight in the orange juice.

The following morning, combine the oats, seeds, sea salt, oil and water or milk in a medium saucepan. Cook, stirring, over medium heat for 8–10 minutes or until thick and cooked. Stir in the coconut cream, then divide evenly among 4 bowls. Top with the soaked prunes and toasted almonds and serve.

Note: Nut oils need to be kept refrigerated to save them from rancidity. Unlike extra virgin olive oil they don't solidify when chilled and last four months if kept well sealed.

Citrus, ginger, lime and coconut smoothie

Spring is all about citrus for me and I celebrate it in all of my cooking. When I want to add apples to my spring recipes, as I do in this smoothie, I know that they are from cold store so I choose Pink Lady as they hold up well to storage, retaining so much flavour and a great sugar–acid balance. This easily made concoction will have you bouncing out of your skin.

SERVES 4

4 oranges, peeled and coarsely chopped
300 ml natural coconut water
3 Pink Lady apples, quartered and cored
Juice of 2 limes
15 g ginger, peeled and chopped
1 tablespoon extra virgin coconut oil, melted
10 large mint leaves
100 g ice cubes

Place all the ingredients in a high-powered blender and blend until smooth. Divide evenly among 4 glasses and serve immediately.

NUTRITION The coconut water is a good source of potassium, manganese, magnesium and fibre.

I love that these super-thin crepes can be made the night before
and stacked on top of each other between sheets of baking paper.

Buckwheat crepes with roasted rhubarb and cinnamon yoghurt

Buckwheat should perhaps be given a new name as it is not a wheat at all, nor a grain. It's a seed of a plant related to rhubarb. It's gluten free, high in protein and full of micronutrients, including iron, magnesium, potassium and zinc. In these crepes the nutty flavour of buckwheat is enhanced by the coconut milk, and the roasted rhubarb is so good it's worth having as much for dessert as for breakfast. Don't leave out the cinnamon with the yoghurt, and I do recommend that you taste before you add any honey – the acidity of natural yoghurts can vary considerably between brands and you may find you don't need any additional sweetness.

SERVES 4

500 g rhubarb, leaves and bases
 discarded
2 tablespoons lightly packed (40 g)
 soft brown sugar
Finely grated zest and juice
 of 2 oranges
2 tablespoons extra virgin olive oil

Cinnamon yoghurt

¾ cup (200 g) thick natural
 probiotic yoghurt
1 teaspoon ground cinnamon
1 teaspoon raw honey (optional)

Crepe batter

300 ml full-cream milk, or milk
 of choice, plus extra if needed
2 free-range eggs
30 g linseeds
2 tablespoons pepitas
 (pumpkin seeds)
2 tablespoons sunflower seeds
1 tablespoon sesame seeds
⅔ cup (100 g) light buckwheat flour
 (see note)
Pinch of sea salt flakes

Rinse the rhubarb stalks well, then cut into 5 cm pieces. Place in a container with the sugar and orange zest and juice. Cover and refrigerate for several hours or overnight.

Preheat the oven to 160°C (fan-forced). Place the rhubarb in a single layer in a roasting tin and pour over the juice and zest. Cover with foil and bake for 20 minutes or until just cooked. Remove from the oven, uncover and set aside to cool.

To make the cinnamon yoghurt, combine all the ingredients in a bowl, cover and refrigerate until needed.

To make the crepe batter, whisk together the milk and eggs, then set aside.

Place all the seeds in a high-powered blender or spice grinder and process until fine. Place in a bowl with the buckwheat flour. Whisk in the milk mixture and salt until well combined. The batter should be the consistency of pouring cream, so if it is a bit thick, add a little extra milk.

Heat a 24 cm frying pan with a little olive oil over low–medium heat. Lift the pan from the heat, then pour in a thin layer of batter and tilt the pan to evenly cover the base. Cook for 2 minutes or until light golden, then gently flip the crepe over and cook for another minute or until just golden. Makes about 8 crepes.

To serve, fill the crepes with rhubarb and a big dollop of yoghurt. Fold into quarters and serve immediately. Left over batter will hold until the next morning.

Note: There are dark and light varieties of buckwheat flour. The dark is made from grinding the seed with the hull and has more fibre and a stronger taste. You will need the finer texture of light (hulled) buckwheat flour for this recipe.

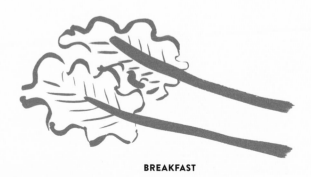

Homemade braised beans on whole-seed bread with avocado

Whether you're having this for breakfast or brunch it's definitely a plan-ahead dish as the beans need to be soaked overnight and their cooking time can vary, depending on how old they are. If the beans are fresh they will take about 40 minutes, but if they are older they can literally take hours. It's also worth noting that the dish develops more flavour if it's made in advance, so do allow time for this.

SERVES 6

2¼ cups (250 g) dried cannellini beans, soaked overnight
2 tablespoons extra virgin olive oil
1 large brown onion, finely chopped
1 clove garlic, smashed and studded with 3 cloves
1 bay leaf
1 large carrot, cut into 1 cm pieces
5 button mushrooms, sliced
2 teaspoons apple cider vinegar
1 x 400 g tin chopped tomatoes
Sea salt flakes and freshly ground black pepper
1 tablespoon Keen's mustard powder
1 tablespoon soft brown sugar
2 tablespoons chopped mint

To serve

2 large ripe avocados
6 thick slices whole-seed, rye or sourdough bread
2 tablespoons flat-leaf parsley leaves

Drain the soaked beans and rinse in a colander. Place in a large saucepan and cover with 4 times the amount of cold water to beans. Bring to the boil over high heat, skimming off any foam that comes to the surface. Reduce the heat to low and simmer for 40 minutes or until tender. Drain.

Heat the olive oil in a large saucepan over medium heat. Add the onion and cook for 10 minutes or until translucent, then add the studded garlic clove and cook for a further minute. Add the bay leaf, carrot and mushroom and cook for 5 minutes or until just soft but not coloured. Stir in the vinegar, then add the tomatoes and a good pinch each of salt and pepper. Combine the mustard powder with 1 tablespoon water, then add to the pan along with the brown sugar. Bring to the boil. Add the cooked beans, cover closely with a piece of baking paper (a cartouche), then cover with a lid. Reduce the heat to as low as possible and simmer for 2 hours, stirring occasionally and adding a little extra water to the pan if necessary, until the beans are tender.

Remove from the heat and stand for about 1 hour. Remove and discard the garlic clove and bay leaf. Stir in the mint and check the seasoning.

To serve, gently warm the beans over low heat. Cut the avocados into thin slices and toast the bread. Top the toast with the avocado, then the warm beans. Scatter with the parsley leaves.

Scrambled eggs, asparagus and hot-smoked salmon

With our busy lives, many of us tend to only have eggs on the weekend, and more often than not for us it's scrambled eggs. Once you are confident with them, you can easily make them for a crowd if you need to. I have to admit I can't make scrambled eggs without cream and a favourite way to make them special is to add the zest of an orange at the end of cooking. When cooking scrambled eggs for two you'll need two pieces of equipment: a 22 cm non-stick frying pan (and yes I throw them away once they're scratched) and a heatproof flexible spatula. I put the smallest amount of butter in the pan to sizzle but not colour before adding the beaten eggs. I let the spatula move the eggs around and as soon as the first curds start to form I move them into the centre. Continue moving the curds with the spatula, then take the pan off the heat when the eggs are shiny but still runny – the residual warmth of the pan and continued movement of the curds will finish the cooking very quickly. The plates need to be warm and the accompaniments ready so you can serve your beautiful eggs immediately.

SERVES 2

1 bunch asparagus, ends trimmed
20 g unsalted butter
160 g hot- or wood-smoked salmon, skin and bones removed

Scrambled eggs

4–6 free-range eggs
2 tablespoons pouring cream
Sea salt flakes and freshly ground black pepper
10 g unsalted butter
½ teaspoon black chia seeds

Place the asparagus in a microwave-safe container with 2 tablespoons water and cook on high for 1 minute. Drain off the water and place the butter on top to melt over the asparagus. Alternatively, drop the asparagus into a large saucepan of lightly salted boiling water and cook for 3–5 minutes, depending on thickness. Drain and top with the butter. Divide the asparagus and salmon between 2 warm plates.

To make the scrambled eggs, whisk the eggs and cream together in a bowl and season to taste. Heat a medium non-stick frying pan over medium heat. Add the butter and let it sizzle and coat the bottom of the pan. Pour the egg mixture into the pan and stir gently with a heatproof spatula just until the eggs start to set. The trick to perfect scrambled eggs is to take the pan off the heat when the mixture is glossy but not yet set as they will continue cooking once off the heat. Divide the eggs between the plates, sprinkle with the chia seeds and serve immediately.

Goat's cheese and spinach omelette with pepitas and cherry tomato salsa

The thing with eggs is not to overcook them. Often when I'm travelling and too tired to go out for an evening meal I'll ask the hotel for an omelette. Perhaps harder than it looks but it's all about having a light touch and taking the omelette off the heat before it is cooked through. The tip about the size of the pan and spatula for the scrambled eggs (see page 73) holds true for this recipe too.

SERVES 2

2½ tablespoons extra virgin olive oil
20 g pepitas (pumpkin seeds)
Sea salt flakes and freshly ground
   black pepper
4 free-range eggs
10 g unsalted butter
120 g English spinach,
   stalks trimmed
60 g goat's cheese, crumbled
1 tablespoon chopped
   flat-leaf parsley

Tomato salsa

¼ small red onion
100 g cherry tomatoes
2 teaspoons extra virgin olive oil
1 teaspoon good-quality
   red wine vinegar
3 large basil leaves, finely chopped
Sea salt flakes and freshly ground
   black pepper

To make the tomato salsa, dice the red onion as finely as you can and place it in a small bowl. Cut the cherry tomatoes in half, then in half again and into 6 pieces. Place in the bowl with the onion and the remaining salsa ingredients, stir and set aside.

Heat 2 teaspoons olive oil in a small frying pan over medium heat. Add the pepitas and stir for 2–3 minutes or until crisp. Drain on paper towel and season lightly with salt.

Crack 2 eggs into a bowl and the remaining 2 eggs into a second bowl. Whisk with a fork until just combined.

Place a well-seasoned, preferably non-stick frying pan over high heat and add the butter. When melted, add the spinach and cook just until wilted. Drain well and season with salt and pepper. Set aside.

Wipe the pan clean with paper towel and place over medium heat with 1 tablespoon olive oil. Pour one of the egg mixes into the pan and, using a spatula move the mix from the outer edge into the centre working your way around the whole pan. Once the egg has just set, top with half the spinach, goat's cheese and parsley and season with salt and pepper. Fold the top third of the omelette over the filling, then fold the bottom third over. Invert onto a serving plate so the loose edges are underneath. Keep in a warm place while you make the second omelette. Top with the tomato salsa, toasted pepitas and a pinch of salt.

NUTRITION Eggs are a rich source of complete protein, as well as vitamin D, B2 and B12, selenium, and they also provide some vitamin K and zinc.

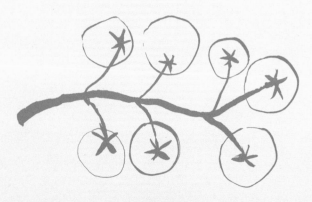

Any hotel that can provide a perfect omelette on room service is one I want to go back to.

Buckwheat porridge with banana and hazelnuts

I had to smile when I read over my first instruction in the method: to soak the buckwheat overnight, and drain and rinse twice during this time. I don't mean you have to get up in the middle of the night to do this, but the draining and rinsing twice before you cook does make a difference. And while I've suggested almond milk here you could easily use any milk, from cow's to soy. When cooking the porridge, make sure you control the simmer so that it cooks slowly but doesn't burn when all the moisture evaporates – you could partially cover it with a lid if that helps. I love the combination of banana and hazelnuts but this is great with any fruit or nuts, and more milk if you like a looser porridge.

SERVES 2

½ cup (100 g) buckwheat kernels
400 ml unsweetened almond milk, preferably homemade (see page 270), plus extra to serve (optional)
1 tablespoon pure maple syrup or raw honey, plus extra to serve (optional)
¼ teaspoon ground cinnamon
Pinch of sea salt flakes
2 small Lady Finger bananas (see note)
3 tablespoons chopped toasted hazelnuts

Soak the buckwheat in 200 ml cold water overnight; drain and rinse twice during the soaking time.

The following morning, place the soaked, drained buckwheat in a saucepan with the milk, maple syrup or honey, cinnamon and salt. Bring to the boil over medium heat, then reduce the heat to low and simmer, stirring regularly, for 25 minutes or until soft and the liquid has evaporated. Remove from the heat and divide between 2 bowls.

Top each bowl with sliced banana, a drizzle of maple syrup, if using, and the chopped toasted hazelnuts. Pour over more almond milk if desired and serve immediately.

Note: Lady Finger bananas need the skin to be generously marked with black to be ripe.

Summer bircher muesli with berries, almonds and yoghurt

This is particularly filling in that wholesome way but I can guarantee you it's delicious too. It's very quick to put together – you just need to be organised the night before. I keep the skin on the apples and drizzle over some lemon juice as soon as I grate them to stop oxidation. You can of course leave out the vanilla, and use cow's milk, soy or almond milk if preferred.

SERVES 4

1 cup (90 g) organic rolled oats
2 tablespoons white chia seeds
240 ml coconut milk, or milk of choice
70 ml natural coconut water
⅔ cup (190 g) natural probiotic yoghurt
½ teaspoon vanilla extract (optional)
2 Granny Smith apples
Finely grated zest and juice of 1 lemon
½ cup (70 g) sliced strawberries
½ cup (70 g) raspberries
3 tablespoons blueberries
3 tablespoons flaked almonds, lightly toasted

In a bowl, combine the oats, chia seeds, coconut milk, coconut water, yoghurt and vanilla, if using. Cover and refrigerate overnight.

The following day, grate the unpeeled apples into a bowl and immediately toss through the lemon zest and juice. Divide the muesli among 4 bowls, then top with the berries and toasted almonds.

NUTRITION ✎ A great start to the day – oats are a good source of fibre, manganese, copper and antioxidants, including the phenolic ferulic acid.

Blueberry, chia and coconut smoothie

Smoothies became an important part of my life a few years ago when I was lucky enough to receive a Vitamix, a blender with a really powerful motor. I tend to be very ad hoc about putting ingredients together, but I definitely take advantage of summer berries from our Saturday Barossa market and try to have properly ripe bananas on hand, which I peel, cut into chunks and freeze. Frozen fruit not only adds flavour, it instantly creates an iced drink. I like to keep a good supply of coconut water, which I buy by the case to be more economical.

SERVES 2

125 g fresh or frozen blueberries

150 g ripe fresh or frozen banana

3 tablespoons raw macadamia nuts (see note)

200 ml natural coconut water

1 tablespoon white chia seeds

1–2 tablespoons lemon juice, to taste

100 g ice cubes (unless using frozen fruit)

Small handful mint leaves, to serve

Place all the ingredients, except the mint, in the jug of a high-powered blender and blend until smooth and creamy. Pour into 2 glasses and serve immediately, topped with mint leaves.

Note: Remember to store macadamias, almonds, hazelnuts, walnuts, pine nuts and brazil nuts in the refrigerator as they are very prone to rancidity.

NUTRITION 🌿 Blueberries will provide you with plenty of anthocyanin antioxidants as well as some vitamin K and C.

Strawberry, blueberry and coconut smoothie

Surprise, surprise: another smoothie! But during summer the strawberry grower at the Barossa market sells huge trays of tempting fruit picked so ripe they are just crying out to be eaten. The only thing to look out for with berries of any kind is that unless you're buying freshly picked fruit direct from the grower they will have been layered on top of each other in punnets and refrigerated, causing them to sweat when taken in and out of the refrigerator. If you are buying them in advance, turn them out onto a plate in a single layer with some absorbent paper and refrigerate to stop them going mouldy.

SERVES 4

250 g strawberries, hulled

125 g blueberries

125 g raspberries

1 banana (see note), peeled

1 tablespoon black chia seeds, plus extra to serve

270 ml coconut milk

2½ cups (625 ml) natural coconut water or water

Mint leaves and extra berries, to serve (optional)

Place all the ingredients, except the mint leaves and extra berries, in the jug of a high-powered blender and blend until smooth and creamy. Pour into 4 glasses and serve immediately, topped with extra chia seeds, berries and mint leaves, if using.

Note: If available use Lady Finger bananas as they have a beautiful flavour, but to be ripe the skin must be marked with black patches, otherwise they are just full of starch and tannin.

Mango, lime and ginger smoothie

This is a particularly luscious smoothie: an irresistible combination of mango and coconut cream with the kick of ginger at the end. I have very fond memories of the Parap Markets in Darwin where there was such an exciting variety of mango smoothies on offer, and we felt it was only right to try as many as we could in the interests of market research! It was the perfect food to enjoy in that tropical heat.

SERVES 4

2 tablespoons coconut cream
3 cm piece ginger, peeled
Finely grated zest and juice of 2 limes
1 ripe mango (about 200 g flesh)
200 ml natural coconut water
150 g banana
80 g ice cubes

Place all the ingredients in the jug of a high-powered blender and blend until smooth and creamy. Pour into 4 glasses and serve immediately.

Almond pancakes with peaches and yoghurt

It's February as I write this and we're picking peaches from our orchard right this minute. The tragedy is that so many ripen at once and we don't really have a local market for fresh fruit (sad but true, as most Australian supermarkets buy from large central producers). I can't bear waste so we dry the larger peaches on trays in the sun, and ripen the smaller ones gradually, then steam them, slip off their skins while they are warm and cryovac them for later use. Peaches are a natural companion for breakfast pancakes, and at the other end of the day they make a great Bellini!

MAKES 18

110 g wholemeal or spelt flour
½ teaspoon bicarbonate of soda
½ teaspoon baking powder
1 tablespoon caster sugar
30 g ground almonds
2 free-range eggs
50 g natural probiotic yoghurt, plus extra to serve
130 ml unsweetened almond milk,
    preferably homemade (see page 270)
40 g unsalted butter
3 large yellow peaches, thinly sliced
Raw honey, to serve

Place the flour, bicarbonate of soda, baking powder, sugar and ground almonds in a large bowl. Whisk to combine well.

In a separate bowl, whisk the eggs, yoghurt and almond milk until well combined. Add to the dry ingredients and stir well to combine.

Melt a knob of butter in a large non-stick frying pan over medium heat. When the butter is foaming, add heaped tablespoons of batter and cook for about 3 minutes on each side until golden. Repeat with the remaining butter and batter. Serve the warm pancakes with the sliced peaches, extra yoghurt and a drizzle of honey.

The scent of our cool room full of peaches is so heady, so perfumed — it's just wonderful.

These crepes are a great way of using leftover caponata which actually improves in flavour after sitting for a day.

Chickpea crepes with caponata and yoghurt

I'm an early riser but would never think of making the caponata just for breakfast - you'll need to have some tucked away in your refrigerator. I often add a tiny bit of grated dark chocolate – just enough to add an intriguing, undefinable flavour. If you are ever asked if you added chocolate you know you have added too much! Chickpea batters are best made the night before, and make sure you skim off any froth before using. This is probably more of a brunch than a breakfast recipe.

SERVES 5

30 g unsalted butter
200 g baby spinach
200 g labneh (see page 271)

Crepes

½ cup (75 g) chickpea flour (besan)
½ cup (80 g) wholemeal plain flour
½ teaspoon sea salt flakes
3 free-range eggs
2 cups (500 ml) milk
Extra virgin olive oil, for cooking

Caponata

3 tablespoons extra virgin olive oil
1 large brown onion, finely chopped
2 large garlic cloves, finely chopped
2 tablespoons red wine vinegar
1 x 400 g tin low-salt crushed
    tomatoes
350 g eggplant (about 1 large),
    cut into 1.5 cm cubes
2 sticks celery, cut into 1 cm
    thick slices
1 tablespoon baby capers
    in brine, drained
Sea salt flakes and freshly ground
    black pepper
3 tablespoons chopped basil

To make the crepes, place the flours and salt in a large bowl and combine well.

In a separate bowl, lightly beat the eggs and milk together. Whisking constantly, add the egg mixture to the flour until smooth and well combined. Pour into a jug, then cover and set aside for 1–2 hours or refrigerate overnight if time permits.

Meanwhile, to make the caponata, heat 1 tablespoon olive oil in a large heavy-based saucepan over low heat. Add the onion and garlic and cook gently for 10 minutes or until translucent. Add the vinegar and simmer for 30 seconds, then stir in the crushed tomatoes. Cover and simmer, stirring occasionally, for 12 minutes or until slightly thickened and reduced.

Heat the remaining olive oil in a wok or large frying pan over high heat. Add the eggplant and saute for 6–8 minutes or until soft and golden. Remove from the pan and add to the tomato sauce once it has thickened, along with the celery. Simmer over high heat for 2 minutes to bring it all together, then stir in the capers and season to taste. Stir in the chopped basil just before serving. Caponata can be made 2 days ahead but only add the basil when you are ready to serve.

To cook the crepes, heat a 24 cm non-stick frying pan over medium heat. Grease the pan with a little olive oil (wipe off the excess or the pancake will slide), then pour in a thin layer of batter, tilting the pan as you go to spread the batter evenly and thinly over the base. Cook for 1 minute on each side or until golden. Transfer to a plate and repeat with the remaining batter, stacking the crepes as you go. Makes about 10.

To serve, heat the butter in a large frying pan over high heat. Add the spinach and saute just until wilted. Remove from the pan and drain well. Place the stack of crepes and the pan of caponata (hot or at room temperature) in the centre of the table for guests to assemble themselves. Fill each crepe with a little caponata and sauteed spinach, then top with a dollop of labneh, roll up and tuck in.

NUTRITION 🌿 Caponata supplies lycopene antioxidant from the tomatoes, polyphenol antioxidants from the onion, and fibre, flavonoid antioxidants and vitamin B6 are provided by the eggplant.

Roasted apricots on grilled spelt toast with ricotta

Such a simple breakfast but it really sets me up for the day. I am particular about my ricotta (and just about everything else) and only buy the fresh ricotta in the open-sided plastic mould that has quite a short use-by date on it. I have no trouble finding lots of ways to use it. As ever, this dish is only as good as the ingredients used to create it. Fresh ripe apricots are only available for a blink in time but are so worth it when you can find them, and of course you could use any other stone fruit or reconstituted dried fruit here too. The honey is only needed if the fruit isn't fulsomely ripe.

SERVES 4

⅓ cup (25 g) flaked almonds
6 ripe locally grown apricots
20 g unsalted butter
1 large sprig rosemary, leaves stripped
4 slices spelt rye or sourdough bread
1½ tablespoons extra virgin olive oil
240 g very fresh ricotta, at room temperature
   (see page 271 if you want to make your own)
Raw honey, for drizzling (optional)

Preheat the oven to 200°C (fan-forced).

Place the almonds on a baking tray and bake for 4–5 minutes or until lightly toasted.

Cut the apricots in half and place cut-side up on a baking tray lined with baking paper. Place a small piece of butter in the centre of each apricot half and scatter with the rosemary leaves, then roast for 8 minutes or until golden and soft. Remove from the oven and set aside to cool, then cut into slices.

Toast the bread, then drizzle with olive oil. Top with the ricotta, then the apricots, flaked almonds and a drizzle of honey, if using, and serve immediately.

Porridge with pistachio and orange

Autumn is the season for fresh pistachios and, luckily for me, a good friend has a small orchard of them. Freshly baked they are wonderful to eat and the trees are just beautiful to look at. Valencia oranges are also in season at this time of year and I love their zingy freshness against the richness of the porridge. If you happen to have roses in the garden and you haven't sprayed them, now is the time to dry a few for scattering over your food.

SERVES 2

4 green cardamom pods, crushed
¾ cup (65 g) organic rolled oats
200 ml coconut milk
1 tablespoon finely grated orange zest
1 orange, segmented
2 tablespoons chopped toasted pistachios
1 tablespoon raw honey

Place the crushed cardamom pods in a small saucepan with the oats, coconut milk and 200 ml water. Bring to the boil, then reduce the heat to low and simmer for 8 minutes or until creamy and the oats are soft. Remove from the heat and stir in the orange zest.

Spoon the porridge into 2 bowls. Top with the orange segments, pistachios and a drizzle of honey. If you happen to have rose petals or pomegranate in the garden, they would make a lovely garnish.

NUTRITION 🌿 A sprinkle of pistachios provides vitamin B6, magnesium, protein and fibre as well as flavonoid antioxidants.

Breakfast baked eggs

I am fussy about lots of things, and enjoying
a regular supply of free-range eggs from our
five chooks who are fed a vegetarian diet have
spoilt me for any commercial egg. I love one-pot
meals at any time, not least because it cuts down
on the washing up! The trick here is choosing your
cooking container wisely as it will influence the
'setting' of the eggs – if, like me, you want your
yolks really runny you'll find a thicker cooking
vessel best as it cooks everything more slowly.

SERVES 2

½ teaspoon cumin seeds
3 tablespoons extra virgin olive oil, plus extra
  for drizzling
2 large red capsicums, peeled with a potato peeler,
  seeds and membrane removed, thinly sliced
2 bay leaves
6 sprigs thyme, leaves stripped
2 tablespoons verjuice
400 g juicy ripe tomatoes, coarsely chopped
½ teaspoon saffron threads
1 cup (250 ml) vegetable stock
1 teaspoon pomegranate molasses
2 free-range eggs
Sea salt flakes and freshly ground black pepper
½ cup flat-leaf parsley leaves, chopped

Preheat the oven to 200°C (fan-forced).

Dry-roast the cumin seeds in a large frying pan over
high heat for 1 minute or until just fragrant. Add
the olive oil, sliced capsicum, bay leaves and thyme
and cook for 5–10 minutes or until golden. Add the
verjuice and simmer until it has nearly evaporated.
Reduce the heat to low, then add the tomatoes, saffron
and stock and simmer for 15 minutes or until slightly
reduced and thickened. If the sauce gets too dry add
a little more stock or water – you're looking for a pasta
sauce consistency. Remove from the heat.

Remove and discard the bay leaves. Stir in the
pomegranate molasses, then adjust the seasoning.
Pour the sauce into an ovenproof frying pan or dish.
Make 2 small evenly spaced indents in the sauce and
crack the eggs into the hollows. Bake for 8 minutes
or until the eggs are just set. Remove from the oven.
Drizzle with olive oil, scatter with parsley and finish
with a grinding of pepper. Serve immediately.

Pomegranate and walnut bircher muesli

I don't want to make you jealous but because
we live on a country property we have so many
food-bearing plants, some 200 pomegranate
bushes amongst them. They are mostly in the form
of hedges, so fruiting is minimal compared with
planting in open rows, but there is no shortage of
this wonderful fruit so I can wait until it starts to
open up to show it's ripe before I pick it. This is
a great advantage as it's not always so easy to
tell when pomegranates for sale look so 'closed'
and perfect.

SERVES 4

¾ cup (65 g) organic rolled oats
⅓ cup (70 g) buckinis (see page 278)
1 tablespoon chia seeds
200 ml almond milk, preferably homemade
  (see page 270) or milk of choice
⅓ cup (35 g) walnuts
2 small pears
Finely grated zest of 1 lemon
120 g natural probiotic yoghurt
Pinch of sea salt flakes
1 large ripe pomegranate, seeded

Place the rolled oats, buckinis, chia seeds, milk and
100 ml water in a medium bowl and stir well. Cover
and refrigerate overnight.

Preheat the oven to 180°C (fan-forced). Place the
walnuts on a baking tray and toast for 8–10 minutes
or until golden. Pour into a clean tea towel and rub off
the skins while still warm. Cool, then finely chop.

When ready to eat, coarsely grate the pears into the
oat mixture. Add the lemon zest, yoghurt, salt and half
each of the pomegranate seeds and walnuts. Stir well,
then divide evenly among 4 bowls. Scatter with the
remaining pomegranate seeds and walnuts.

Kale and fruit smoothie

This is the base recipe for a smoothie I have after my early-morning walk. Whether I make it with cavolo nero, curly kale, spinach or sorrel changes with the season but it's always a bunch out of my garden. And when I have coriander in flower it adds an amazing dimension to the smoothie. As we have an orchard of apples, pears, apricots and peaches I have a particular love of pears but because they all ripen at about the same time, no matter how much fruit we have, there are times during the year when we have to rely on green pears in cold storage, which I leave to ripen in the fruit bowl before I use them. At other times of the year I use kiwifruit, mangoes, banana, loquats or papaya – whatever is going.

SERVES 2

125 g kale, leaves stripped (50 g trimmed),
   or other greens such as cavolo nero or spinach
2 kiwifruit, peeled, plus extra to serve
1 tablespoon finely chopped ginger
½ cup (140 g) natural probiotic yoghurt
1 cup (250 ml) natural coconut water
80 g ice cubes

Place all the ingredients in a high-powered blender and process on high speed until smooth. Pour into 2 cups or glasses, top with extra sliced kiwifruit and serve immediately.

Note: I use a Vitamix as it has a very high speed, and with the exception of kiwifruit, I use all the peel and the pulp of the fruit.

Autumn fruit smoothie

In the first draft of recipes for this book I found that I had 18 dishes with pomegranate arils (seeds) in them. I had to pare this back as getting ripe full-flavoured pomegranates isn't always easy but I do love the sweet and sour flavour of this amazing fruit and there are so many ways to use it, starting with breakfast and moving right through the day.

SERVES 2

1 large dark red ripe pomegranate (see note)
25 seedless red grapes
2 cm piece ginger, peeled and chopped
300 ml natural coconut water
2 teaspoons extra virgin coconut oil, melted
1 large ripe banana
80 g ice cubes

Cut the pomegranate in half and tease out a small amount of seeds for serving. Squeeze the juice from the remaining pomegranate by using an old-fashioned orange juicer.

Place all the ingredients in a high-powered blender and blend on high until smooth. Divide between 2 glasses and sprinkle with the reserved seeds.

Note: If you are growing your own pomegranates as I do in the Barossa, pick them at the first sign of them starting to split as this indicates they are ripe. It's harder to tell when you buy perfect ones from the supermarket. Once they are established they are very easy to grow with minimum water, especially in Mediterranean climates.

Pomegranate arils are not just for breakfast!
When the day is coming to an end, they give
a whole new meaning to 'pink gin'.

Pear and nut muesli

Macadamias work really well here. We are lucky enough to have 10 trees and a rustic-looking but very effective cracking apparatus on the back verandah, which our grandchildren learn to use at a very young age – I mean so they can eat freshly cracked macadamias, not slave labour shelling them for me! If preferred, replace the macadamias with walnuts or hazelnuts, or just use all almonds. I always store nuts in the refrigerator for freshness.

SERVES 4

⅓ cup (55 g) almonds
60 g macadamia nuts
3 tablespoons sesame seeds
2 small–medium ripe pears, grated with skin on
3 tablespoons extra virgin coconut oil, melted
400 g natural probiotic yoghurt, plus extra
   to serve (optional)
⅔ cup (50 g) desiccated coconut
2½ tablespoons chia seeds
Pinch of sea salt flakes
Finely grated zest of 1 lemon
Extra thinly sliced pear, to serve (optional)

Preheat the oven to 180°C (fan-forced).

Place the almonds and macadamias on a baking tray and bake for 8–10 minutes or until golden. Remove from the oven, stand until cool, then coarsely chop. Place the sesame seeds on the tray and bake for 6–8 minutes or until golden.

Place the nuts, seeds, grated pear, coconut oil, yoghurt, desiccated coconut, chia seeds, salt and lemon zest in a medium bowl. Add 2 tablespoons warm water and combine well. Cover and refrigerate overnight.

Remove the muesli from the refrigerator 20 minutes before serving and stand at room temperature. Divide among 4 bowls, then top with extra yoghurt and sliced pear, if using.

Nut and dried pear muesli

If you're a nut lover you're in luck here, as long as you prepare this muesli the night before. The combination of nuts, seeds and apple gives a great mix of sweetness and acidity, and the dried pear halves I've already waxed lyrical about are just great eating. You might think I'm the nut but I always feel quite virtuous when I've been organised enough to make this for the next day's breakfast.

SERVES 4

65 g sunflower seeds
30 g pepitas (pumpkin seeds)
60 g macadamia nuts
75 g blanched almonds
2 dried Australian pear halves
30 g sultanas
1 Pink Lady apple
1 teaspoon finely grated lemon zest
3 teaspoons lemon juice
½ cup (125 ml) apple juice or verjuice
½ cup (140 g) natural probiotic yoghurt,
   plus extra to serve

Place the seeds and nuts in separate bowls, cover with cold water and stand overnight. If the pear halves are plump, there's no need to soak them.

The following day, drain all the soaked ingredients and rinse through a fine sieve. Transfer to a blender. Add the dried fruit, apple, lemon zest and juices and blend on high until smooth – you may need to add a little water. Stir in the yoghurt.

To serve, divide among 4 bowls and top with extra yoghurt, if using.

NUTRITION 🌰 Our most loved indigenous food, macadamias provide monounsaturated fatty acids, as well as fibre and magnesium.

Poached quince, yoghurt and almond crumble

I can't imagine life without a quince tree – it's such a wonderful addition to the garden if you have space. We have six different varieties in our home orchard so I can have a spread of quinces over the whole season, which is a delight as there is so much more to do with them than make quince paste (as much as I love that). This breakfast recipe is a perfect example.

SERVES 6

2 quinces (see note)
½ lemon
2 tablespoons raw honey
Thick natural probiotic yoghurt,
   to serve

Crumble

1 cup (80 g) flaked almonds
1 cup (90 g) organic rolled oats
1 teaspoon ground cinnamon
Pinch of sea salt flakes
½ cup (80 g) extra virgin coconut
   oil, melted
½ cup (125 ml) pure maple syrup

Note: Quinces only develop their beautiful ruby colour when cooked for a couple of hours. Cooked for just 25 minutes in this breakfast recipe they will be a warm golden colour.

Wash, peel and core the quinces, reserving the skins and cores. Squeeze the lemon into a large bowl of cold water. Cut into quarters or eighths depending on the size, placing them into the acidulated water as you go to prevent discolouration.

Place the reserved skins and cores, honey and just enough water to cover in a saucepan over medium heat and simmer for 30 minutes. Add the quince wedges and enough water to cover them and cook for 25 minutes or until tender but not falling apart.

Preheat the oven to 180˚C (fan-forced). Line a baking tray with baking paper.

Meanwhile, to make the crumble, combine the almonds, oats, cinnamon and salt in a large bowl. Stir through the melted coconut oil and maple syrup until well combined. Spread the mixture evenly over the lined tray and bake for 30 minutes or until golden, stirring halfway through. Allow to cool for 5 minutes, then serve warm or allow to cool completely and store in an airtight container.

Serve the warm or cold poached quince with the crumble and a big dollop of yoghurt.

Dried pear
and rice porridge

Have you ever tried plump Australian dried pear halves? Let me tell you that they are possibly even better than dried apricots and, given that we dry our own apricots, peaches and pears, that's quite a statement from me. This porridge takes just minutes to make and I'm not hiding the fact that it needs the flavour of the coconut oil (as little as it is), honey and pear to make it moreish, but that's what cooking is all about.

SERVES 1

½ cup (55 g) brown rice flakes (see glossary page 279)

1 cup (250 ml) unsweetened almond milk, preferably homemade (see page 270) or milk of choice, plus extra if needed

2 dried Australian pear halves, thinly sliced

1 teaspoon extra virgin coconut oil

1 teaspoon raw honey

Pinch of freshly grated nutmeg

Pinch of sea salt flakes

1 tablespoon toasted flaked almonds

½ small ripe pear, sliced

Place the rice flakes, milk and dried pear in a small saucepan and bring to the boil over medium heat. Once boiling, reduce the heat to as low as possible and simmer, stirring occasionally for 4–5 minutes or until thickened and the flakes are cooked.

Remove from the heat, stir in the coconut oil and honey, then add the nutmeg and salt to taste. If you prefer a moister porridge, stir in a little extra milk. Spoon into a serving bowl, top with the almonds and pear slices and serve immediately.

NUTRITION 🍃 Pears are a source of antioxidant anti-inflammatory flavonoids and some fibre, especially if you don't peel the fresh one.

Orange almond winter smoothie

While the green smoothie on page 88 is my everyday one, in winter this smoothie is a real tonic and the more variety we have in our food the better. I confess I'm stuck in bit of a rut with the routine of coming back from my walk and picking the greens from the garden as I go past without thinking, so sometimes I have to remind myself just how special this winter smoothie is and make sure I have the ingredients on hand to treat myself.

SERVES 4

1 tablespoon chia seeds
350 ml unsweetened almond milk,
   preferably homemade (see page 270)
1 large ripe banana
1 lime, peel, white pith and seeds removed
2 oranges, peel, white pith and seeds removed
1 tablespoon extra virgin coconut oil, melted
15 g ginger, peeled and chopped
35 g raw honey

Place all the ingredients in a high-powered blender and process until smooth and creamy. Divide among 4 glasses and serve.

Old-fashioned oats with banana and sultanas

This doesn't take long to make on the stove top but has nothing to do with 'instant' oats. I've been known to cook oats in the microwave when in a hurry and although it has all the same goodness, it just doesn't taste like it. I love a Lady Finger banana but make sure it's really ripe (with black spots on the skin) and that drizzle of honey might not be needed but it does make a nice addition.

SERVES 4

1 cup (90 g) organic rolled oats
3 tablespoons sultanas
1 tablespoon chia seeds
½ teaspoon ground cinnamon
2 cups (500 ml) milk (cow's, nut or coconut)
1 tablespoon extra virgin coconut oil
1 tablespoon raw honey, plus extra to serve (optional)
2 Lady Finger bananas, sliced
3 tablespoons shaved macadamia nuts

Place the oats, sultanas, chia seeds, cinnamon and milk in a medium saucepan. Cook over low heat, stirring constantly, until the porridge boils and thickens. Remove from the heat and stir in the coconut oil and honey.

Divide among 4 bowls and top with sliced banana, shaved macadamias and a drizzle of extra honey, if desired.

NUTRITION Bananas provide vitamin B6, manganese and water- soluble fibre.

Coconut oil granola with macadamias and raisins

This makes a good batch of granola that keeps well in an airtight container. Using extra virgin coconut oil rather than extra virgin olive oil makes it less likely to become rancid if you take your time getting through it. I find so many granolas are too sweet for me so I hold back on the honey as there's already a lot of sweetness in the dried pears and raisins, but if this isn't right for you just adjust it to suit your palate.

MAKES ABOUT 1.6 KG

500 g organic rolled oats
45 g puffed millet
1 cup (75 g) shredded coconut
135 g pepitas (pumpkin seeds)
80 g sunflower seeds
50 g linseeds (flaxseeds)
250 g macadamia nuts, chopped
1 teaspoon ground cinnamon
Sea salt flakes
3 tablespoons extra virgin coconut oil
⅓ cup (120 g) raw honey or ⅓ cup (80 ml)
   pure maple syrup
175 g raisins
100 g dried Australian pears, thinly sliced

Preheat the oven to 160°C (fan-forced). Line 2 large baking trays with baking paper.

In an extra-large bowl, combine the oats, millet, coconut, seeds, nuts, cinnamon and a little salt.

Melt the coconut oil and honey or maple syrup in a small saucepan over low heat. Stir through the dry ingredients until well combined.

Spread the mixture evenly over the lined trays. Bake for 30–40 minutes or until golden, stirring every 15 minutes to make sure the mixture toasts evenly. Remove from the oven and stand to cool completely, then stir in the dried fruit. Store in an airtight container for up to 2 weeks.

Tahini and coconut muesli

Another recipe with lots of seeds, nuts and dried fruit but the difference here is the tahini, which adds a great savoury flavour to the mix. I'd always just used orange zest in this until one day I happened to have a pile of mandarins and I dried the skins in a very old home-style dehydrator that I bring out from the back of a cupboard occasionally. I ground the dried skins to a powder and added some to the muesli. The result was fabulous, but it's definitely optional.

SERVES 8-10 (MAKES ABOUT 800 G)

125 g brown rice flakes (see page 278)
125 g organic rolled oats
60 g coconut flakes
70 g blanched almonds
35 g pepitas (pumpkin seeds)
40 g sesame seeds
1 tablespoon finely grated orange zest
¼ teaspoon sea salt flakes
1 tablespoon extra virgin coconut oil
2 tablespoons raw honey
50 g unhulled tahini
½ cup (80 g) sultanas
⅓ cup (60 g) dates, seeded and very thinly sliced
60 g dried peaches or pears, very thinly sliced
2 teaspoons mandarin skin powder (see page 275)
   (optional)

Preheat the oven to 180°C (fan-forced). Line 2 large baking trays with baking paper.

Combine the rice flakes, oats, coconut flakes, almonds, seeds, orange zest and salt in a large bowl.

Place the coconut oil, honey and tahini in a small saucepan. Bring to the boil over low heat, then pour over the dry ingredients and mix well, taking care to coat all the dry ingredients. Spread the mixture evenly over the lined trays and bake, stirring occasionally for 20–30 minutes or until golden and toasted. To check whether the flakes are crisp, take a small amount and cool out of the oven, then taste. Remove the muesli from the oven and set aside to cool completely. Stir in the dried fruit and mandarin skin powder, if using. Store in an airtight container for up to 2 weeks.

Lunch

Sweet potato fritters with smashed avocado and salmon

The beauty of this recipe is that you don't need to precook any of the ingredients so it's a quick process, particularly if you have a helper. The salmon could be cooked, raw or from a tin and well drained. Like all fritters they don't take long but they need to cook at a low temperature to make sure the raw grated vegetables are cooked through and soft. The best avocados are those that haven't been refrigerated, but when you consider the logistics of moving food around the country these days that's more and more unlikely, so my tip is to buy them when they're still hard and ripen them yourself at room temperature, which can easily take up to 10 days.

SERVES 4
(MAKES 8 FRITTERS)

1 ripe Hass avocado
Juice of 1 lime
2 tablespoons extra virgin olive oil, plus extra to serve
200 g salmon fillet, cooked and flaked (see note) or smoked or tinned salmon
Dill or chervil sprigs and lime wedges, to serve

Fritters

400 g sweet potato, peeled
Sea salt flakes and freshly ground black pepper
2 large leaves silverbeet, finely chopped
1 spring onion, finely chopped
2 free-range eggs
1 teaspoon chopped coriander
2 tablespoons extra virgin olive oil

Preheat the oven to 150°C (fan-forced).

To make the fritters, coarsely grate the sweet potato, then place in a bowl and mix in 1 teaspoon sea salt. Stand for 10 minutes, then drain the sweet potato and squeeze out any excess liquid.

In a separate bowl, place the chopped silverbeet, spring onion, eggs and coriander. Add the sweet potato, season to taste and mix well.

Heat the olive oil in a large frying pan over medium heat. Working in 2 batches, place 3 tablespoons of mixture for each fritter into the pan and press down with a spatula. Cook on both sides for 2–3 minutes or until golden, then drain on paper towel. Place on a baking tray, cover with foil and keep warm in the oven while you cook the remaining fritters.

Smash the avocado flesh and lime juice in a bowl until smooth. Stir in the olive oil and season to taste.

To serve, place 2 fritters on each plate. Top with the smashed avocado, salmon and sprigs of dill or chervil. Drizzle with olive oil and serve with lime wedges.

Note: If using fresh salmon, drizzle a little olive oil in a frying pan over high heat. Add the fish, skin-side down and cook for 3 minutes or to the point where it will almost burn. Remove the salmon, then quickly wipe out the pan with paper towel, being careful not to burn yourself. Add a drizzle of oil or a bit of butter to the pan, reduce the heat to low–medium and return the salmon to the pan, skin-side up. Cook for 2 minutes, then rest for 10 minutes. Remove and discard the skin, then flake the fish.

Avocados are a staple in my kitchen as different varieties ripen throughout the year and there are so many ways to use them.

Tofu with broccolini, smoked almonds and pickled ginger

I actually prefer silken tofu to other varieties but it can be a little tricky to cook as it falls apart easily so I've selected extra-firm tofu for this recipe. Still, for texture and mouthfeel silken is always my first choice — give it a try once you've had some experience with tofu. In case you haven't read any of the other recipes and come straight to this one, I need to tell you that I'm very comfortable with cooking vegetables in the microwave, particularly greens. One of my food heroes, Harold McGee, wrote in his book *Keys to Good Cooking*: 'Microwaving is a very efficient and rapid way to cook small portions of vegetables and preserves their vitamins and flavour better than boiling or steaming.' It's also a wonderful way to retain the vibrant colour of cooked greens. I recommend tossing them with some water and oil or butter to prevent them from drying out.

SERVES 4

400 g extra-firm tofu (preferably packed in water)
2 bunches broccolini, bases trimmed
3 tablespoons extra virgin olive oil, plus extra for drizzling
Sea salt flakes
1 tablespoon pickled ginger with 1 teaspoon of the pickling juices
100 g smoked almonds, coarsely chopped
Watercress sprigs or other herbs, to serve

Marinade

3 tablespoons lemon juice
1 tablespoon extra virgin olive oil
1 clove garlic, minced
2 teaspoons oregano leaves
Sea salt flakes and freshly ground black pepper

To make the marinade, whisk all the ingredients together in a small bowl.

Drain and rinse the tofu, then pat dry. Cut the block crossways into eight 1 cm thick slices and place in a shallow dish. Add the marinade and turn to coat. Cover and refrigerate for at least 30 minutes or for up to 8 hours.

Place the broccolini in a microwave-safe container. Add a dash of water and cover with a lid. Cook on high for 1½ minutes, then drain. Alternatively, cook the broccolini in a saucepan of lightly salted boiling water for 3–4 minutes or until just tender but still firm to the bite, then drain.

Drain the tofu from the marinade and pat dry on paper towel. Heat the olive oil in a large frying pan over high heat. Cook the tofu for 1 minute on each side or until golden, then remove from the pan. Drain all but 1 tablespoon olive oil from the pan. Add the drained broccolini, season with salt and toss until coated in the oil and heated through. Add the pickled ginger and the pickling juice

To serve, scatter the broccolini over a large serving plate. Top with the tofu and any pan juices, then scatter with the smoked almonds and watercress sprigs or fresh herbs. Drizzle with a little extra olive oil and serve immediately.

NUTRITION 🍃 Broccolini is a very good source of vitamins C and K, folate, and anti-inflammatory sulphur-containing compounds.

Roasted garlic mushrooms on toast with avocado

This dish needs big meaty open mushrooms that are just packed with flavour. Once the ingredients are prepared it takes less than 10 minutes to get it on the table. Again, I've used avocado but it is an optional extra. The vital part is to have good bread toasted and ready so you can pile the mushrooms on top and let all the juices soak into the bread. Any freshly chopped herb will finish it nicely. See page 100 for a tip about buying avocados – it's worth knowing.

SERVES 4

30 g unsalted butter
3 tablespoons extra virgin olive oil, plus extra
  for drizzling
500 g large flat-capped mushrooms, thickly sliced
1 clove garlic, smashed
6 sprigs lemon thyme, leaves stripped
Sea salt flakes and freshly ground black pepper
3 tablespoons verjuice
4 thick slices sourdough, multigrain or rye bread
1 large ripe avocado, thinly sliced
½ cup chopped flat-leaf parsley

Heat the butter and olive oil in a large frying pan over medium heat. When the butter is foaming, add the mushroom, garlic and thyme leaves and season with salt. Toss for 3–4 minutes or until the mushrooms are tender. Increase the heat to high, then add the verjuice and cook for another minute or until nearly evaporated. Remove from the heat.

Toast the bread, then top with avocado and divide among 4 plates. Spoon over the mushrooms, then scatter with chopped parsley and season. Drizzle with extra olive oil and serve immediately.

Spring slaw of red cabbage, beetroot, bok choy and asparagus with walnuts

This dish is as beautiful as a piece of art but only if the ingredients are super fresh and thinly sliced or grated. The good thing is the ingredients are interchangeable: if there is no bok choy, use broccoli instead, slicing the stems really thinly crossways separately to the heads. No red cabbage? Green cabbage will do, particularly a sugarloaf one. This versatile slaw makes a great accompaniment to a chop on the barbecue, pan-fried chicken livers or a grilled chicken thigh, or enjoy it with something even simpler like some tinned sardines on toast.

SERVES 6

⅛ red cabbage, thinly sliced
½ beetroot, peeled and grated
1 carrot, grated
½ bunch bok choy, thinly sliced
½ red onion, thinly sliced
½ bunch asparagus, ends trimmed and thinly sliced
½ cup flat-leaf parsley leaves, chopped
⅓ cup (35 g) chopped toasted walnuts

Dressing

1 teaspoon Dijon mustard
2 tablespoons sherry vinegar
⅓ cup (80 ml) extra virgin olive oil
Sea salt flakes and freshly ground black pepper

To make the dressing, whisk all the ingredients together in a small bowl.

Place all the sliced or grated vegetables in a large bowl. Add the dressing and parsley and toss to coat. Stand for 10 minutes, then scatter with walnuts and serve.

Verjuice carrots, barley and currant salad with Persian feta

This dish evolved from an occasion when all the cooks and producers of the Barossa put on a picnic for some 80 members of the media for one of the early Tasting Australia festivals. Each cook was paired with a producer and had to cook a dish for up to 40 people, depending on whether it was an accompaniment or the 'main game'. I worked with the Schmidt family, the local carrot producers at the time, and in huge pans cooked blanched young carrots in extra virgin olive oil and butter and deglazed with verjuice. That simple dish was a great hit and I've extended it here by adding a barley salad with lots of currants and herbs tossed through. I often have small amounts of barley, lentils or chickpeas left over from another dish and they are a great addition to almost any salad.

SERVES 4

3 tablespoons dried currants
3 tablespoons verjuice
½ cup (100 g) raw pearl barley
1½ cups (375 ml) chicken or
    vegetable stock or water
Sea salt flakes and freshly ground
    black pepper
2 bunches young Dutch carrots
    (about 16), rinsed and tops
    trimmed to about 2 cm
60 g unsalted butter
3 tablespoons chopped
    flat-leaf parsley
3 tablespoons chopped mint
½ cup (100 g) crumbled Persian
    feta or fresh curd
Extra virgin olive oil, for drizzling

Place the currants and verjuice in a small bowl and stand for at least 45 minutes to rehydrate. Overnight is ideal.

Place the barley in a saucepan with the stock or water and bring to the boil over medium–high heat. Reduce the heat to low, then cover and simmer for 40–50 minutes or until tender and most of the liquid has been absorbed. Remove from the heat and stand for 5 minutes. Season to taste.

Fill a large saucepan with water and bring to the boil over high heat. Add the carrots and cook for 3–5 minutes or until just half cooked. To check if the carrots are ready, remove one from the boiling water and slide a clean cloth over it – the skin should come away easily. When ready, drain the carrots and remove the skin with the cloth while the carrots are still warm. If the carrots are really fresh then leave the skins on. Allow to cool.

Heat the butter in a large frying pan over medium heat until melted and beginning to sizzle. Add the carrots, then increase the heat to high and cook for 3–5 minutes or until the carrots are tender and the butter is nut brown. Drain the currants, then add the verjuice to the pan and cook for 1 minute. Remove from the heat and season.

Combine the barley, currants, parsley and mint in a large bowl. Divide among serving plates, top with the carrots and scatter the feta over the top. Drizzle with a final flourish of olive oil and serve.

NUTRITION Carrots are a rich source of beta-carotene, fibre, the antioxidants lutein and ferulic acid, and vitamin K.

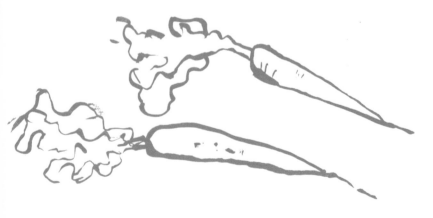

As long as it's super fresh,
raw fish is one of my favourite
things in life to eat.

Salmon ceviche with celeriac, apple, walnut and lime

I call this a ceviche rather than sashimi because the vinaigrette 'cooks' the salmon a little. In our household, Colin prepares it this way so the ceviche step is just for him. For myself I just add extra virgin olive oil and salt flakes as I love the fish totally raw. While I've used salmon here, another wonderful fish to eat raw is Hiramasa kingfish, which is also readily available as a farmed fish. As ever, you have options too so just make it the way you like it.

SERVES 4

600 g very fresh skinless salmon, bones removed
1 tablespoon lime juice
2 tablespoons verjuice
2 tablespoons extra virgin olive oil
2 tablespoons finger lime pearls (if available)
Sea salt flakes

Dressing

1½ tablespoons sour cream
½ teaspoon Dijon mustard
1 teaspoon lemon juice, plus extra if needed
1 teaspoon freshly grated horseradish
1½ tablespoons extra virgin olive oil
1½ tablespoons walnut oil
Sea salt flakes and freshly ground black pepper

Salad

Juice of ½ lemon
2 small heads celeriac
2 small Granny Smith apples
1 teaspoon finely grated lemon zest
80 g walnuts, toasted and coarsely chopped
small handful of chervil, chopped

Thinly slice the salmon against the grain and place in overlapping slices on each serving plate. Keep the salmon as cold as possible while working with it. Slice it in advance, cover with plastic film and refrigerate until ready to serve.

To make the dressing, whisk together the sour cream, mustard, lemon juice and horseradish. Combine the olive and walnut oils. Whisking constantly, gradually add the oils in a thin, steady stream until emulsified. Adjust the seasoning with salt, pepper and more lemon juice if needed.

To make the salad, squeeze the lemon into a large bowl of water. Trim the bases and tops from the celeriac, then cut down the sides to remove the skin. Using a strong vegetable peeler or mandolin, shave slices from the celeriac, dropping them into the bowl of acidulated water as you go to stop discolouration. Quarter and core the apples, then thinly slice and add to the water.

Just before serving, remove the salmon from the refrigerator. Drizzle with the lime juice, verjuice and olive oil. Scatter with finger lime pearls, if using, and a little sea salt. Stand for no longer than 5 minutes to allow the vinaigrette to 'cook' the salmon.

Meanwhile, drain the apple and celeriac well, then return to the bowl. Add the dressing and remaining salad ingredients (reserving a little of the chervil and sprinkling it over the salmon) and toss to combine. Serve the salmon immediately with the salad on the side.

NUTRITION Salmon is a rich source of complete protein, omega-3 fatty acids, vitamins B3, B12, D, and selenium.

Dukkah-crusted chicken livers with pistou and green beans

The first dish I ever cooked myself when I was about eight years old was a panful of chicken livers, and I remember my father telling me to stop picking at them or there'd be nothing left for dinner. The love of every part of the animal comes from my childhood, and livers are the most accessible offal, and the cheapest. The dukkah crust will encourage someone who is not sure about eating livers to give them a try and the pistou adds another temptation to the mix.

SERVES 4

500 g chicken livers
2 free-range eggs
2 tablespoons milk
⅔ cup (100 g) plain flour
2 tablespoons extra virgin olive oil, plus extra for drizzling
30 g unsalted butter
400 g baby green beans, topped
¾ cup (60 g) toasted flaked almonds

Pistou

125 g English spinach leaves
30 g blanched almonds
Juice of ½ lemon
½ cup (125 ml) extra virgin olive oil
1 tablespoon grated parmesan
Sea salt flakes and freshly ground black pepper

Dukkah crumb

60 g dry sourdough or rye crumbs
40 g dukkah (see page 275)
Finely grated zest of ½ lemon

To make the pistou, place all the ingredients in a food processor and blend until combined but not too fine. Season to taste.

To make the dukkah crumb, combine all the ingredients in a bowl.

Drain the chicken livers of any blood if they have come in a cryovac pack. Gently pat dry using paper towel. Cut out any connective tissues that are dominant but try and keep them as whole as possible.

Whisk the eggs and milk in a bowl, then place the flour and dukkah crumb in two separate bowls. Working with one at a time, dust the livers in flour, then dip in the egg wash allowing the excess to drain before coating evenly in the dukkah crumb.

Heat the olive oil and butter in a large frying pan over medium heat. When the butter is foaming, add the livers and gently pan-fry until golden on both sides. Drain on paper towel.

While the livers are cooking, cook the beans in a saucepan of lightly salted boiling water for 3–4 minutes or until just tender but still firm to the bite. Drain and drizzle with a little olive oil.

To serve, spread the pistou onto a serving dish. Top with the green beans, pan-fried livers and toasted almonds.

Grilled peach, labneh, rocket and smoked trout salad

I created this recipe to utilise some smoked trout I found in the local community co-op. If you were to buy about 500 grams of smoked trout and remove the skin and bones to carefully flake the flesh you would end up with round 320 grams, which in this salad would be enough for four people. The alternative is just as lovely and the next time I made this I used a 160 gram packet of hot smoked salmon, which is just the right amount for two people. Wood-smoked salmon would also be fine.

SERVES 2

½ cup (50 g) walnuts (optional)
3 small or 2 large ripe peaches
10 g unsalted butter
Large handful young rocket
Handful sorrel leaves (or an assortment of herbs and leaves)
160 g smoked trout, or wood- or hot-smoked salmon, flaked
100 g labneh (see page 271)
3 tablespoons basil leaves

Dressing

2 tablespoons verjuice
2 tablespoons walnut oil
½ teaspoon Dijon mustard
Sea salt flakes and freshly ground black pepper

Preheat the oven to 180°C (fan-forced). Place the walnuts on a baking tray and toast for 8–10 minutes. Pour into a clean tea towel and rub their skins off while still warm.

Preheat the grill to the highest heat possible.

Cut the peaches in half, remove the seeds and place, cut-side up, on a baking tray lined with baking paper. Place a dot of butter in the centre of each peach half and cook under the grill for 6–8 minutes or until golden but not overcooked.

Divide the rocket and sorrel leaves between 2 plates. Place the peaches on the leaves and scatter with the flaked fish, dollops of labneh, basil and toasted walnuts (if using).

To make the dressing, place all the ingredients in a small jar. Seal and shake until well combined. Drizzle over the salad and serve immediately.

Tri-colour roasted beetroot salad with thyme, walnut, goat's cheese and herb salad

I remember the first time I ever served goat's curd for a lunch. It was a long long time ago after a trip to France where I'd bought a bottle of amazing walnut oil. Gabrielle Kervella from Western Australia was a pioneer in making fresh goat's curd of such quality and it was available for the first time in Adelaide. I simply made a mound of it, drizzled it with the aforementioned walnut oil and toasted walnuts and served it with some roasted beetroot and leaves from the garden. I have to say it was the equal of anything I had eaten in France. This is just an extension of the simplicity of that dish.

SERVES 4

3 small–medium yellow beetroot

3 small–medium purple beetroot

3 small–medium white or
    red beetroot

Rock salt

18 sprigs thyme

60 g walnuts

6 large thin slices sourdough bread,
    or similar

2 tablespoons extra virgin olive oil,
    plus extra for drizzling

Sea salt flakes and freshly ground
    black pepper

2 tablespoons vino cotto or
    balsamic vinegar

½ cup young beetroot leaves
    or rocket

½ cup flat-leaf parsley leaves

200 g fresh goat's cheese, cut into
    bite-sized pieces

2 tablespoons walnut oil

2 tablespoons verjuice

Preheat the oven to 165°C (fan-forced).

Tear 9 pieces of foil large enough to wrap each beetroot. Weigh the beetroot and work out 6% of the total weight (for example, if the beetroots weigh 100 g in total, you will need 6 g rock salt). Divide the salt among the pieces of foil, top with the beetroot and 2 sprigs of thyme, then wrap up each beetroot to seal. Place on a baking tray and roast for 1 hour or until a skewer inserts easily into the centre of the beetroot. (Remember that the beetroot will continue to cook while cooling.) Remove from the oven and stand until cool.

Increase the oven temperature to 180°C (fan-forced). Place the walnuts on a baking tray and toast for 8–10 minutes. Pour into a clean tea towel and rub their skins off while still warm.

Brush both sides of the bread with a generous amount of olive oil and season with salt and pepper. Place on a baking tray in a single layer and toast for 8–12 minutes or until golden. Remove from the oven and set aside to cool.

Unwrap the cooled beetroot and rub their skins off – they should come off easily. (You may choose to wear a pair of disposable gloves to keep your fingers from turning purple.)

Take 2 small bowls and place 1 tablespoon olive oil and 1 tablespoon vino cotto into each. Cut the beetroot into quarters or rounds and place the red and purple pieces of beetroot into one bowl and the yellow into the other. Toss to coat well.

To serve, scatter the beetroot leaves or rocket over a large serving platter. Top with the beetroot, parsley leaves and walnuts. Break the toast into shards and scatter over the top, followed by the goat's cheese. Place the walnut oil and verjuice in a small jar, season to taste, then seal and shake well. Pour over enough dressing to just coat the salad. Serve immediately.

NUTRITION ✎ Walnuts and walnut oil will provide you with protein, polyunsaturated fatty acids, manganese and copper.

Nori rolls with dukkah-crusted sweet potato, sprouts and oven-baked tomatoes

Now this is a great lunch to take to work as long as it stays well chilled, which helps to keep it tightly wrapped. Don't leave out drizzling the avocado with the lemon juice though or it will spoil it. I love the crunch of the dukkah on the sweet potato but it's still good without it, and although the roasted tomatoes with the vino cotto add a great dimension of flavour, I'm just as likely to use fresh tomatoes if I'm strapped for time and the tomatoes are ripe. The star for me is the nori so if you love it too let your imagination go wild with other fillings.

SERVES 4

500 g unpeeled and scrubbed
    sweet potato
2½ tablespoons extra virgin olive oil
Sea salt flakes and freshly ground
    black pepper
2 tablespoons dukkah (see page 275)
Finely grated zest of ½ orange
12 cherry tomatoes, halved
1 teaspoon vino cotto or
    balsamic vinegar
1 teaspoon chopped thyme
2 ripe avocados
Juice of ½ lemon
4 nori sheets
50 g bean sprouts
16 young rocket leaves

Preheat the oven to 200°C (fan-forced).

Cut the sweet potato into 3 cm thick rounds, then into half-moons. Place on a baking tray lined with baking paper, drizzle with 1½ tablespoons olive oil and season with salt. Toss to coat well, then roast in a single layer for 30 minutes. Reduce the oven temperature to 180°C (fan-forced). Turn the sweet potato over, sprinkle evenly with dukkah and roast for another 10 minutes. Remove from the oven, scatter with orange zest and stand until cool.

Place the cherry tomatoes, cut-side up, on a baking tray lined with baking paper. Sprinkle with the vino cotto or balsamic and thyme, then bake for 8 minutes or until slightly soft. Remove from the oven and set aside to cool.

Place the avocado flesh, lemon juice and remaining tablespoon of olive oil in a bowl. Using the back of a fork, mash together, then season to taste.

To assemble, place one sheet of nori, shiny-side down, and with the long side facing you on a dry surface or a sushi mat if you have one. Leaving a 2 cm border at the top, spread with one quarter of the avocado. Place one quarter of the sweet potato across the centre of the avocado, then top with one quarter of the bean sprouts, tomatoes and rocket. Roll up tightly, then repeat with the remaining ingredients. Cut in half and serve.

Sardines and roasted beetroot on sourdough

I always have tins of sardines in my larder and have eaten them all my life. These sardines have been tizzied up beautifully to be a luncheon you'd be happy to serve to a discerning friend — the marriage of the beetroot with the touch of parmesan is magic. Yet in truth, nine times out of ten I would serve my tinned sardines for my own lunch on toasted rye bread with nothing more than a squeeze of lemon. And sometimes with some finely chopped red onion on top. Couldn't live without them.

SERVES 4

1 large beetroot, about 280–300 g
2 teaspoons rock salt
2 sprigs thyme
1 cup (80 g) grated parmesan
  or pecorino
3 tablespoons extra virgin olive oil,
  plus extra for drizzling
4 slices good-quality sourdough or
  rye bread
2 x 120 g tins best-quality sardines
  in olive oil, drained
3 tablespoons finely chopped mint
Lemon wedges, to serve

Preheat the oven to 140°C (fan-forced).

Wrap the beetroot in foil with the salt and thyme, then roast for 1 hour or until a skewer inserts easily. Remove from the oven and set aside to cool. Unwrap the cooled beetroot and rub the skin off – it should come off easily. (You may choose to wear a pair of disposable gloves to keep your fingers from turning purple.)

Place the beetroot, parmesan or pecorino and a dash of the olive oil in a food processor and pulse to a medium coarseness.

Heat the remaining olive oil in a large frying pan over medium heat. Add the bread slices and cook until golden and crisp on both sides. Drain on paper towel. Alternatively, just brush the bread with olive oil and cook under the grill.

Spread the beetroot mixture over the toasted bread. Top with the sardines, chopped mint and a drizzle of olive oil. Serve with lemon wedges.

Eggplant, zucchini, caramelised onion and feta tart with brown rice and almond pastry

I do love pastry but it has to have real flavour as well as being a vehicle for a filling. The combination of the rice and almond crust and these wonderful summer vegetables nestling in custard is sublime. And did I mention the salty feta?! If you're feeling extravagant and want to make this even more special, add toasted pine nuts to the filling. The oregano could easily be replaced with flat-leaf parsley, if you prefer it.

SERVES 6

Pastry

¾ cup (120 g) brown rice flour
1 cup (120 g) ground almonds (see note)
½ teaspoon baking powder
2 tablespoons cornflour
½ teaspoon sea salt flakes
3 tablespoons extra virgin olive oil
1 free-range egg, plus 1 free-range egg yolk

Filling

⅓ cup (80 ml) extra virgin olive oil, plus extra for drizzling
1 large red onion, thinly sliced
Sea salt flakes and freshly ground black pepper
2 tablespoons red wine vinegar
120 g eggplant, cut into 1 cm dice
120 g zucchini, cut into 1 cm dice
100 g good-quality feta
3 free-range eggs
¾ cup (180 ml) thickened cream
1 tablespoon finely chopped oregano

Preheat the oven to 180°C (fan-forced). Grease a 13 cm x 35 cm non-stick fluted rectangular tart tin with removable base.

To make the pastry, place the dry ingredients in a large bowl and whisk to combine. In a separate bowl, whisk together the olive oil and eggs. Add the wet ingredients to the dry ingredients and stir until the dough just comes together. Turn out onto a workbench and pinch off a walnut-sized ball. Keep this aside in case you need to patch any fine cracks after baking. Shape the dough into a rectangle about 10 cm x 20 cm. Place the pastry inside the greased tart tin and press evenly across the base and up the sides. Bake for 8–10 minutes or until light golden. Don't be tempted to cook the pastry too long or it will start to crack. Remove from the oven and reduce the temperature to 165°C (fan-forced).

Meanwhile, to make the filling, heat 2 tablespoons olive oil in a frying pan over medium–high heat. Add the onion and a large pinch of sea salt flakes and cook for 5–6 minutes until the onion starts to collapse. Reduce the heat to low, add the vinegar and cook for another 10 minutes. This long slow cooking will bring out the sweetness in the onion. Remove from the heat and set aside.

Heat the remaining 2 tablespoons olive oil in a wok or large saucepan over high heat. Add the eggplant and saute for 4–5 minutes or until light golden and almost cooked through. Add the zucchini and toss for another 2 minutes or until tender. Season to taste, then pour into a sieve to drain off any excess moisture. Stand to cool slightly.

Combine the onion, eggplant and zucchini together and check the seasoning. Scatter the vegetables evenly over the base of the tart shell, then crumble the feta over the top.

Whisk together the eggs and cream and pour into the tart shell. Bake for 30–35 minutes or until the custard is just set and the top is golden. Remove from the oven and allow to cool slightly.

To serve, remove from the tin, scatter with chopped oregano and drizzle with a little olive oil.

Note: If desired, you can replace the ground almonds with 1 cup (150 g) chickpea flour (besan).

This tart is so moreish I have to resist the temptation of going back for more than I need.

Such an easy yet comforting dish — there's something very satisfying about the warm crunchiness of fish cakes.

Spring onion, sweet potato and caper fish cakes with tomato and avocado salsa

Fish cakes are a quick and simple dish for lunch, and while you might think the fish flavour is drowned out by the sweet potato and onions there is method to my madness if someone in the family thinks they don't like fish (and it does happen!). You can leave out the anchovies if you must. Given that this recipe only calls for half of a 45 gram tin and one of my pet hates is leaving leftover anchovies to oxidise, I have a solution for we fish lovers. Drain the remaining anchovies and mash into some butter (preferably unsalted) then wrap carefully in plastic film and put it in the freezer. You now have a very quick anchovy butter for next time you're cooking a lamb chop on the barbecue.

SERVES 3-4

150 g piece unpeeled and scrubbed
  orange sweet potato
40 g unsalted butter
⅓ cup (80 ml) extra virgin olive oil
½ large brown onion, finely chopped
1 clove garlic, finely chopped
200 g skinless raw fish (anything
  from mulloway to salmon),
  bones removed
2 tablespoons capers in brine, rinsed
2 tablespoons finely chopped spring
  onion greens
½ cup lemon thyme leaves (see note)
1 x 45 g tin anchovies in extra virgin
  olive oil, half drained and
  finely chopped
35 g freshly ground almonds
1 teaspoon finely grated lemon zest
Sea salt flakes and freshly ground
  black pepper
½ cup (65 g) spelt flour
1 free-range egg
2½ tablespoons milk
30 g panko breadcrumbs
30 g LSA
Lemon wedges, to serve

Tomato and avocado salsa

1 large avocado, finely diced
2 vine-ripened tomatoes,
  finely diced
½ red onion, very finely diced
Lemon juice, to taste
2 tablespoons finely chopped
  flat-leaf parsley
2 tablespoons extra virgin olive oil

Cook the sweet potato in lightly salted boiling water until soft, then drain and stand until cool. Remove the skin if you think you need to, then mash with the butter until smooth.

Preheat the oven to 200°C (fan-forced).

Heat 2 tablespoons olive oil in a small frying pan over medium heat, add the onion and cook for 10 minutes or until translucent. Add the garlic and cook for 1–2 minutes or until soft. Remove from the heat.

Pulse the fish gently in a food processor until finely chopped but not a paste. Transfer to a large bowl and add the capers, spring onion, thyme, anchovies, ground almonds, lemon zest, mashed sweet potato and the onion mixture. Combine well, then season to taste. Using damp hands, shape the mixture into 6 patties.

Place the flour in a shallow bowl. In a separate bowl, whisk together the egg and milk, then in another bowl, combine the breadcrumbs and LSA. Dust the patties in the flour, then dip in the egg mixture and coat in the breadcrumbs.

Heat the remaining 2 tablespoons olive oil in a large ovenproof frying pan over low heat. Cook the fish cakes on both sides until golden, being careful not to burn the breadcrumbs. Once golden, transfer the pan to the oven and cook for 5 minutes or until cooked through.

Meanwhile, to make the salsa, combine all the ingredients in a small bowl, then season to taste. Drain the fish cakes on paper towel, then serve with the salsa and lemon wedges.

Note: If you don't have the luxury of having plenty of lemon thyme growing in the garden as I do, use half the amount of either chopped flat-leaf parsley or chives.

NUTRITION 🍃 Avocado provides plenty of monounsaturated fatty acids, as well as vitamin K, fibre, folate and copper.

Grilled zucchini salad

You might think of zucchini as an afterthought but I find them invaluable. They are so easy to grow and embarrassingly abundant, but do pick them when they're small to get them at their very best. They are grilled here (and have a great flavour because of it), but if you slice freshly picked zucchini very thinly you can serve it raw with exactly the same vinaigrette.

SERVES 4 AS A SIDE

4 small zucchini (about 200 g in total)
2 tablespoons extra virgin olive oil
1 tablespoon finely grated lemon zest
Sea salt flakes and freshly ground black pepper
1 tablespoon verjuice
Mint leaves, to serve

Preheat a barbecue grill to high.

Using a large sharp knife or mandolin, cut the zucchini lengthways into 3 mm thick slices. Place in a bowl with the olive oil and lemon zest, then season with salt and pepper and toss to coat well.

Grill for 1 minute each side, then place on a serving plate. Drizzle with verjuice, scatter with mint leaves and serve.

NUTRITION ✎ Eat zucchini for copper, manganese and some vitamin C and fibre.

Sashimi blue-eye trevalla

This could be sashimi of almost any fish. It just happened that blue-eye was the freshest fish available on the day and for sashimi that's what you need. This combination of umeboshi (the Japanese salty sour plum) with a little vino cotto came from an amazing meal I had years ago at Southern Ocean Lodge, presented by Tim Bourke, their chef at the time when I was taking part in their 'Food Safari'. It's a combination I've used again and again in different guises and I'm so grateful for it. Thanks Tim!

SERVES 2

200 g sashimi-grade blue-eye trevalla
    or other super-fresh fish fillet
25 g umeboshi (pickled Japanese plums)
3 teaspoons vino cotto
3 teaspoons extra virgin olive oil, plus extra for drizzling
1 tablespoon finely chopped spring onion, green ends only
1 tablespoon finely chopped chives
Sea salt flakes

Cut the fish against the grain into thin slices and arrange on a plate.

Peel the umeboshi, discard the seed and place in a small bowl. Use a fork to mince the plum. Stir in the vino cotto and olive oil, then add the chopped spring onion greens to make a paste. Place the umeboshi paste in the centre of the sashimi. Drizzle with extra olive oil and sprinkle with chives and a little sea salt. Serve immediately.

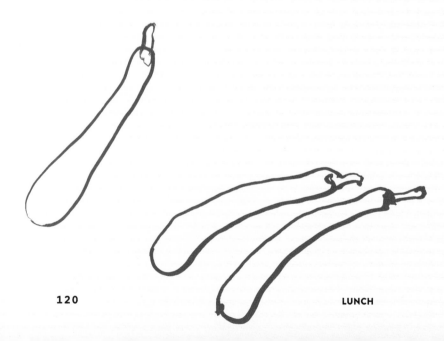

Tomato and beetroot soup with basil

I'm sure you've all made tomato soup before but adding the beetroot gives such a great viscosity and colour. While I've added a variety of herbs, I do this simply because I have them all to hand and yes, they do add flavour, but even one herb from your garden would make a difference. If you decide to include the mozzarella then it's definitely a meal in itself and best served cold, but resist the urge to cut it into slices; it really tastes so much better when you tear off pieces of mozzarella and finish with a drizzle of extra virgin olive oil if you feel so inclined. And guess who would? Without the mozzarella it's still a great soup, hot or cold.

SERVES 2

⅓ cup (80 ml) extra virgin olive oil, plus extra for drizzling

3 brown onions, finely chopped

2 cloves garlic, finely chopped

1.5 kg ripe tomatoes, coarsely chopped

1 beetroot, peeled and cut into chunks

4 sprigs thyme

2 fresh bay leaves, crushed for maximum flavour

2 sprigs rosemary

Sea salt flakes and freshly ground black pepper

1 tablespoon lemon juice

150 g fresh mozzarella (optional)

6 cherry tomatoes, quartered

Small basil leaves, to serve

Heat the olive oil in a medium saucepan over medium heat. Add the onion and cook for 10 minutes or until translucent but not coloured. Add the garlic and cook for another 2 minutes or until fragrant. Add the tomato, beetroot and herbs, then season to taste. Reduce the heat to as low as possible and cook, stirring occasionally, for 25 minutes or until thickened.

Remove and discard the herbs. Transfer the soup to a blender and process until smooth. Strain through a fine sieve into a bowl and stand until cool. Refrigerate overnight for maximum flavour.

Just before serving, stir in the lemon juice and adjust the seasoning if necessary. Ladle the soup into serving bowls, then tear over the mozzarella, if using. Top with the cherry tomatoes, basil leaves and a drizzle of olive oil.

Beetroot, cabbage and vino cotto soup

I'm not trying to make a borscht here but if you like beetroot, and I certainly do, this is definitely a meal in itself for lunch. The trick to retaining as much colour as possible is to cook the carrot and onion right through first before adding the cabbage, beetroot and celery, and then cooking it as quickly as possible. While I say vegetable stock I often use chicken stock for a fuller flavour, and if you don't have vino cotto (or balsamic) a good squeeze of lemon juice will give that acid touch. It's best of all served straight after pureeing without reheating, but it's also great as a chilled soup. Serve it with a side of grilled zucchini (see page 120) for a more substantial lunch.

SERVES 6

2 tablespoons extra virgin olive oil, plus extra for drizzling
2 red onions, thinly sliced
2 carrots, peeled and thinly sliced
¼ red cabbage (about 500 g), thinly sliced
2 tablespoons vino cotto
800 ml hot vegetable stock
2½ tablespoons verjuice or water
1 large stick celery, thinly sliced
1 medium–large beetroot, scrubbed and grated
½ teaspoon sea salt flakes
¼ teaspoon freshly ground black pepper
3 tablespoons natural probiotic yoghurt (optional)
Coarsely chopped flat-leaf parsley and crusty bread, to serve
1 tablespoon finely grated orange zest (optional)

Heat the olive oil in a large deep frying pan over low–medium heat. Gently saute the onion and carrot for 10 minutes or until soft. Increase the heat to high, then add the cabbage, half at a time but quickly, and stir until it begins to wilt. Add the vino cotto.

Meanwhile, place the stock and verjuice or water in a saucepan over medium heat until hot (this helps speed up the cooking time for the vegetables to keep the colour as vibrant as possible).

Add the celery and beetroot to the onion mixture and stir for 1–2 minutes. Increase the heat to high and add the hot stock mixture. Bring the soup back to a rolling boil and cook just until all the vegetables are tender. Remove from the heat and stand until slightly cooled.

Blend the soup until fairly smooth. Season with salt and pepper, then ladle into bowls. Top with a dollop of yoghurt, if using, then drizzle with olive oil and scatter with parsley and orange zest, if using. Serve with crusty bread.

Miso, eggplant and soba noodle salad

I love the umami flavour of miso, and my many trips to Japan have shown me how versatile it is. I seek out the unpasteurised miso as it has the best flavour, not to mention health benefits, and sometimes will just have a spoonful in a mug of boiling water if I'm hungry between meals. Miso has a natural affinity with eggplant, and also with noodles. Soba are hands down my favourite Japanese noodles, and they make a great last-minute addition to many dishes. Definitely worth a place in the larder!

SERVES 4

4 eggplants
3 tablespoons extra virgin olive oil
Sea salt flakes and freshly ground
    black pepper
2 tablespoons sesame oil
1 tablespoon julienned ginger
1 tablespoon unpasteurised white
    (shiro) miso
2 tablespoons verjuice
100 ml vegetable stock
2 teaspoons sweet soy sauce
    (kecap manis)
2 bundles (180 g) soba (buckwheat)
    noodles
⅓ cup (50 g) toasted sesame seeds
½ cup coriander leaves

Vinaigrette

1 tablespoon extra virgin olive oil
1 tablespoon verjuice
1 teaspoon soy sauce

Preheat the oven to 220°C (fan-forced). Line 2 baking trays with baking paper.

Peel the eggplant and cut into 2.5 cm cubes. Place in a bowl, pour over the olive oil and season well. Toss to coat, then spread over the lined trays. Roast for 25 minutes or until golden and tender, but not mushy. Remove and set aside.

Meanwhile, heat the sesame oil in a small saucepan over medium heat. Add the ginger and saute for 2 minutes. Stir in the miso, then add the verjuice and simmer until nearly evaporated. Add the stock and bring to the boil. Reduce the heat to low, stir in the soy sauce and simmer for 5–6 minutes or until slightly thickened. Remove from the heat.

To make the vinaigrette, whisk together all the ingredients in a small bowl.

Bring a large saucepan of lightly salted water to the boil. Add the noodles and cook according to manufacturer's instructions or until tender. Drain and place in a large bowl with the vinaigrette and toss to coat. Add the eggplant and sauce and combine well. Divide among serving plates and scatter with the sesame seeds and coriander leaves.

Soft poached egg, braised lettuce and capers

I usually serve this at lunchtime but it also makes a terrific weekend breakfast. But only on days when I'm not rushing somewhere, as – without you thinking I'm being silly – making the perfect poached egg needs attention, and one poached in advance simply doesn't cut the mustard. Never underrate a good egg!

SERVES 4

1 tablespoon apple cider vinegar
4 free-range eggs
50 g unsalted butter
1 tablespoon capers in brine, rinsed
Dill sprigs, to serve

Braised lettuce
2 baby cos lettuce
1 tablespoon extra virgin olive oil
½ teaspoon sea salt flakes
150 ml chicken or vegetable stock

To make the braised lettuce, remove the outer cos leaves, revealing the tender hearts and cut in half lengthways.

Heat the olive oil in a large non-stick frying pan over medium heat. Slide the cos hearts into the pan, cut-side down, and season with the salt. Add the stock and simmer for 2 minutes or until just tender. Remove from the heat and divide among warm plates.

Meanwhile, bring 2 litres water to the boil in a large saucepan. Add the vinegar, then reduce the heat to low – the water should be just bubbling. Crack the eggs into 4 separate cups or ramekins, taking care not to break the yolks. Using a large spoon, stir the water clockwise to create a whirlpool. Gently tip the eggs into the centre of the whirlpool, one at a time, and simmer gently for 2–3 minutes, depending on how runny you like the egg. Remove the eggs with a slotted spoon and pat dry on a clean tea towel. Place on top of the warmed braised lettuce.

Working quickly, place the butter in a small frying pan over high heat and cook until nut brown in colour. Add the capers and remove from the heat. Spoon the butter and capers over the eggs, scatter with dill sprigs and serve immediately.

Roasted pumpkin with salad of massaged kale, pomegranate and pepitas

A long time ago when I was young (please don't block your ears like my grandchildren do) I lived overseas, and found that pumpkin simply wasn't part of my diet. I can't tell you how much I missed it, and when I came home I wanted it to be part of every meal, every day for a long time – that's how much I love it. You'll notice I leave the skin on in this recipe. I nearly always use the skin because it adds so much flavour and texture. The pumpkin shines here with pomegranates, kale and creamy hummus. I've specified tinned chickpeas for the hummus only for convenience but if you have time to soak and cook dried chickpeas the flavour will be even better.

SERVES 4

400 g Queensland Blue or Jap
  pumpkin, seeded, skin on
2 tablespoons extra virgin olive oil,
  plus extra for drizzling
Sea salt flakes
125 g curly kale, leaves stripped off
  and stalks discarded
1 tablespoon lemon juice
60 g pepitas (pumpkin seeds)
½ pomegranate, seeds removed

Hummus

1 x 400 g tin chickpeas, drained
  and rinsed
1 clove garlic, crushed
70 ml extra virgin olive oil
1½ teaspoons ground cumin
2 tablespoons lemon juice
Sea salt flakes and freshly ground
  black pepper

Preheat the oven to 220°C (fan-forced). Line a baking tray with baking paper.

Cut the pumpkin into 3 cm thick wedges and place on the lined tray. Drizzle with olive oil and season with salt, then roast for 30–40 minutes or until golden and tender.

Meanwhile, coarsely chop the kale leaves and place in a large bowl. Add the lemon juice, 1 tablespoon olive oil and a good pinch of salt and massage into the kale for 5 minutes or until it starts to soften.

Place the remaining 1 tablespoon olive oil in a medium frying pan over medium heat. Add the pepitas and toss for 2–3 minutes or until the seeds are golden and toasted. Drain on paper towel and season with salt. Allow to cool.

To make the hummus, place all the ingredients in a food processor and blend until smooth. Adjust the seasoning and add a little cold water if needed to produce a smooth, creamy hummus.

To serve, place the roasted pumpkin overlapping on a large platter. Scatter with the kale, toasted pepitas and pomegranate seeds. Serve the hummus alongside.

Eggplant, tomato and feta salad

Some years I grow up to six different varieties of eggplant in our garden and we enjoy eating them between February and May, though interestingly each year a different variety seems to be the star. One year we had the white 'Cosmo' eggplant that was still bearing through until June in great condition, and the next year not so. I can't wait to see what happens with the next batch. Ripe tomatoes add freshness and flavour to this simple salad, contrasting with the tart creaminess of Persian feta.

SERVES 2

1 large eggplant (about 350 g)
2 tablespoons verjuice
3 tablespoons extra virgin olive oil
Sea salt flakes and freshly ground
 black pepper
250 g ripe cherry tomatoes
100 g Persian feta, drained and
 broken into bite-sized pieces
½ cup flat-leaf parsley leaves
½ cup mint leaves, torn at the
 last moment

Dressing

½ teaspoon fennel seeds, toasted
1 clove garlic, peeled
1½ tablespoons lemon juice
1 tablespoon raw honey
1 tablespoon pomegranate molasses
2 tablespoons extra virgin olive oil

Preheat the oven to 220°C (fan-forced). Line a baking tray with baking paper

Slice the eggplant into 2 cm thick rounds and place in a single layer on the lined tray. Combine the verjuice and 2 tablespoons olive oil in a small bowl, then brush over both sides of the eggplant. Season with salt and bake for 30 minutes or until golden, turning over halfway through cooking. Remove the eggplant from the oven and allow to cool. Cut into quarters and place on a serving plate.

Cut the cherry tomatoes in half and place in a bowl. Drizzle with the remaining 1 tablespoon olive oil and season to taste.

To make the dressing, pound the fennel seeds in a mortar and pestle with the garlic until a paste forms. Add the lemon juice, honey and molasses and mix well. Stirring constantly, gradually add the olive oil in a thin steady stream until emulsified.

Scatter the cherry tomatoes, feta and herbs over the eggplant. Pour over the dressing, season and serve.

Mushroom souffle omelette

This is not a souffle to be nervous about; however, it does require your family or guests to be sitting at the table when you put it in the oven as it deserves an audience when it comes out. Serve it simply with a fresh salad and take compliments on how clever you are.

SERVES 6

40 g unsalted butter
⅓ cup (80 ml) extra virgin olive oil
1 small brown onion, finely diced
250 g Swiss brown mushrooms,
    thinly sliced
10 sprigs thyme
2 tablespoons verjuice
Sea salt flakes and freshly ground
    black pepper
6 free-range eggs, separated
1 tablespoon lemon thyme leaves,
    chopped
½ cup (40 g) finely grated parmesan

Preheat the oven to 180°C (fan-forced). Grease a 25 cm ovenproof frying pan or baking dish.

Heat the butter and half the olive oil in a large saucepan over medium heat. Add the onion and cook for 5 minutes or until softened. Add the remaining olive oil, then the mushroom and thyme and saute for 5–8 minutes or until golden and cooked through. Add the verjuice and simmer until nearly evaporated, then season to taste and remove from the heat.

Remove the thyme sprigs and pulse the mixture in a food processor, retaining some texture. Set aside to cool.

In the bowl of an electric mixer fitted with a whisk attachment, whisk the egg whites until medium peaks form.

In another bowl of the electric mixer, whisk the egg yolks until thick and pale. Gently fold one third of the whites into the yolks, along with the lemon thyme, parmesan and cooled mushroom mixture. Fold in the remaining whites, keeping as much air in the mixture as possible. Pour into the greased pan or dish and bake for 12–18 minutes or until golden and set. Remove from the oven and serve immediately.

NUTRITION 🍃 Mushrooms contain selenium, vitamins B2, B3 and some vitamin D.

Pumpkin, ginger and coconut soup

Towards the end of autumn when the weather starts to cool down a bowl of soup is just what I feel like for lunch, and so easy – when you're not making it on the day. I know you can freeze soup but it never seems to be quite the same so I make a large enough batch to enjoy several meals of the same soup (quelle horreur!) within a week, and store the balance in the refrigerator. Pumpkin and coconut are great together so I have no problem eating this for a few days in a row.

SERVES 4

1.2 kg butternut pumpkin, peeled
   and seeded
3 tablespoons extra virgin olive oil
Sea salt flakes and freshly ground
   black pepper
1 large sprig rosemary
2 large brown onions, thinly sliced
30 g ginger, peeled and grated
1 litre vegetable or chicken stock
1 x 440 ml tin coconut milk
Juice of 1 lime
3 tablespoons chopped
   toasted walnuts
3 tablespoons chopped
   flat-leaf parsley
Toasted sourdough or spelt bread,
   to serve

Preheat the oven to 220°C (fan-forced). Line a baking tray with baking paper.

Cut the pumpkin into 2 cm thick wedges and place on the lined tray. Drizzle with 1 tablespoon olive oil, season to taste and add the rosemary sprig. Roast for 30–40 minutes or until golden and tender. Remove from the oven, discard the rosemary sprig and set aside.

Heat the remaining olive oil in a large saucepan over medium heat. Add the onion and cook for 10 minutes or until translucent. Add the ginger and cook for another 2–3 minutes. Add the roasted pumpkin and stock. Bring to the boil, then reduce the heat to low and simmer for 25 minutes or until reduced by one third. Stir in the coconut milk and remove from the heat. Blend the soup until smooth, then season with lime juice, salt and pepper. Ladle into bowls, then scatter with the walnuts and parsley and serve with toasted sourdough or spelt bread.

Baked sweet potato with labneh, kale pesto and dukkah

A word of advice: don't get between me and a roast sweet potato, particularly the 'old-fashioned' white or purple variety. And this is one of my favourite ways to enjoy them. Before you finish this book (and I do hope you'll stick with me on this) I'll have you loving kale, I promise; the only proviso is to make sure it's fresh and vibrant when you buy or pick it.

SERVES 4

3 tablespoons rock salt
2 small purple, orange or white
   sweet potatoes, about 250 g each,
   unpeeled and scrubbed
100 g labneh (see page 271)
2 tablespoons extra virgin olive oil,
   plus extra for drizzling
2 tablespoons dukkah
   (see page 276)
Purple or green basil leaves,
   to serve

Kale pesto

½ bunch kale (about 110 g), leaves
   stripped, stalks discarded
⅓ cup (25 g) finely grated parmesan
1 clove garlic, peeled
1 tablespoon toasted pine nuts
   or walnuts
15 g basil leaves
100 ml extra virgin olive oil
Sea salt flakes

Preheat the oven to 220°C (fan-forced). Line a baking tray with baking paper.

Place 1 heaped tablespoon rock salt under each sweet potato on the lined tray. Prick the sweet potatoes with a fork so steam can escape during cooking. Bake for 30–50 minutes or until golden, cooked through and soft. Remove from the oven and set aside to cool slightly.

Meanwhile, to make the pesto, drop the kale into a saucepan of lightly salted boiling water and simmer for 1 minute. Drain and cool, then squeeze out as much water as possible. Coarsely chop and place in a food processor with the remaining ingredients. Pulse together leaving some texture, then adjust the seasoning.

Place the labneh in a bowl, then stir in the olive oil and season to taste.

Cut the sweet potatoes in half lengthways and place on serving plates. Squash down lightly with the back of a fork, then top with a generous amount of pesto, labneh and dukkah. Scatter with the basil leaves and finish with a final flourish of olive oil.

Chickpea, pumpkin and tamarind stew

This dish began as a soup but it's so rich in chickpeas and winter vegetables that it should really be termed a stew, even though that word doesn't carry an elegance with it. Not only is it hearty and satisfying but there is a real sweetness from the carrots, parsnips and pumpkin which is offset by the tamarind in a delightful way. My preference is for chicken stock as it has more body and flavour but use vegetable if you want to make this a vegetarian meal. Make it the day before to give the flavours time to meld.

SERVES 4

½ cup (100 g) dried chickpeas, soaked overnight in cold water

2 tablespoons extra virgin olive oil, plus extra to serve

1 large red onion, cut into 1 cm dice

Sea salt flakes and freshly ground black pepper

2 carrots, peeled and cut into 1 cm dice

2 parsnips, peeled and cut into 1 cm dice

1 tablespoon finely grated ginger

1 teaspoon ground cinnamon

½ teaspoon ground turmeric

150 g pumpkin, peeled, seeded and cut into 2 cm dice

1 tablespoon tamarind paste

1 x 400 g tin low-salt crushed tomatoes

1 litre chicken or vegetable stock

2 sticks celery, cut into 1 cm dice

1 tablespoon lemon juice

Thick natural probiotic yoghurt, toasted pepitas (pumpkin seeds) and coriander leaves, to serve

Drain and rinse the soaked chickpeas and place in a medium saucepan with 4 times the amount of cold water. Bring to the boil over high heat, then reduce the heat to low and simmer for 40 minutes or until soft. Drain and set aside.

Heat the olive oil in a saucepan over medium heat. Add the onion and ½ teaspoon salt and saute for 10 minutes or until soft. Add the carrot and parsnip and cook for another 10 minutes. Add the ginger, cinnamon and turmeric and stir for 2 minutes or until the spices become aromatic. Add the pumpkin, tamarind, tomatoes and stock. Simmer for 30 minutes or until the vegetables are tender. Stir in the drained chickpeas and celery and simmer for 5 minutes (celery is always best when still left with texture). Season with salt and pepper, then stir in the lemon juice.

To serve, divide among warm bowls. Drizzle with extra olive oil, then top with a dollop of yoghurt and scatter with pepitas and coriander leaves.

NUTRITION 🍃 Chickpeas are full of protein and fibre and are a source of molybdenum, manganese, folate and copper.

Celeriac is such a prehistoric-looking
vegetable, but it's definitely worth making
its acquaintance for its unique flavour.

Celeriac and green lentil soup

When choosing celeriac at the farmers' market, look for the blond smaller ones just out of the ground as they taste the best – or grow them yourself if you can. I have to admit, though, that I have great difficulty growing these to a good bulb. They take a long time in the ground and in my impatience I've often pulled them up too early. I specify green or black lentils here but that's simply because I prefer them to red lentils – it's fine to use whichever you have in your pantry.

SERVES 4

⅓ cup (80 ml) extra virgin olive oil, plus extra for drizzling
1 large brown onion, cut into 1 cm dice
1 clove garlic, finely chopped
1 large sprig rosemary
Sea salt flakes and freshly ground black pepper
200 g celeriac, peeled and cut into 2 cm dice
150 g green or black lentils, rinsed in cold water, drained
2 litres chicken or vegetable stock
2 sticks celery, cut into 1 cm dice
2 tablespoons lemon juice
2 tablespoons extra virgin olive oil
½ cup young celery leaves (if your celery is super fresh) or flat-leaf parsley leaves
Finely grated zest of 1 lemon

Heat 1 tablespoon olive oil in a large saucepan over medium heat. Add the onion and cook for 8 minutes or until transparent. Add the garlic, rosemary and a pinch of salt and cook for another 5 minutes or until tender. Add the celeriac, remaining olive oil and drained lentils and cook for 4–5 minutes or until the celeriac is lightly coloured.

Add the stock and bring to a gentle boil, skimming off any impurities that rise to the surface. Reduce the heat to low and simmer for 30–40 minutes or until the lentils and celeriac are tender. Add the celery and check the seasoning, then cook for another 5 minutes (celery is always best when still left with texture). Just before serving, stir through the lemon juice.

To serve, heat the olive oil in a small frying pan over medium heat. When the oil is hot, add the celery or parsley leaves and quickly toss for 1 minute – you want the leaves to go crisp but not brown. Drain on paper towel and season with salt. Ladle the soup into bowls, then scatter with the celery leaves and lemon zest.

NUTRITION 🌿 Celeriac is a source of vitamins K and B6, phosphorus and fibre.

Miso, mushroom and soba noodles

My love affair with Japanese food means I always have unpasteurised miso in my refrigerator. This is more of an idea than a recipe, and you should feel free to vary it according to what you have to hand (such as replacing the nuts with tofu). It's so quick to throw together and could easily be taken to work or school for lunch in two containers: put the cold cooked soba noodles and accompaniments together and heat the stock separately, then pour it over the noodles and enjoy the beautiful clean flavours.

SERVES 2

8 g dried shiitake mushrooms
2 tablespoons extra virgin olive oil, plus extra for drizzling
180 g fresh shiitake mushrooms, stalks discarded, caps thinly sliced
2 tablespoons unpasteurised white (shiro) miso
3 cups (750 ml) vegetable or chicken stock
Freshly ground black pepper
1 bundle (90 g) soba (buckwheat) noodles
80 g sugar snap peas, topped and cut lengthways into thirds
60 g toasted cashews or peanuts, finely chopped
½ cup coriander leaves

Soak the dried shiitake mushrooms in warm water for 1 hour. Drain, then remove and discard the stalks. Cut the caps into 4 mm thick slices.

Heat the olive oil in a medium saucepan over medium heat. Add the sliced fresh and soaked mushroom caps and cook for 4–5 minutes until soft. Stir in the miso, then add the stock and bring to the boil. Reduce the heat to low and simmer for 5 minutes. Add pepper to taste.

Meanwhile, bring 2 medium saucepans of water to the boil. Add the noodles to one and simmer for about 6 minutes or until soft. Drain and toss in a little extra virgin olive oil. Add the sugar snap peas to the other pan, cook for 1 minute, then drain.

Working quickly, divide the noodles and sugar snap peas between warm bowls. Top with the mushrooms and soup, then scatter with nuts and coriander leaves and serve.

Jerusalem artichoke and coconut soup

Jerusalem artichokes have such a wonderful flavour that the temptation is there to have a second serving. The issue is that for many people this amazing vegetable can cause flatulence or stomach pains. In his terrific book *On Food and Cooking*, Harold McGee suggests that cooking them long and slow might address the problem so I decided to test the theory and use my slow cooker. I'm happy to say it worked for me so do give it a try – this is a flavour you really don't want to miss. The soup doesn't freeze well so make it when you have the right number of people at your table to eat it in one sitting.

SERVES 6

1 kg Jerusalem artichokes
1.5 litres chicken stock, plus extra if needed
1 teaspoon sea salt flakes
1 x 270 ml tin coconut cream
½ bunch chives, finely chopped

Scrub the artichokes really well and cut off any really dark bits. Coarsely chop and place in a slow cooker with the stock and salt. Put the slow cooker on high for 40 minutes or until it comes to a simmer. Turn down to the lowest setting and cook for 6 hours. Allow to cool a little, then transfer to a blender and add 230 ml coconut cream. Blend until smooth and creamy. Adjust the seasoning if necessary.

To serve, gently reheat the soup over low heat. If necessary, thin the soup with a little extra chicken stock. Ladle into warm bowls. Top with a spoonful of the remaining coconut cream, then sprinkle with chopped chives.

NUTRITION ✎ The high level of inulin (type of sugar) in Jerusalem artichokes is considered to be good for type 2 diabetes, partly by providing prebiotic energy for the bacteria in your digestive system. The artichokes are also full of fibre and are a good source of iron and copper.

Chicken soup with leek and barley

Chicken soup has always been a favourite comfort food in my family. As a child it's what I asked Mum for when I was not feeling well or down about something, and my own children have the same feeling for it so it really is worth making it from scratch with the best ingredients. I like to cook the barley separately and add it in the final stages to stop it becoming glue-like from long cooking. But that's a personal preference. Someone very close to me loves it like that: so thick with barley you could cut it into pieces!

SERVES 6-8

¾ cup (150 g) raw organic pearl barley, rinsed
2 tablespoons extra virgin olive oil
1 large brown onion, finely diced
2 carrots, cut into 1 cm dice
1 leek, halved lengthways, washed well and cut into 5 mm thick slices
10 sprigs thyme
25 g unsalted butter
Sea salt flakes and freshly ground black pepper
3 tablespoons verjuice
2 sticks celery, cut into 1 cm dice
½ cup chopped flat-leaf parsley
Crusty bread, to serve

Chicken stock

1 x 2 kg Barossa or other well-brought-up chook, cut into quarters and left on the bone
1 brown onion, quartered
1 carrot, quartered
2 sticks celery, cut into 5 cm pieces
1 leek, green and white parts, washed well and cut into 5 cm pieces
2 cloves garlic, thinly sliced
2 bay leaves, crushed
1 teaspoon black peppercorns
½ teaspoon sea salt flakes

To make the stock, place all the ingredients in a large heavy-based saucepan with 4 litres water. Bring to the boil over high heat, then reduce the heat to low and simmer very gently for 1–1½ hours. Remove from the heat and set aside to cool completely, then refrigerate overnight.

The following day, place the rinsed barley in a large saucepan with 4 times the amount of water. Bring to the boil over high heat, then reduce the heat to low and simmer for 30–40 minutes or until tender. Drain, then cover with a cloth so it doesn't dry out and set aside.

Skim off any fat that has risen to the surface of the chicken stock. Remove the chicken pieces and discard the skin and bones. Shred the meat into bite-sized pieces. Place the cold stock in a large saucepan and heat until just warm, then strain and discard the solids. Return the stock to the pan and bring to the boil, skimming off any impurities, fat and foam that rises to the surface. Reduce the heat to low and simmer gently.

Meanwhile, heat the olive oil in a large saucepan over medium heat. Saute the onion for 10 minutes or until translucent. Add the carrot, leek, thyme and butter, then season with salt and pepper. Simmer for another 5 minutes or until the vegetables are tender. Remove the thyme sprigs. Add the verjuice and simmer until nearly evaporated, then add the hot stock. Bring to the boil, then reduce to a simmer. Stir in the shredded chicken meat, cooked barley and celery and simmer for 5 minutes or until heated through. Check the seasoning.

To serve, ladle the soup into warmed bowls, scatter with the chopped parsley and serve with crusty bread.

> **NUTRITION** 🍃 The goodness in chicken soup has been proclaimed for centuries in so many cultures around the world. This soup will be no exception, with garlic, onion and leek to provide anti-inflammatory, antioxidant and anti-microbial components.

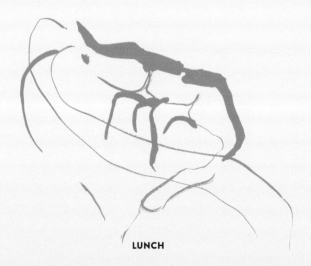

Aromatic coconut soup
with prawns and coriander

Those who know me well will be surprised I've actually added chilli to a dish, being the chilli wimp I am. In 20 years of writing recipes, this would only have happened a couple of times before. The chilli here just gives an underlying flavour rather than a blast of heat, but if you love chilli add more as this soup could take it. I love the combination of coconut milk, lime and coriander, and if you have any coriander that's going to seed, add the flowers at the last moment too. One last word of advice:
don't overcook the prawns!

SERVES 6

12 large raw prawns
40 g extra virgin coconut oil
3 large golden shallots, thinly sliced
2 cloves garlic, finely chopped
60 g ginger, peeled and finely grated
1 tablespoon ground turmeric
1 long fresh red chilli, coarsely
   chopped (or more if you like
   things hot)
1 teaspoon coriander seeds
4 lemongrass stalks, pale ends
   only, crushed
4 kaffir lime leaves, crushed
½ cup coriander roots and stalks,
   rinsed well
2 litres chicken or vegetable stock
2 cups (500 ml) coconut milk
2 tablespoons fish sauce
2 tablespoons lime juice
Sea salt flakes and freshly ground
   black pepper
1 tablespoon extra virgin olive oil
½ cup coriander leaves
3 tablespoons fried shallots (available
   from Asian supermarkets)

Peel the prawns, leaving the heads and tails on. Reserve the shells. Use a skewer to devein the prawns, then place in an airtight container and refrigerate until needed.

Melt the coconut oil in a large saucepan over medium heat. Add the shallot and cook, stirring regularly, for 10 minutes or until translucent. Add the garlic and ginger and cook for 3 minutes. Add the turmeric, chilli, coriander seeds, lemongrass, lime leaves, coriander roots and stalks and the prawn shells and cook for 3–4 minutes or until aromatic.

Add the stock and bring to the boil, skimming off any impurities that rise to the surface. Reduce the heat to low and simmer for 10 minutes. Add the coconut milk and cook for another 10 minutes. Remove from the heat and stand for 20 minutes before straining. Discard the solids, then return the soup to a clean pan. Stir in the fish sauce and lime juice and season to taste.

Just before serving, heat the olive oil in a large frying pan over high heat. Cook the prawns, in 2 batches, for 2 minutes on each side or until just cooked through. Remove the heads and tails, then cut the prawns in half lengthways.

To serve, ladle the soup into bowls. Add the prawns, then scatter with coriander leaves and fried shallots.

NUTRITION ✎ This soup is full of anti-inflammatory power from the ginger, garlic and turmeric.

Green frittata

Getting a frittata right should be one of the basics for young people leaving home and cooking for themselves for the first time. The base ingredients of eggs, vegetables and cheese can be prepared and cooked in less than 20 minutes, and almost any kind of vegetable will do. It's simple, versatile, full of flavour and goodness, and, depending on the extravagance of the cheese, can be a real budget dish. But all of these good points can be ruined by overcooking. Practise with the oven you're working with to get this right.

SERVES 4

3 tablespoons extra virgin olive oil, plus extra for drizzling
1 large brown onion, thinly sliced
Sea salt flakes and freshly ground black pepper
125 g chard stalks, washed and cut into 2.5 cm pieces
125 g broccoli, florets cut into 1 cm thick slices, stalk peeled and finely chopped
1 leek, halved lengthways, washed well and cut into 1 cm thick slices
125 g chard leaves, torn into bite-sized pieces
20 g unsalted butter
2 tablespoons verjuice
½ teaspoon finely grated lemon zest
4 free-range eggs
⅓ cup (25 g) finely grated parmesan
½ cup (100 g) ricotta (see page 271), crumbled

Preheat the oven to 175°C (fan-forced). Grease and line a 24 cm ovenproof frying pan or similar with baking paper, leaving the sides overhanging.

Heat the olive oil in a large saucepan over medium heat. Add the onion and a pinch of salt and cook for 10 minutes or until soft but not coloured. Add the chard stalks, broccoli florets and stalks and the leek and saute for 8–12 minutes or until the broccoli is al dente. Stir in the chard leaves and butter and cook until the leaves have wilted. Add the verjuice and simmer until nearly evaporated. Remove from the heat, stir in the lemon zest and season with salt and pepper. Pour the mixture into the prepared pan.

In a bowl, whisk together the eggs, parmesan and ricotta. Pour over the top of the chard mixture, then place the pan on a baking tray and bake for 15–20 minutes or until just set. Remove from the oven and rest for 10 minutes. Drizzle with a flourish of olive oil and serve.

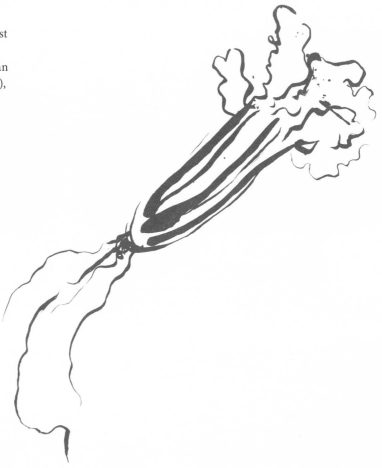

There's something about the way the
sweet potato takes up the spices in
this recipe that makes it special.

Spiced sweet potato with black barley and honey turmeric walnuts

I can't resist white sweet potato; I've loved it since childhood. For you it might be orange or purple sweet potato, both of which I use often as well. It's important that the spices are fresh. Forgive me for repeating myself but you should only buy spices in small quantities and roast them before grinding for maximum freshness and flavour. Black barley is my new favourite grain – so much so that I'm working on some South Australian growers to plant it. Might take a few seasons but watch this space!

SERVES 4

½ cup (100 g) raw black barley
(see page 278)
1.2 kg white, orange or purple sweet
potatoes, unpeeled, scrubbed and
chopped into 3 cm chunks
2–3 tablespoons extra virgin olive oil
½ teaspoon freshly grated nutmeg
½ teaspoon ground cinnamon
1 teaspoon ground cumin
¼ teaspoon ground allspice
Sea salt flakes and freshly ground
black pepper
1 cup flat-leaf parsley leaves
½ cup mint leaves, torn
160 g Persian feta, crumbled

Honey turmeric walnuts

1 cup (100 g) walnuts
1 tablespoon raw honey
½ teaspoon ground turmeric
Pinch of sea salt flakes

Vinaigrette

3 tablespoons extra virgin olive oil
3 tablespoons walnut oil
3 tablespoons orange juice
1 tablespoon lemon juice
Sea salt flakes and freshly ground
ground pepper

Preheat the oven to 220°C (fan-forced). Line a baking tray with baking paper.

Place the black barley in a sieve and rinse under cold water. Place in a medium saucepan with 1 litre water and bring to the boil over medium heat. Simmer for 30 minutes or until the barley is tender, then drain. Tip into a large bowl and cover with a cloth to prevent it drying out.

Meanwhile, place the sweet potato, olive oil and spices in a large bowl. Season with salt and pepper and toss to combine well. Spread over the lined tray and roast for 30–35 minutes or until golden and tender. Reduce the oven temperature to 180°C (fan-forced).

To make the honey turmeric walnuts, place the walnuts on a baking tray and cook for 8–10 minutes or until lightly toasted. Pour into a clean tea towel and rub off the skins while still warm.

In a small bowl, combine the honey, turmeric, salt and just enough water to make a thick paste. Add the toasted walnuts and stir to coat well. Spread over a baking tray lined with baking paper and bake for 10 minutes or until the walnuts are crunchy but still a bit sticky.

To make the vinaigrette, place all the ingredients in a jar. Seal, then shake until well combined.

To serve, add the sweet potato, herbs and half the vinaigrette to the barley and combine well. Place in a serving bowl, scatter with the walnuts and feta and serve with the remaining dressing alongside.

NUTRITION 🥄 Sweet potato is rich in beta-carotene, vitamin C, manganese, copper and fibre.

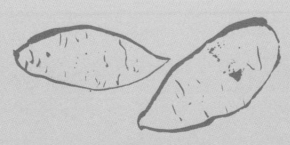

Dinner

Braised leek and butter bean ragout with mushrooms and ricotta

Also known as lima beans, butter beans are fantastic eating but it's difficult to predict the cooking time of dried beans as it depends how old they are. Unfortunately you can't glean this information from the packet. There are times when I'm tempted to use tinned butter beans as long as they don't have preservatives added and you rinse them well before using them. Of course tinned beans are already cooked so they will only need to be warmed through. The combination of leeks and mushrooms could be spooned over a bowl of pasta and make a delightful meal, but there is something special about a plump butter bean so they are definitely worth the trouble.

SERVES 4

1 cup (190 g) dried butter beans, soaked overnight in cold water

1 clove garlic, crushed

3 bay leaves

6 black peppercorns

½ cup (125 ml) extra virgin olive oil, plus extra for drizzling

12 pencil leeks or 3 medium–large leeks, washed well and green tops trimmed

1 tablespoon verjuice

1 lemon, zest removed in wide strips using a peeler, juiced

20 g unsalted butter

400 g button mushrooms, sliced

1 teaspoon sea salt flakes

½ teaspoon freshly ground black pepper

60 g Kalamata olives, pitted

½ cup oregano leaves, chopped

½ cup (100 g) ricotta (see page 271), or any fresh curd

Drain the soaked butter beans, then place in a heavy-based saucepan with the garlic, bay leaves, peppercorns and 1 litre water. Bring to a simmer over high heat, then immediately reduce the heat to as low as possible and cook for 1 hour or until tender. During cooking, skim off any impurities that come to the surface. Once cooked, drain and while the beans are still warm, pop them out of their skins into a bowl. Drizzle with a little of the olive oil and set aside.

Heat 3 tablespoons olive oil in a large frying pan over medium heat. Add the leeks (if using pencil leeks, leave them whole; if using larger leeks, cut them in half crossways to fit in the pan but note they will need a slightly longer cooking time). Cook for 5 minutes, then add the verjuice and reduce the temperature to very low. Cover and cook for 8 minutes or until tender. Add the lemon zest at the last moment. If you used large leeks, cut them into 2.5 cm lengths.

Melt the butter and 2 tablespoons olive oil in a large frying pan over medium heat. Add the mushrooms and salt and cook for 3–4 minutes or until tender. When almost cooked, add the pepper and toss to combine well. Remove from the heat.

Once all the components are cooked, place the beans, leeks, mushrooms, olives and oregano in a bowl and gently toss to combine. Divide among 4 shallow bowls, then finish each plate with a grinding of pepper and a drizzle of lemon juice. Scatter with dollops of ricotta or curd, then drizzle with a final flourish of olive oil.

NUTRITION ❧ Leeks are high in polyphenols, as well as beta-carotene and vitamin K.

Spring lamb rack with olive crumb on a bed of spinach and tomato sugo

As with any ingredient, but particularly meat, the quality will be influenced by the breed and by the farming practices. It's not a level playing field so finding a butcher you can trust to share this knowledge with you is important. We often have either our own Wiltshire lamb or the local Suffolk lamb – both are breeds where the texture of the lamb is noticeably different. The olive crumb needs a careful hand and brushing the tapenade on first helps the crumb to stay in place. Spinach, silverbeet and chard grow like the clappers in my garden and would in yours too. Although the photo might not show lots of it, it's worthy of a big dish on its own when it's freshly picked.

SERVES 4

2 tablespoons extra virgin olive oil
1 rack of lamb with 8 cutlets, French trimmed (ask your butcher to do this)
Sea salt flakes and freshly ground black pepper
50 g black olive tapenade or minced pitted olives
500 g baby spinach, washed and coarsely chopped
2 cups (500 ml) good-quality tomato sugo
16 Kalamata olives, pitted
2 tablespoons chopped flat-leaf parsley

Crumb

60 g fine sourdough breadcrumbs
1 tablespoon black chia seeds
1½ tablespoons linseeds (flaxseeds), blended to a coarse crumb
½ cup (50 g) LSA
1 teaspoon thyme leaves
Sea salt flakes
20 g unsalted butter, melted

Preheat the oven to 200°C (fan-forced). Place a wire rack over a baking tray.

To make the crumb, combine the breadcrumbs, seeds, LSA, thyme and salt in a bowl. Stir in the melted butter until well combined.

Heat 1 tablespoon olive oil in a large frying pan over high heat. Season the lamb rack to taste, then add to the pan, fat-side down first, and cook for 10 minutes or until golden on all sides. Brush the top side of the lamb with a thick layer of olive tapenade then press the crumb mixture on top. Place, crumb-side up, on the prepared rack and roast for 10–12 minutes for rare–medium rare lamb. Remove from the oven and rest for at least 10 minutes.

While the lamb is resting, heat the remaining tablespoon of olive oil in a large frying pan over high heat. Add the spinach and toss for 1–2 minutes or until just wilted. Remove from the heat and season to taste.

Warm the tomato sugo in a small saucepan, then spread over a large serving platter. Top with the spinach. Carve the lamb into cutlets and place on top, scatter with the olives and parsley and serve.

NUTRITION 🌿 The chia seeds and linseeds in the crumb are both rich in omega-3 fatty acids, and are good sources of copper, manganese, calcium and magnesium.

Barbecued lemon myrtle prawns with sorrel mayonnaise

I'm afraid I've made this a little trickier to manage than a regular skewered prawn recipe. Normally you'd spear the prawns onto the skewers first but because this dish is so flavour driven you'll get much better results from tossing the loose prawns in the marinade to make sure every part of the prawn is in contact with those wonderful flavours. It's not a bad idea to put on some kitchen gloves for threading the skewers after this. I've made a sorrel mayonnaise as I have lots in the garden and I love its sharp citrus flavour but any mayonnaise you make with a good balance of lemon juice will work well here.

SERVES 4

16 x 20 cm bamboo skewers soaked in
    water for 2 hours to avoid burning
16 very fresh large raw king or
    tiger prawns
Extra virgin olive oil, for cooking
Lime wedges, to serve

Marinade

2 tablespoons lemon myrtle powder
2 tablespoons chilli sauce
3 tablespoons finely chopped
    golden shallots
⅓ cup (80 ml) fish sauce
⅓ cup (80 ml) lemon juice
100 ml extra virgin olive oil
Sea salt flakes and freshly ground
    black pepper

Sorrel mayonnaise

½ cup (125 ml) mellow extra virgin
    olive oil
½ cup (125 ml) grapeseed oil
2 free-range egg yolks, at room
    temperature
1 cup trimmed sorrel leaves
    (about 1 bunch)
Sea salt flakes and freshly ground
    black pepper
Juice of ½ lemon

Preheat a barbecue grill plate to high or an overhead grill to the highest setting possible.

To make the marinade, place all the ingredients in a blender and process until smooth.

Peel the prawns, leaving the heads and tails intact. Use a skewer to devein the prawns, then toss them in the marinade and stand for 30 minutes.

Meanwhile, to make the sorrel mayonnaise, pour both the oils into a small jug. Place the egg yolks in a blender or a small food processor. Add the sorrel, a good pinch of salt and a good squeeze of lemon juice and process until smooth. With the motor running, gradually add the combined oils, drop by drop at first, then in a slow steady stream until thick and emulsified. Adjust the seasoning with salt, pepper and lemon juice as needed. This recipe will make more than you need but the leftover mayonnaise will keep well in the refrigerator for about a week.

Using a clean cloth to hold the slippery prawns, thread the prawns onto the soaked skewers, starting from the tail end. Place the skewers on a baking tray and brush with a little olive oil. Cook on the barbecue or under the grill for 2 minutes or until they turn bright red. Turn them over, brush with a little more olive oil and cook for another minute or until just cooked through. Be careful not to overcook the prawns – remember they will continue to cook once off the heat. Serve immediately with the sorrel mayonnaise and some lime wedges.

NUTRITION 🦐 Prawns are a good source of complete protein, vitamins B3 and B12, and selenium.

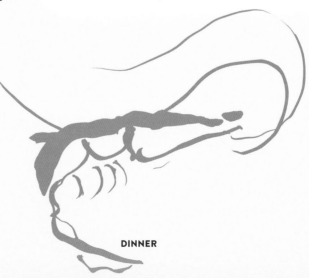

Roast chook with broccoli tabbouleh and turmeric buttermilk dressing

I remember a time on MasterChef when I cooked this chicken, giving important details like adding verjuice during the final stages of cooking and turning it over to rest for 20 minutes. That segment led to so much comment by email, social media and people stopping me on the street, telling me they'd tried the recipe and couldn't believe how wonderful it was.

SERVES 6

2 kg Barossa or other well-brought-up chook (for me it's always Saskia's)
125 g unsalted butter, softened
⅓ cup French tarragon leaves
Sea salt flakes and freshly ground black pepper
2 tablespoons extra virgin olive oil
3 tablespoons verjuice
Lemon wedges, to serve

Broccoli tabbouleh

1 head broccoli (about 360 g)
⅓ cup baby spinach
3 spring onions
⅔ cup finely chopped flat-leaf parsley
1 cup finely chopped mint
1 large ripe avocado, cut into small cubes
⅓ cup (45 g) slivered almonds, toasted

Dressing

1 tablespoon raw honey
1 teaspoon ground turmeric
Finely grated zest and juice of ½ lemon
½ cup (125 ml) buttermilk

Take the chook out of the refrigerator 1 hour before cooking to bring it to room temperature.

Preheat the oven to 200°C (fan-forced).

Place the butter and tarragon in a food processor and whiz to combine the ingredients but don't process it too much or the butter will split. Add seasoning to taste.

Place the chicken in a roasting tin and carefully slide your fingers under the skin around the legs and across both breasts to separate it from the meat. Place the butter under the skin by pushing it in with your fingers.

Tuck the wings under, then rub the skin of the chook with the olive oil and season to taste. Place a piece of foil just over the chicken breast so it won't dry out. Roast the chicken for 30 minutes, then reduce the oven temperature to 180°C (fan-forced). Remove the foil and roast for another 30 minutes. Open the oven and pour the verjuice over the bird, then close the oven and cook for another 10 minutes. Remove the chicken from the oven and turn it over in the roasting tin to rest upside down for 20 minutes before carving. After 5 minutes of resting, check whether the chicken is cooked by inserting a skewer into the thickest part of the thigh – there should not be any pink juices. Alternatively, the internal temperature should be 68°C. Leave to rest for another 15 minutes as it will keep warm in this time.

Meanwhile, to make the broccoli tabbouleh, as close as possible to serving, use a large knife to shave the head off the broccoli to give you fine pieces (see note). Chop the spinach and spring onions as finely as you can and place in a bowl with the broccoli. Gently stir in the remaining ingredients.

To make the dressing, whisk all the ingredients together.

Carve the chook and drizzle with all of the resting juices. Just as you're about to serve, toss the tabbouleh with most of the buttermilk dressing.

To serve, spoon the broccoli tabbouleh onto a serving platter and pour over the last bit of dressing. Serve with lemon wedges.

Note: While you only use the finely shaved broccoli head for the tabbouleh, the stalk is delicious too. Peel and cut it into fingers, then blanch and toss in extra virgin olive oil. Serve as a side with the chook or another dish.

A good-quality, well-brought-up chook is more expensive to buy but will go further as a well-raised chicken has a far superior texture and flavour so you need less per person.

Blue-eye trevalla baked in paper with bok choy, ginger, miso and soy

This is a great cooking method if you don't like the smell of fish lingering in your kitchen. You simply bundle each portion of the fish and flavourings together in a parcel made of baking paper or foil and bake it. The Asian flavours of miso, soy, garlic and ginger work beautifully as a dressing, but the trick is to not overcook the fish. I've suggested 8–10 minutes for what was a thick piece of fish, but keep in mind that it will continue to cook as it rests and you want it be only just cooked when you serve it.

SERVES 2

2 small heads baby bok choy,
  cut into 2 cm pieces
2 spring onions, green ends only,
  thinly sliced
2 x 200 g fillets skinless blue-eye
  trevalla, bones removed

Dressing

30 g unpasteurised white
  (shiro) miso
1½ tablespoons good-quality
  soy sauce
2 tablespoons verjuice
2 tablespoons extra virgin olive oil
1 clove garlic, very thinly sliced
15 g ginger, peeled and finely grated

Preheat the oven to 180°C (fan-forced).

To make the dressing, combine all the ingredients in a small bowl.

Place one head of bok choy in the centre of a large piece of baking paper and top with half the spring onion. Place the fillet on top and pour half the dressing over the fish. Bring up the two long sides of the baking paper and pleat to seal, then bring up the ends and pleat to form a secure parcel. Repeat for the second serve.

Place on a baking tray and bake for 8–10 minutes, depending on the thickness of the fillets. Remove and check that the fish is cooked. Allow to rest for a few minutes, then open up the parcel and drizzle over the remaining dressing.

Butterflied quail with orange and barley salad

Barbecuing quail and being given leave to eat with your fingers really delights me (though make sure you have a finger bowl close by). Here, the vino cotto marinade gives the quail a quick burnish that really accentuates the flavour. The barley salad with orange and lemon is the essence of spring and could be paired with any meat or poultry cooked on the barbecue.

SERVES 2

2 x 320 g jumbo quail
2 tablespoons vino cotto or balsamic
2 tablespoons extra virgin olive oil,
   plus extra for drizzling
Rocket leaves, to serve

Orange and barley salad

½ cup (100 g) pearl barley
3 tablespoons currants
½ cup (125 ml) verjuice or water
⅓ cup (55 g) almonds, lightly toasted
   and coarsely chopped
1 orange, cut into thin slices,
   seeds removed and each slice
   cut into eighths
⅓ cup chopped flat-leaf parsley
1 tablespoon extra virgin olive oil
1 tablespoon almond oil
Finely grated zest of 1 lemon
1 tablespoon lemon juice
Sea salt flakes and freshly ground
   black pepper

To prepare the quail, use a pair of kitchen scissors to cut down either side of the spine, then discard the spine. Place the quails, skin-side up, on a workbench and press down firmly with your hand to flatten. Place in a shallow bowl. Combine the vino cotto and olive oil in a bowl, then pour over the quail and marinate for at least 1 hour at room temperature, turning halfway through.

Meanwhile, to make the salad, place the barley in a saucepan and cover well with cold water. Bring to the boil over medium–high heat, then reduce the heat to low and simmer for 40–50 minutes or until tender. Meanwhile, place the currants and verjuice or water in a bowl and stand for 45 minutes to rehydrate. Drain the barley, then place in a bowl with all the remaining ingredients and combine well.

Heat a barbecue flat plate to high. Add the quail, skin-side up, and cook for 6 minutes. Reduce the heat to medium, turn the quail and cook, skin-side down, for another 2 minutes or until golden and cooked through. Remove and rest, skin-side down, for 5 minutes.

Serve the quail and any resting juices with the barley salad and rocket drizzled with a little olive oil. Don't forget a finger bowl.

Soba noodles with pickled carrot and cucumber and sesame ginger sauce

Soba noodles are so handy to have in the pantry. They taste great, cook quickly and can be served warm or at room temperature with these quick pickled veggies, or they can be cooked in advance and used as part of a cold salad. In this recipe the tofu and cashews make it a delicious light meal, but without those the noodles and pickled veggies would make a lovely accompaniment to miso-coated grilled salmon.

SERVES 6

3 bundles (270 g) soba
   (buckwheat) noodles
2 tablespoons extra virgin olive oil,
   plus extra for drizzling
300 g silken tofu
Sea salt flakes and freshly ground
   black pepper
120 g chopped toasted cashews
20 g (1 cup) mint leaves or very
   young shiso leaves, very
   thinly sliced
20 g (1 cup) Thai basil leaves, torn
Soy sauce or tamari, to serve

Pickles

70 ml rice wine vinegar
1 tablespoon sugar
1 teaspoon salt
½ telegraph cucumber, peeled
   lengthways with a peeler
   into thin ribbons
2 carrots, scrubbed, then peeled
   lengthways into thin ribbons

Sesame ginger sauce

50 g unhulled tahini
3 teaspoons rice vinegar
1 tablespoon finely grated ginger
1 heaped tablespoon unpasteurised
   white (shiro) miso
3 teaspoons soy sauce or tamari
3 teaspoons sesame oil
1 tablespoon sesame seeds, toasted

To make the pickles, combine the vinegar, sugar and salt in a large bowl. Add the vegetable ribbons, toss to combine and stand for 20 minutes, turning occasionally.

Meanwhile, to make the sesame ginger sauce, place all the ingredients in a small bowl and whisk until combined. Gradually whisk in up to ½ cup (125 ml) cold water until you reach a thick coating consistency.

Bring a large saucepan of salted water to the boil and cook the soba noodles according to the packet instructions until al dente (don't overcook them!). Drain and immediately lay out on a tray lined with baking paper to impede any more cooking. Drizzle with a little olive oil and cover with plastic film until needed.

Drain the tofu and gently pat dry on a clean tea towel. Cut into 1.5 cm cubes. Heat the olive oil in a large frying pan over high heat. When the oil is hot, add the tofu and cook, gently shaking the pan once or twice, until the tofu is golden. Season to taste, then gently pour into a sieve placed over a bowl to drain.

Place the soba noodles in a large bowl and toss with the sesame ginger sauce (depending on how saucy you like your noodles, you may have some sauce left over). Add the drained pickles, cashews and herbs and toss to combine well. Place on a large serving plate, top with the tofu and a drizzle of soy sauce or tamari and serve immediately.

NUTRITION ✎ Soba noodles are high in complete protein, fibre, manganese, magnesium and copper, as well as flavonoid antioxidants.

Stuffed squid and black barley

Here we have another of my favourite foods: squid. I love it in all its forms, whether it's simply cleaned, cut up and cooked briefly in a hot pan or, as here, stuffed with onion, breadcrumbs, fresh herbs and anchovies and cooked whole. Squid is wonderful with the nutty flavour of black barley but at the moment I can only find an expensive imported version. I'm hoping this will change in the near future, with the help of PIRSA, our state Primary Industries agency, and a few farmers who are keen to grow it. If you want to try this dish and can't find black barley just cook it the same way with black rice, which is much more affordable and accessible.

SERVES 4

4 medium squid, cleaned, tentacles reserved
Extra virgin olive oil, for cooking
Squeeze of lemon juice
Finely grated zest of 1 lemon
8 Kalamata olives, pitted and coarsely chopped

Stuffing

2 tablespoons extra virgin olive oil, plus extra for drizzling
2 brown onions, finely chopped
2 cloves garlic, finely chopped
⅔ cup (50 g) fresh sourdough breadcrumbs
2 tablespoons rinsed and finely chopped preserved lemon rind (see note)
2 anchovy fillets, finely chopped
½ cup chopped flat-leaf parsley

Black barley salad

½ cup (100 g) raw black barley (see glossary page 279)
3 tablespoons extra virgin olive oil
⅓ cup (55 g) pepitas (pumpkin seeds), toasted
¼ preserved lemon, pith discarded, rind finely chopped
2 tablespoons finely chopped sun-dried tomatoes
1 small red onion, halved and thinly sliced
½ cup coriander leaves, chopped
¼ bunch chives, finely chopped
2 tablespoons lemon juice
Sea salt flakes and freshly ground black pepper

To make the stuffing, heat the olive oil in a large frying pan over low–medium heat. Add the onion and cook, stirring often, for 10 minutes or until translucent. Add the garlic and stir for another 2–3 minutes or until fragrant. Add the breadcrumbs, preserved lemon and anchovy and combine well. Remove from the heat and stand until cool, then stir through the parsley.

Meanwhile, to make the barley salad, bring a large saucepan of water to the boil. Add the barley and cook for 15–30 minutes or until tender. The cooking time will depend on the age of the barley. Drain, then place in a bowl and stir through the olive oil. Stand until cool. Just before serving, stir through the remaining ingredients gently but well.

Preheat the oven to 200°C (fan-forced).

Fill the cleaned squid tubes with the stuffing to about 2.5 cm from the top of the tube. Thread a toothpick through the top to prevent the stuffing coming out during cooking.

Heat a drizzle of olive oil in a large ovenproof frying pan over medium heat. Cook the stuffed squid and tentacles for 2 minutes on each side or until lightly coloured. Remove the tentacles from the pan and set aside. Transfer the pan to the oven and cook for another 4–6 minutes, depending on the size of the squid. Remove from the oven, then drizzle the squid with a little extra olive oil and a squeeze of lemon juice. Leave to rest in the pan for 5 minutes. Remove the toothpicks.

Serve the squid with all the pan juices on top of the barley salad. Add the tentacles, lemon zest and chopped olives, and a last flourish of extra virgin olive oil.

Note: If you don't have any preserved lemon on hand, simply use the same quantity of very thinly sliced lemon rounds, cut into eighths.

NUTRITION Squid is particularly nutritious as it provides complete protein, vitamins B3, B6 and B12, iron, zinc and selenium. It also provides some omega-3 fatty acids.

I have only come across black barley relatively
recently and I think it has so much potential.
The flavour is so nutty and delicious.

Mushroom and tempeh barbecue patties

Who says you have to have buns to have a hamburger? Instead, select some beautiful large open mushrooms of a similar size and I can assure you no one will go hungry. As with so many of my recipes you should view this as a starting point only. You could replace the rice with lentils or chickpeas if you have them left over from another dish, or try adding beetroot slices or leftovers from the Grilled zucchini salad on page 120 instead of spinach or lettuce.

MAKES 8

16 open Swiss brown mushrooms, about 6 cm wide, stalk removed
3 tablespoons olive oil, plus extra for brushing
Sea salt flakes and freshly ground black pepper
100 g baby spinach or small cos lettuce leaves
2 large vine-ripened tomatoes, sliced
8 large slices Gruyere

Patties

¾ cup (150 g) brown rice
1 carrot, peeled and grated, excess liquid squeezed out
100 g grated zucchini, excess liquid squeezed out
½ red onion, very finely diced
1 clove garlic, finely grated
3 tablespoons chopped flat-leaf parsley
3 tablespoons chopped basil
125 g tempeh, finely chopped
35 g hulled tahini
30 g coconut amino sauce (see glossary page 278) or tamari
1 tablespoon white chia seeds
35 g ground almonds
Sea salt flakes and freshly ground black pepper
Spelt flour, for dusting (optional)

To make the patties, rinse the rice well, then place in a medium saucepan with 1 litre water. Bring to the boil over medium heat, then cover and reduce the heat to low. Simmer for 30–40 minutes or until tender. Remove from the heat and stand for 5 minutes, then drain off any excess water. Set aside to cool.

Place all the patty ingredients, except the spelt flour, in a large bowl and mix until well combined. Refrigerate for 10 minutes to help firm up the mixture. Shape the mixture into 8 patties about the same diameter as your mushrooms, pressing the mixture together tightly. If the mixture appears wet, dust the patties in a little spelt flour.

Preheat a barbecue grill plate or chargrill pan to medium–high. Brush the top of the mushrooms with olive oil and season with salt and pepper. Cook, top-side down, for 8 minutes, then turn and cook for another 2 minutes or until cooked through. Remove from the heat, cover and keep warm.

Meanwhile, heat the olive oil in a large frying pan over low heat. Add the patties and pan-fry for 3–4 minutes on each side or until golden – they will be slightly fragile so take care when turning. Remove from the pan.

To assemble the burgers, place half the mushrooms, cap-side down, on plates. Top with half the spinach or cos, then a slice of tomato and the patties. Finish with the cheese slices (if you work quickly the heat of the patties will melt the cheese nicely). Top with the remaining spinach and mushroom caps, then serve immediately.

NUTRITION 🍃 Tempeh is a good source of protein, manganese, copper, vitamin B2 and fibre.

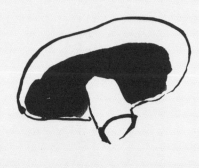

These 'burgers' are as much fun to eat as they are to make — just have lots of serviettes at the ready.

The tabbouleh is so good it could actually be enjoyed as a lunch dish on its own, perhaps with a boiled egg to boot.

Yoghurt marinated chicken with Turkish-style tabbouleh

I need to declare a bias and that is that I would never cook chicken without the skin. Remember mine is a recipe for life, not a diet, but I absolutely understand if you prefer to remove it. If so, please cook the chicken at the lowest possible temperature so it doesn't dry out. Alternatively, you could cook the chicken with the skin on and then throw it away, but in a dish like this the seasonings on the skin protecting the chicken would be lost.

SERVES 4

2 cloves garlic, minced
3 tablespoons thick natural probiotic yoghurt, plus extra to serve (optional)
1 tablespoon thyme leaves
Finely grated zest and juice of ½ lemon
1 tablespoon extra virgin olive oil
Sea salt flakes and freshly ground black pepper
4 x 160–200 g chicken thighs, skin on
½ cup (60 g) toasted ground almonds or dukkah (see page 275)
Vino cotto, for drizzling

Turkish-style tabbouleh
150 ml chicken stock
½ cup (100 g) wholemeal couscous
Sea salt flakes and freshly ground black pepper
1 cup flat-leaf parsley leaves, rinsed and patted dry
½ cup mint leaves, rinsed and patted dry
1 tablespoon lemon juice
3 vine-ripened tomatoes, cut into 1 cm dice
2 spring onions, green ends only, finely chopped
1 large avocado, cut into 1 cm dice
2 tablespoons extra virgin olive oil

Place the garlic, yoghurt, thyme, lemon zest, lemon juice and olive oil in a large bowl. Season the chicken, then add to the marinade and toss to coat well. Cover and refrigerate for 30 minutes.

Preheat the oven to 230°C (fan-forced).

Meanwhile, to make the tabbouleh, place the stock in a saucepan and bring to the boil. Place the couscous in a heatproof bowl. Pour over the hot stock, then cover with a plate or a piece of plastic film and stand for 5 minutes. Use a fork to fluff up and separate the grains. Season to taste and stand until cool.

Gather the parsley leaves in a tight wad in your hand and finely shred the leaves with a very sharp knife, almost in a shaving action. Repeat with the mint leaves. Add to the cooled couscous with the remaining ingredients and gently mix through. Season and set aside.

Remove the chicken from the marinade, shaking off any excess. Place the chicken, skin-side up, on a baking tray lined with baking paper and sprinkle the ground almonds or dukkah evenly over the top. Bake for 12–18 minutes or until the chicken is golden and cooked through. Remove from the oven and leave to rest for 10 minutes.

Serve the chicken drizzled with a good glug of vino cotto, and the tabbouleh topped with a dollop of yoghurt, if using.

NUTRITION 🌿 The herbs in the tabbouleh, parsley and mint, are rich sources of vitamins K and C, some beta-carotene, folate and flavonoids.

Wholewheat and yellow zucchini pasta with anchovies

This is the perfect last-minute meal if you have your own vegetable patch, and if so, being summer, I'm sure you'll have plenty of zucchini. If you're buying them get the smallest ones you can find, whether they are yellow or green or indeed baby squash. I keep packets of Pangkarra wholewheat pasta in my pantry. It's a great product from a Clare Valley farming family. Follow the instructions on your pasta packet so it's ready with the other ingredients and toss them through the moment you've drained the pasta. To make a more substantial meal, serve this with my Grilled zucchini salad on the side (see page 120).

SERVES 3-4

½ cup (50 g) walnuts
250 g wholewheat pasta
   (shape of your choice)
½ cup (125 ml) extra virgin olive oil
Sea salt flakes and freshly ground
   black pepper
8 small yellow (or green) zucchini
   (about 45 g each), cut into
   2 cm thick rounds
1 x 45 g tin anchovies in extra virgin
   olive oil, drained, patted dry and
   cut into thirds
⅓ cup basil or flat-leaf parsley leaves
120 g ricotta (see page 271),
   crumbled

Preheat the oven to 180°C (fan-forced).

Toast the walnuts on a baking tray for 8–10 minutes. Pour into a clean tea towel and rub off the skins while still warm. Coarsely chop and set aside.

Bring a large saucepan of lightly salted water to the boil over high heat. Add the pasta and cook according to the packet instructions until al dente. Drain and return to the pan, then add ⅓ cup (80 ml) olive oil and season to taste.

Meanwhile, place the zucchini in a microwave-safe container with a lid. Drizzle with the remaining olive oil and microwave on high for 60 seconds. Alternatively, add the zucchini to a saucepan of lightly salted boiling water and cook for 2 minutes only, then drain.

Add the cooked zucchini and anchovies to the hot pasta and toss to combine well. Divide among serving bowls, then scatter with the toasted walnuts. Gather the basil or parsley in a tight wad in your hand and finely shred the leaves with a very sharp knife, almost in a shaving action. Scatter over the pasta, followed by the ricotta, and serve immediately.

Note: I use a lot of walnuts in my cooking and tend to toast a whole tray at a time. Keep them in airtight containers in the refrigerator or freezer so you'll always have a readily available supply.

Quail with quandong and snake beans

The quandong is a native peach and is generally only available dried, and even then it's expensive and not particularly accessible. But my goodness what a unique flavour! I was recently given a large bag of dried quandongs and was intrigued to try different ways of cooking with them. I rehydrated them overnight (actually in verjuice as I have lots to hand but water is the norm) and in the end I decided I preferred their flavour in savoury dishes rather than sweet. For this dish I just tossed them in extra virgin olive oil and allowed their natural sugars to burnish them and bring out the flavour but if you want to use quandongs in a dessert they are great cooked in a light sugar syrup.

SERVES 4

½ cup (25 g) dried quandongs
4 x 320 g jumbo quail
2 tablespoons vino cotto
⅓ cup (80 ml) extra virgin olive oil
1 tablespoon rosemary leaves
Sea salt flakes and freshly ground
    black pepper
1 bunch snake beans

Soak the quandongs overnight in ¾ cup (180 ml) water.

To butterfly the quail, use a pair of kitchen scissors to cut along the spine, then press down firmly with your hands to flatten evenly. Place in a shallow bowl with 1 tablespoon vino cotto, 2 tablespoons olive oil and the rosemary leaves and toss to coat well. Cover and refrigerate for at least 1 hour, turning halfway through.

Preheat a barbecue grill plate to high.

Season the quail all over with salt and pepper. Place, skin-side up, on the grill and cook for 4–6 minutes (depending on the size of the quail) or until golden and almost cooked through. Turn and cook, skin-side down, for 2 minutes or until the breast is just cooked through but still pink. Remove from the heat and place on a shallow tray. Drizzle with 1 tablespoon each of olive oil and vino cotto, and rest, skin-side down, for 5 minutes.

Meanwhile, drain the soaked quandongs well and toss with the remaining 1 tablespoon olive oil.

Steam or microwave the snake beans on high for 2–3 minutes or until tender (no squeaky beans) but still with good colour. Alternatively, drop into a saucepan of lightly salted boiling water and cook until tender. Serve the quail with the resting juices, beans and quandongs with a finger bowl for the quail.

Spelt pasta rags with tomato, olives and ricotta

It's great fun making pasta of any kind, particularly with children who love the involvement as much as they love getting flour all over themselves. Sometimes I will make deliciously silky pasta from hard white wheat flour but for every day I love the rustic texture and flavour of spelt, and making rags is definitely the easiest shape of all as it's meant to be 'unstructured'. The only actual cooking in this dish is that of the pasta as all the other ingredients are just cut up and tossed in. There are lots of ways you could make it more special if you feel the need: you could drizzle the olives with a little extra virgin olive oil and roast them in a 200°C (fan-forced) oven for 10 minutes, or you could add your favourite toasted nuts and grated lemon zest. As ever, just use what you love and what you have to hand.

SERVES 6 (OR 4 VERY HUNGRY DINERS)

400 g ripe heritage tomatoes
Sea salt flakes and freshly ground
    black pepper
⅓ cup (80 ml) extra virgin olive oil
20 Kalamata olives, pitted
160 g ricotta (see page 271),
    coarsely crumbled
Small handful basil leaves

Spelt pasta

500 g spelt flour
4 x 55 g free-range eggs
6 free-range egg yolks,
    plus extra if needed

To make the pasta, tip the flour onto a workbench and make a well in the centre. Whisk the eggs and egg yolks together, then pour into the well and use a fork to gradually incorporate them into the flour. This is a stiff dough but you may need to add an extra yolk if the dough is too dry. Knead for at least 10 minutes or until a smooth shiny dough forms. Alternatively, place the flour and egg mixture in a food processor and pulse just until the dough starts to come together – it won't need much pulsing. Tip the dough out onto a work surface and knead by hand. Shape into a rectangle, wrap in plastic film, then refrigerate for 30 minutes.

Cut the rested dough crossways into 10 even pieces and cover with a tea towel. Take a piece of dough and press it as flat as you can with the palm of your hand. Feed it through the rollers of a pasta machine set on the widest aperture. Fold the rolled dough in thirds, then pass the narrow end through the machine another 8–10 times until the pasta is shiny and silky. Pass the dough through each of the remaining settings 3–4 times until you reach the second-last setting. Cut the sheet into irregular shapes, then place on a clean tea towel and cover with plastic film. Repeat with the remaining pieces of dough.

Twenty minutes before serving, cut the tomatoes in half, then season and toss with a drizzle of olive oil – this creates lovely juices which will add to the dish.

To cook the pasta, bring 4 litres water to the boil in a tall saucepan, then add a generous amount of salt. Tip in the pasta and stir gently to keep it well separated. Cook until done, testing a piece after 3 minutes. Drain the pasta and reserve a little of the cooking water in case you want to moisten the completed dish. Do not run the cooked pasta under water, as you will lose the precious starch that helps the sauce or oil adhere.

Return the hot pasta to the pan. Toss through the olive oil, olives, tomatoes and any juices, and season to taste. Divide among bowls and scatter with the ricotta. Gather the basil in a tight wad in your hand and slice with a very sharp knife. Scatter over the pasta and serve immediately.

Resting meat before carving is really important to make the most of the flavour and texture.

Star anise and vino cotto beef with red vegetable salad

Most people are comfortable cooking a steak on the barbecue so there is nothing to fear here. I have simply taken a larger piece of beef, rubbed it with ground star anise, extra virgin olive oil and vino cotto (though you could easily use balsamic) and left it to marinate at room temperature. Use your judgement with this, especially if you're in the middle of a heatwave – you just need the meat to be at room temperature when you put it on the grill.

SERVES 2

1 tablespoon vino cotto
¼ teaspoon ground star anise
1 tablespoon extra virgin olive oil
2 x 160 g trimmed Porterhouse
    steaks
Horseradish cream or Dijon
    mustard, to serve (optional)

Red vegetable salad

3 ripe tomatoes
2 tablespoons extra virgin olive oil
3 red onions
2 teaspoons vino cotto
2 large red capsicums

Dressing

3 tablespoons extra virgin olive oil
1 tablespoon red wine vinegar
1 tablespoon chopped flat-leaf
    parsley
1 teaspoon lemon thyme leaves
Sea salt flakes and freshly ground
    black pepper

Preheat the oven to 220°C (fan-forced).

Combine the vino cotto, star anise and olive oil in a small bowl. Rub all over the steaks and allow to stand at room temperature for at least 2 hours.

Meanwhile, to make the vegetable salad, cut the tomatoes into eighths and place on a baking tray. Drizzle with 1 tablespoon olive oil and roast for 20–25 minutes or until burnished. Remove from the oven and set aside to cool.

Cut the red onions into eighths and remove the outer layer of skin. Place on a baking tray, drizzle with a little olive oil and roast for 20 minutes or until soft, collapsed and burnished. Remove from the oven, drizzle with the vino cotto and allow to cool.

Place the whole capsicums on a baking tray and rub all over with the remaining olive oil. Roast for 20 minutes or until at least 60% of the skin has blackened. Remove from the oven and place in a bowl, then cover with plastic film and stand until cool. Peel and seed the cooled capsicum (don't wash them or you will wash away all the lovely juices). Tear into rough pieces and place in a large bowl. Add the cooled tomato and red onion.

To make the dressing, whisk all the ingredients together in a bowl. Pour over the vegetable salad and toss lightly with your hands.

Preheat a barbecue grill plate or chargrill pan to high. Cook the steaks for 4 minutes on one side, then turn and cook the other side for 2–3 minutes. The cooking time will depend upon the thickness of the meat. Remove and rest for at least 5 minutes. Serve the steaks drizzled with any resting juices, along with the red vegetable salad and horseradish or mustard, if using.

NUTRITION 🌿 This red salad packs a nutritional punch – red onions are a rich source of antioxidant polyphenols, manganese and anthocyanins. Red capsicum is a good source of vitamins C and B6 and beta-carotene, and the tomatoes provide the antioxidant lycopene and vitamin C.

Moroccan-style baked fish

My introduction to the wonderful spice blend 'ras el hanout' was actually in Morocco about 10 years ago. We were travelling with friends and visited what looked like an apothecary with shelf after shelf of tall glass jars filled with vibrantly coloured spices. I will never forget the headiness of the scent. Ras el hanout is a combination of the 'top drawer' or more literally 'head of the shop' spices. I have read of it being made with up to 28 spices but we make ours (in small quantities) with cumin, coriander, cinnamon, ginger, turmeric, cardamom and black pepper. I make a lot of Mediterranean dishes so I often use it in my cooking these days – it adds such a special note.

SERVES 4

4 x 180 g skinless white fish or
  salmon fillets, bones removed
2 tablespoons extra virgin olive oil
1 teaspoon sea salt flakes
1 tablespoon ras el hanout
2 tablespoons thinly sliced
  flat-leaf parsley
⅔ cup (50 g) toasted flaked
  almonds (optional)

Tomato base

2 tablespoons currants
2 tablespoons verjuice
⅓ cup (80 ml) extra virgin olive oil
2 brown onions, finely chopped
1 teaspoon finely chopped garlic
½ teaspoon ras el hanout (see note)
½ teaspoon saffron threads
1 lemon, zest removed in wide strips
  using a peeler
1 x 400 g tin chopped tomatoes

Couscous

1 cup (200 g) wholemeal couscous
2 cups (500 ml) chicken or
  vegetable stock
30 g unsalted butter, softened
2 carrots, quartered lengthways
  and sliced on the diagonal
Sea salt flakes and freshly ground
  black pepper

To make the tomato base, soak the currants in verjuice for 1 hour or overnight if time permits.

Preheat the oven to 220°C (fan-forced).

Heat the olive oil in a large saucepan over medium heat. Add the onion and cook for 10 minutes or until translucent but not coloured. Add the garlic and cook for another 2 minutes. Stir in the ras el hanout and saffron threads and cook for 1 minute or until fragrant. Add the currants and verjuice and simmer for 30 seconds, then add the lemon zest and tomatoes. Simmer for 8–10 minutes or until thickened. Pour the sauce into a shallow ovenproof baking dish.

Meanwhile, to make the couscous, place the stock in a small saucepan and bring to the boil. Place the couscous into a heatproof bowl, stir in the boiling stock, then cover immediately and leave for 5 minutes. Add the butter and use a fork to fluff up and separate the grains. Cook the carrots in lightly salted boiling water for 2–3 minutes or until tender. Drain and stir into the couscous, then season to taste, cover and keep warm.

Rub the fish with olive oil, then season with salt and ras el hanout. Place on top of the tomato base and bake for 7 minutes or until the fish is just cooked. Remove from the oven and stand for 5 minutes. Scatter with the parsley and toasted almonds, if using, and serve with the warm couscous.

Note: Ras el hanout can be bought ready made from Herbie's Spices online or from other good spice suppliers.

NUTRITION 🍃 Couscous is a good source of fibre, manganese, magnesium and some B-vitamins.

Dukkah-crusted chicken schnitzel with heritage tomato salad

I don't want to sound like a stuck record but eating well is about making choices with lots of variety and balance. I always eat the skin of chicken but many people avoid it and if you are one who does then I repeat the advice of cooking slowly so you don't dry out the chicken. You can buy dukkah, but it's so easy to make your own. Store it in the refrigerator as it is predominantly made with almonds, and all nuts should be kept refrigerated. Tomatoes, on the other hand, shouldn't be refrigerated unless they are so ripe they are going to burst. Cutting tomatoes half an hour in advance and sprinkling over a little extra virgin olive oil, salt and pepper brings out the flavour enormously.

SERVES 2

2 x 230 g chicken breast fillets, skin on (use a Barossa or other well-brought-up chook)
Plain flour, for dusting
⅓ cup (45 g) dukkah (see page 275)
1 free-range egg
2 tablespoons extra virgin olive oil
Basil leaves, to serve

Heritage tomato salad
250 g heirloom tomatoes, halved
1 tablespoon extra virgin olive oil
1 tablespoon basil leaves
2 teaspoons verjuice
Sea salt flakes and freshly ground black pepper

Preheat the oven to 180°C (fan-forced).

Pat dry the chicken breasts with paper towel. Place the flour and dukkah on separate plates and lightly beat the egg in a shallow bowl. Dust the chicken with flour, dip into the beaten egg, then coat in the dukkah.

Heat the olive oil in an ovenproof frying pan over medium heat. Add the chicken and cook gently for 2 minutes on each side or until light golden. Transfer the pan to the oven and cook for 6–8 minutes, depending on the thickness of the breasts. Remove from the oven and rest for at least 8 minutes before slicing.

Meanwhile, to make the tomato salad, toss all the ingredients together in a bowl.

To serve, thickly slice the chicken against the grain, then serve with the tomato salad and basil leaves.

Spiced lamb with roasted eggplants

The spices of the Middle East are so accessible these days and give so much life to minced lamb. If you can, it's best to keep whole spices and roast and grind them as needed, but if you know you just won't go to that trouble try to buy them from a reliable source such as Herbie's Spices that has such a high turnover they will always be fresh. If you like leftovers for lunch this dish is even better the next day as the flavours mature and meld together.

SERVES 4

2 eggplants
Sea salt flakes and freshly ground
    black pepper
⅓ cup (80 ml) extra virgin olive oil,
    plus extra for drizzling
2 small brown onions,
    finely chopped
1 tablespoon ras el hanout (see
    page 170)
2 tablespoons verjuice
500 g lamb mince
3 tablespoons chopped
    flat-leaf parsley
3 tablespoons chopped mint
½ cup (80 g) toasted pine nuts
½ cup (140 g) natural probiotic
    yoghurt, plus extra to serve
Lemon juice, to taste
Flat-leaf parsley or mint leaves,
    to serve

Preheat the oven to 220°C (fan-forced). Line a baking tray with baking paper.

Cut the eggplants in half lengthways. Score the flesh lightly. Season both sides with salt and drizzle with 1 tablespoon olive oil. Place on the tray, cut-side down, and roast for 20–30 minutes or until tender. Allow to cool slightly. Using a metal spoon, scoop out the eggplant flesh, leaving a 1 cm border. Finely chop the flesh and place the shells on the baking tray.

Heat the remaining olive oil in a large saucepan over medium heat. Add the onion and cook for 8–10 minutes or until translucent. Add the ras el hanout and stir for 1–2 minutes, then add the verjuice and simmer until nearly evaporated.

Meanwhile, heat a drizzle of olive oil in another saucepan over high heat. Add the lamb mince and cook, breaking up any lumps with a wooden spoon, for 12 minutes or until browned. Drain off the excess fat, then add the mince to the onion and combine well. Remove from the heat. Stir in the chopped herbs, eggplant flesh, pine nuts and yoghurt. Adjust the seasoning.

Fill the eggplant shells with the mince mixture. Cover the tray with foil and bake for 10 minutes or until heated through. Serve topped with a dollop of extra yoghurt, a drizzle of olive oil, a squeeze of lemon juice and the parsley. Finish with a grinding of pepper.

Pan-fried whiting with celery and pomegranate salad

With the exception of keen anglers who can catch their own, most of us have to buy our fish. Whiting is such a delicate and delicious fish so do buy it when you see it! All it needs is a quick fry in butter, with a bit of salt and pepper, a squeeze of lemon and perhaps a sprinkling of parsley. You could serve it with some purple potatoes made into chips just think of that colour! The salad is a wonderful accompaniment to the simply cooked fish, but it could easily be made into a stand-alone dish for lunch with some fresh ricotta. I love this style of cooking. It's just about pulling ideas together and combining great flavours with a minimum of fuss.

SERVES 4

4 x 160–180 g skinless whiting fillets, bones removed
Sea salt flakes and freshly ground black pepper
2 tablespoons extra virgin olive oil, plus extra for drizzling
40 g unsalted butter
Finely grated zest and juice of 1 lemon
2 tablespoons chopped flat-leaf parsley

Celery and pomegranate salad

80 g green lentils
2 tablespoons extra virgin olive oil
1 bulb fennel, tough outer leaves removed
1 tablespoon lemon juice
2 large sticks celery, thinly sliced
½ small Lebanese cucumber, halved lengthways and thinly sliced
1 cup flat-leaf parsley leaves
1 pomegranate, seeds removed
Sea salt flakes and freshly ground black pepper

To make the salad, rinse the lentils, then place in a saucepan with 4 times the amount of cold water. Bring to the boil, then reduce the heat to low and simmer for 20 minutes or until tender. Drain well and spread out on a tray so they don't continue to cook. Place in a bowl and drizzle with a little of the olive oil. About 10 minutes before serving, using a mandolin, thinly slice the fennel into a bowl. Toss through the remaining olive oil and the lemon juice and stand for 10 minutes. Just before serving, add the celery, cucumber, parsley, pomegranate seeds and lentils and toss to combine well. Season to taste.

Heat 2 large frying pans over high heat so you don't overcrowd the pan and 'poach' the fish rather than pan-fry it (see note). Season the fish, add a drizzle of olive oil to both pans and, when hot, add 2 fillets to each pan. Cook for 2 minutes on each side, then divide the butter, lemon zest, lemon juice and parsley between the pans. Shake to gently combine, then serve immediately with the salad.

Note: If you don't have 2 large frying pans that can fit comfortably on your stove top, preheat the oven to 150°C (fan-forced) and keep half the cooked fish warm (covered loosely with foil) while you cook the remaining fillets, but be careful not to overcook it.

NUTRITION 🍃 Whiting is a very good source of omega-3 fatty acids and protein, it also provides selenium, and vitamins B3, B6 and B12.

It's such a treat to get your hands on fresh whiting.

Lemongrass and buttermilk poached chicken with saffron tomato ragu

I adore buttermilk. Poaching white meat in it adds a delightful zing to the dish and, although this is a pretty instant recipe here, if you have the time to slow cook the chicken on the barest simmer I encourage you to go the extra step of letting it cool completely in the strained juices, which will set into a natural jelly. If I cooked this in summer I'd help it along by adding some gelatine to the juices so it could set enough to be cut into squares as part of a salad dish. Again, just another extension; a way of making the most of all the ingredients.

SERVES 4

600 ml buttermilk
2 fresh bay leaves, lightly crushed
20 g ginger, peeled and sliced
2 lemongrass stalks, lightly crushed
    and cut into 5 cm lengths
2 large free-range chicken breasts,
    skin on (about 320 g each)
2 tablespoons extra virgin olive
    oil (optional)
Basil leaves, to serve
Steamed broccolini, to serve
    (optional)

Tomato ragu

3 tablespoons extra virgin olive oil
2 brown onions, finely diced
2 carrots, peeled and finely diced
2 sticks celery, finely diced
1 fresh bay leaf, lightly crushed
8 sprigs lemon thyme
2 tablespoons tomato paste
2 tablespoons verjuice
2 teaspoons saffron threads
1 x 800 g tin roma tomatoes,
    coarsely chopped
1 cup (250 ml) vegetable or
    chicken stock
Sea salt flakes and freshly ground
    black pepper
3 tablespoons chopped basil

To make the tomato ragu, heat the olive oil in a deep frying pan over low–medium heat. Add the onion and cook for 10 minutes or until soft and golden brown. Add the carrot, celery, bay leaf and thyme and cook for 10–12 minutes or until tender. Add the tomato paste and cook for 2 minutes, then add the verjuice and simmer until nearly evaporated. Stir in the saffron, tomatoes and stock, then season to taste. Cover with a lid, reduce the heat to low and simmer, stirring occasionally, for 30 minutes or until thickened and reduced. Just before serving, remove the bay leaf and thyme sprigs, and stir in the chopped basil.

Meanwhile, place the buttermilk, bay leaves, ginger and lemongrass in a deep non-stick frying pan over medium heat. Bring to a simmer, then add the chicken, skin-side down. Cover with a lid and gently simmer for 5 minutes. Turn the chicken over and cook for another 4–5 minutes or until cooked through – the cooking time will depend on the thickness of the breasts. If you have a digital thermometer, remove the chicken once the internal temperature reaches 62°C.

If you are going to serve the skin (and I certainly do), heat the olive oil in another non-stick frying pan over medium–high heat. Pat the chicken lightly with paper towel to dry. Once the pan is hot, add the breasts, skin-side down, and pan-fry for 1 minute or until you get a slight caramelisation on the skin. Remove from the pan and rest, skin-side up, in a warm place for 10 minutes.

Spread the ragu over a serving plate. Thickly slice the chicken against the grain, then place on top of the ragu and scatter with basil leaves. Serve with steamed broccolini on the side, if desired.

Sweet potato, ras el hanout and fennel tart with olive oil pastry

This is a delightfully free-form tart. The pastry is straightforward and very forgiving, and in fact can be made in a food processor as long as you just pulse to bring all the ingredients together. You could add a bit of cinnamon to the filling if you like – it's one of the ingredients in ras el hanout, a Middle Eastern spice blend that is so worth looking out for. If you have some pomegranate seeds, or 'arils' as they are properly known, scatter them over the tart just before serving. They'll finish it off beautifully.

SERVES 6

350 g white, red or purple sweet
   potato, peeled and cut into
   3 cm chunks
⅓ cup (80 ml) extra virgin olive oil
Sea salt flakes and freshly ground
   black pepper
2 tablespoons verjuice
2 small bulbs fennel, trimmed
   and cut into 1 cm thick slices
1 tablespoon ras el hanout
   (see page 170)
100 g mozzarella cheese, torn
   into small pieces
3 tablespoons raisins
3 tablespoons toasted pine nuts
½ cup chopped flat-leaf parsley

Pastry

2 cups (260 g) organic white
   spelt flour
⅓ cup (25 g) finely grated parmesan
½ cup (125 ml) extra virgin olive oil
2 free-range eggs
3 tablespoons iced water

Preheat the oven to 220°C (fan-forced).

To make the pastry, place the flour, parmesan, olive oil and eggs in a food processor. Pulse until just combined, then gradually add enough iced water to bring the pastry together. Do not overwork. Turn out onto a workbench, shape into a rectangle, then wrap in plastic film and refrigerate for 30 minutes.

Meanwhile, toss the sweet potato in a bowl with 2 tablespoons olive oil, then season with salt and pepper. Spread over a baking tray lined with baking paper and roast for 25 minutes. Pour over the verjuice and roast for another 10 minutes or until golden and tender. Remove from the oven and set aside to cool. Reduce the oven temperature to 180°C (fan-forced).

Heat the remaining 2 tablespoons olive oil in a frying pan over low heat. Add the fennel and saute for 12–15 minutes or until tender. Add the ras el hanout and stir for another 1–2 minutes or until fragrant. Remove from the heat.

Roll out the pastry between 2 sheets of baking paper into a rough rectangle about 3 mm thick. Remove the top sheet of paper, then trim the sides to neaten a little. Place on a baking tray and refrigerate until needed.

To assemble, toss the cooled sweet potato and half the mozzarella in a bowl and spread over the centre of the pastry, leaving a 6 cm border. Fold up the edges of the tart, pleating where necessary to encase the filling, leaving the middle open. Scatter with the fennel, raisins and pine nuts. Bake for 35–40 minutes or until golden. Remove from the oven and stand for 10 minutes. Scatter with the chopped parsley and serve with the remaining mozzarella on the side or scattered on top.

NUTRITION 🍃 This nutritious pastry will provide you with fibre and protein, iron and magnesium from the flour, complete protein from the eggs, and monounsaturated fatty acids as well as antioxidant and anti-inflammatory polyphenols from the olive oil.

If you ever have the chance to try wild barramundi I'd certainly grab it as it's very special but not easy to find.

Roasted barramundi with kale, anchovies and lemon

Farmed fish is the way of the future, given the diminishing stocks of the sea, and I have tasted some great farmed barramundi at Parndana Area School on Kangaroo Island (and I know there are others). The students there are responsible for growing the barramundi in tanks and the school has a purpose-built hospitality centre where they cook the barramundi in every way imaginable. Colin visited a few months ago and declared their salt and pepper barramundi the best he had eaten!

SERVES 2

1 bulb garlic

2 tablespoons extra virgin olive oil, plus extra for drizzling

1 lemon, zest removed in wide strips using a peeler

2 x 170 g barramundi or other white fish fillets, skin on, bones removed

Sea salt flakes and freshly ground black pepper

30 g unsalted butter

1 bunch curly kale (about 200 g), stems removed and leaves torn into bite-sized pieces

1 x 45 g tin anchovies in extra virgin olive oil, drained (see note)

Preheat the oven to 180°C (fan-forced).

Place the garlic bulb on a piece of foil and drizzle with olive oil. Wrap up to make a parcel, then place on a baking tray and roast for 30 minutes or until soft and caramelised. Remove from the oven and set aside to cool slightly. When cool enough to handle, squeeze the soft garlic out of the skins into a bowl. Reserve half the garlic and place the remainder in an airtight container for another use.

Using a small sharp knife, remove and discard any white pith from the underside of each strip of lemon zest. Place the lemon zest in a small saucepan of water and bring to the boil. Simmer for 2 minutes, then drain. Repeat the process once more – this will remove all bitterness from the lemon.

Pat the fish dry with paper towel, then season on both sides. Heat 1 tablespoon olive oil in a large frying pan over medium heat. Place the fish, skin-side down, in the pan and cook, without moving, for 3–4 minutes or until golden. Turn the fish and reduce the heat to low. Cook for another 2 minutes or until just cooked through (the cooking time will depend on the thickness of the fish). Add the butter and a squeeze of lemon juice. Remove from the heat and set aside to rest.

While the fish is resting, heat the remaining tablespoon olive oil in a large frying pan over high heat. Add the kale, season with salt and pepper and toss for 3–4 minutes or until wilted. Add the lemon zest and the reserved roasted garlic cloves and toss to combine well. Divide the kale between 2 plates and serve with the fish and 4 anchovies each.

Note: There are 10–12 anchovies in these small 45 g tins so, rather than let the remainder of the tin oxidise, I finely chop the balance and fold it through some unsalted butter (at room temperature), then roll it into a cylinder and freeze. It makes a wonderful but very simple compound butter to put on a piece of grilled fish.

NUTRITION 🌿 Kale is rich in vitamin C, beta-carotene, and another antioxidant carotenoid – lutein.

Spelt pappardelle with pumpkin, sage and walnuts

While I love making pasta myself and have such fond memories of making it with my grandchildren when they were young, I have to be honest and say that 9 times out of 10 my pasta will be from a packet. But that packet will be well chosen – I usually have spelt and wholewheat pasta, something seductively Italian and a packet of fine egg noodles sitting in my larder. It's great to see that there are some really good Australian dried pastas available now, and this simple pumpkin and sage mixture is the perfect way to show it off.

SERVES 4

1 cup (100 g) walnuts

400 g Queensland Blue or other ripe pumpkin, peeled, seeded and cut into 2 cm x 3 cm pieces

120 ml extra virgin olive oil, plus extra for drizzling

2 sprigs rosemary

Sea salt flakes and freshly ground black pepper

2 tablespoons verjuice

3 tablespoons flat-leaf parsley leaves

1 tablespoon lemon juice

1 clove garlic

25 small sage leaves

250 g good-quality spelt pappardelle pasta

80 g Persian feta (optional)

Preheat the oven to 180°C (fan-forced).

Place the walnuts on a baking tray and cook for 8 minutes or until lightly toasted. Pour into a clean tea towel and rub off the skins while still warm. Stand until cool. Increase the oven temperature to 220°C (fan-forced).

Place the pumpkin in a bowl with 2 tablespoons olive oil, the rosemary and a good pinch of salt. Toss to coat well, then spread over a baking tray lined with baking paper. Roast for 25–30 minutes or until golden and tender. Drizzle with the verjuice and bake for another 5 minutes. Remove from the oven and set aside.

Meanwhile, place ¾ cup (75 g) toasted walnuts, the parsley leaves, lemon juice, garlic, a good pinch of salt and a splash of olive oil in a high-powered blender and blend to a paste. With the motor running, gradually add another 3 tablespoons olive oil in a steady stream until well combined. Check the seasoning and consistency (you may need to thin the mixture with a little bit of water).

Heat the remaining olive oil in a medium frying pan over medium heat. Once warm, add the sage leaves and fry until crisp, turning once the sizzling has stopped on the first side. When the entire sage leaf is dark green and crisp, remove and drain on paper towel. Season with salt.

Bring a large saucepan of salted water to the boil. Add the pasta and stir to separate the strands, then cook for 6–8 minutes or until al dente. Drain and return to the pan, then drizzle with a little olive oil and toss to coat. DO NOT RUN IT UNDER WATER. Toss the walnut sauce through the hot pasta, then place the pasta in a large serving bowl. Top with the roasted pumpkin, crisp sage leaves, remaining toasted walnuts and feta, if using, and serve immediately.

NUTRITION 🍃 As you might guess from its colour, pumpkin is an excellent source of antioxidant beta-carotene.

This is such a cosy dinner for cooler autumn nights — some Persian feta scattered over the top would add a luscious creaminess.

Turmeric, soy and ginger chicken

Chicken is quite a staple in our house but then we do have my daughter Saskia's birds on hand, and the difference a well-brought-up chook makes in flavour and texture is incredible. The great thing is that each state of Australia has wonderful producers and they need to be encouraged as it costs a lot more to grow out a free-range bird to full maturity. The marinade here is definitely 'finger-licking good' in the true sense of those words and it adds wonderfully to the caramelisation of the skin. You're a stronger person than me if you can peel that off before you eat.

SERVES 6

6 x 230 g chicken thighs, skin on, bone in
⅓ cup (80 ml) extra virgin olive oil
Sea salt flakes
Roasted carrots, kale and hazelnuts (see page 186), to serve

Marinade

1 tablespoon soy sauce
Finely grated zest of 1 lime
1 tablespoon lime juice
1 teaspoon finely grated orange zest, plus extra to serve
1 tablespoon fish sauce
1 clove garlic, finely grated
1 tablespoon finely grated ginger
1 lemongrass stalk, pale end only, finely chopped
1 teaspoon finely grated turmeric
1 teaspoon raw honey
Sea salt flakes and freshly ground black pepper

To make the marinade, place all the ingredients in a bowl and whisk until well combined.

Place the chicken in an airtight container, pour over the marinade, then place the lid on the container and shake well. Refrigerate for 2–4 hours.

Preheat the oven to 200°C (fan-forced).

Heat the olive oil in a large frying pan over medium heat. Remove the chicken from the marinade and shake off the excess. Season with salt, then place half the chicken, skin-side down, in the pan and cook for 2 minutes on each side or until golden. Take care not to burn the marinade. Remove from the pan and place, skin-side up, and spaced well apart on a baking tray lined with baking paper. Repeat with the remaining chicken thighs. Transfer to the oven and bake for 4–5 minutes or until just cooked through. Remove from the oven and allow to rest in a warm place for 8–10 minutes. Scatter with extra orange zest and drizzle with any resting juices. Serve with the roasted carrots, kale and hazelnuts.

NUTRITION 🍃 Turmeric contains the polyphenol curcumin which has antioxidant, anti-inflammatory, anti-cancer and anti-diabetes properties. See page 28 for more on this special spice.

Roasted carrots, kale and hazelnuts

I could eat a plate of roasted vegetables any time as a meal in itself and perhaps simply add some more nuts for protein. This dish could just as easily be an accompaniment for a dinner to be shared. I can't resist the natural sweetness of the well-roasted carrots and onions and the kale, though raw, becomes soft from massaging it with the lemon and provides just the right counterbalance of flavour.

SERVES 4 AS AN ACCOMPANIMENT

5 medium carrots, halved
    lengthways
⅓ cup (80 ml) extra virgin olive oil,
    plus extra for drizzling
Sea salt flakes and freshly ground
    black pepper
2 large red onions, unpeeled
    and halved crossways
½ cup (70 g) hazelnuts
½ bunch (110 g) kale, stems removed
    and torn into bite-sized pieces
1 tablespoon lemon juice
½ cup flat-leaf parsley leaves

Dressing

100 ml blood orange juice
    or regular orange juice
1 tablespoon vino cotto or
    balsamic vinegar
2 tablespoons hazelnut oil
Sea salt flakes

Preheat the oven to 220°C (fan-forced). Line a baking tray with baking paper.

Place the carrots on the lined tray, toss with 2 tablespoons olive oil and season with salt and pepper. Add the onion halves and drizzle with a little olive oil. Arrange the carrot and onion, cut-side-down, on the tray and roast for 20–30 minutes or until tender and beginning to brown. Remove from the oven and set aside to cool. Once cold, remove and discard the skin from the onions, then cut each half into 4 pieces. Reduce the oven temperature to 180°C (fan-forced).

Place the hazelnuts on a baking tray and cook for 8–10 minutes or until lightly toasted. Pour into a clean tea towel and rub off the skins while still warm.

Place the torn kale leaves into a large bowl. Add the lemon juice and remaining olive oil. Toss to coat well, then stand for 5 minutes. Sprinkle with a little salt and massage until the leaves start to soften.

To make the dressing, place all the ingredients in a small jar, then seal and shake well.

To serve, add the roasted carrots and onion to the kale, along with the parsley leaves and hazelnuts. Toss to combine well, then place on a large serving platter and pour over the dressing. Serve immediately.

Buckwheat, mushroom, bok choy and tofu

During my search for buckwheat I learnt that unless you're looking for buckwheat or soba noodles made from buckwheat flour, it is most commonly sold as 'buckinis', which is 'activated' buckwheat. It looks like a wheat but it's actually the seed of a plant like rhubarb and sorrel, and has loads of flavour and nutritional benefits. It's used a lot in Japanese cooking, hence the accompanying ingredients I have chosen here.

SERVES 2

2 dried shiitake mushrooms, soaked in warm water for 30 minutes
2 tablespoons extra virgin olive oil, plus extra for drizzling
3 golden shallots, finely chopped
1 clove garlic, finely chopped
2 cm piece ginger, peeled and grated
150 g buckinis
1 litre chicken or vegetable stock
40 g unsalted butter
250 g medium Swiss brown mushrooms, thinly sliced
Sea salt flakes and freshly ground black pepper
2 heads baby bok choy, chopped
100 g silken tofu, cut into bite-sized pieces
Finely grated zest of 1 lemon
2 tablespoons chopped chives

Drain the shiitake mushrooms. Cut off and discard the woody stalks, then thinly slice the caps.

Heat the olive oil in a medium saucepan over medium heat. Add the shallot and cook for 2–3 minutes or until soft. Add the garlic, ginger and shiitake mushrooms and cook for another 5 minutes or until the mushrooms are soft. Add the buckinis and stock and simmer for about 25 minutes or until the buckinis are tender.

Meanwhile, heat the butter and a drizzle of olive oil in a frying pan over medium heat. Add the fresh mushrooms and season to taste. Cook for 5 minutes or until golden and tender. Add the cooked mushrooms and bok choy to the buckinis for the last 5 minutes of cooking.

To serve, divide the buckini mixture between 2 bowls. Place the tofu on top, then scatter with lemon zest and chives and serve immediately.

The secret to crispy skin on your fish fillet is to be
sure the skin is dry and the pan is smoking hot!

Crispy skin salmon with winter vegetables

Given that we live in the country, I'm grateful that salmon freezes really well, and it's the closest thing to a convenience food I'm likely to have on hand. Ocean trout freezes quite well too, it's all about the fat content, but I don't freeze any other type of fish. Of course, always source salmon from a sustainable producer. I buy it by the side of salmon with skin on and cut it into serving-sized pieces, which I carefully wrap and keep in the freezer. This dish is all about maximising the vegetables of winter together with some quinoa, and could in fact be a stand-alone meal without the fish. Having said that, it's decidedly moreish when the salmon skin is really crisp but the flesh is only just cooked.

SERVES 4

8 small Jerusalem artichokes
½ cup (95 g) quinoa
100 ml extra virgin olive oil
1 leek, green tops discarded,
  cut into 2.5 cm lengths
2 tablespoons verjuice
8 Brussels sprouts, bases trimmed
  and scored
4 x 180 g salmon or white fish fillets,
  skin on, bones removed
Sea salt flakes and freshly ground
  black pepper
20 g unsalted butter
200 g red cabbage, torn into
  bite-sized pieces
1 tablespoon lemon thyme leaves
Juice of 1 lemon
3 tablespoons chopped chervil
  (optional)

Place the Jerusalem artichokes in a medium saucepan, cover with cold water and bring to the boil over high heat. Reduce the heat to low, cover and simmer for 10 minutes or until half-cooked. Drain and set aside until cool enough to handle, then rub off the skins and cut into 2.5 cm pieces.

Meanwhile, place the quinoa in a medium saucepan and cover with 4 times the amount of cold water. Bring to the boil over high heat, then reduce the heat to low and simmer for 30 minutes or until tender. Drain, then cover to keep warm.

Heat 1 tablespoon olive oil in a small saucepan over medium heat. Add the leek and cook for 3 minutes or until slightly wilted. Add the verjuice, then reduce the heat to low, cover and simmer for 8–10 minutes or until tender.

Place the Brussels sprouts in a microwave-safe container with 2 tablespoons water, cover and cook on high for 2 minutes. Remove and stand with the lid on for 5 minutes to continue cooking through. Alternatively, cook the sprouts in lightly salted boiling water for 4–5 minutes or until just tender. Drain the sprouts, then cut in half.

Heat 2 tablespoons olive oil in a frying pan over medium–high heat. Fry the Jerusalem artichokes until cooked through and golden on both sides.

Season the fish. Heat another tablespoon of olive oil in a large non-stick frying pan over high heat. Add the fish, skin-side down, and cook for 3 minutes or until the skin is golden and crisp. Remove the fish from the pan and wipe it out with paper towel. Add the butter and return the fish to the pan, skin-side up. Cook for another 2 minutes only, then remove from the heat and allow to rest for 5 minutes. The cooking time will vary, depending on the thickness of the fillets.

While the fish is resting, heat the remaining 1 tablespoon olive oil in a large frying pan over medium–high heat. Add the cabbage and thyme and saute for 6–8 minutes or until wilted. Add the quinoa, sprouts, Jerusalem artichoke, leek and its cooking juices and stir to combine well, then season with salt, pepper and lemon juice.

To serve, divide the winter vegetables among plates, top with a piece of salmon and any resting juices, then scatter with chervil, if using.

Fish curry

This is not a curry for aficionados of the genre. It's a gentle but beautifully spiced curry, and yes all right, slightly heavy on the coconut cream. I'm certainly not known for having a delicate touch! I'm always going for a hit of flavour, but I also want balance and in this case it's the fresh lime juice that brings that to the dish so don't leave it out.

SERVES 6

3 tablespoons extra virgin
    coconut oil
1 large brown onion, finely diced
30 g ginger, peeled and finely grated
2 cloves garlic, crushed
1 long fresh red chilli, halved
    lengthways, seeded and
    thinly sliced
1 tablespoon ground turmeric
2 teaspoons ground cumin
1 teaspoon coriander seeds
1 teaspoon sweet smoked paprika
1 cinnamon stick
1 cup (250 ml) chicken stock
600 ml coconut cream
2 tablespoons lime juice
1 tablespoon fish sauce
Sea salt flakes and freshly ground
    black pepper
4 x 160 g skinless white fish fillets,
    bones removed
½ cup coriander leaves
3 tablespoons toasted coconut flakes
⅓ cup thinly sliced spring onions,
    green ends only

Couscous

1 cup (250 ml) chicken, vegetable
    or fish stock
1 cup (200 g) wholemeal couscous
40 g unsalted butter

Melt 1 tablespoon coconut oil in a medium saucepan over medium heat. Add the onion and saute for 8–10 minutes or until transparent. Add the ginger and garlic and cook for another 3 minutes. Add the chilli and spices, then stir for 2 minutes or until aromatic. Stir in the stock and coconut cream and simmer for 20 minutes. Remove from the heat and stand for 5 minutes. Strain and discard the solids, then return the sauce to a clean pan. Stir in the lime juice and fish sauce, then adjust the seasoning if necessary.

Meanwhile, to make the couscous, place the stock in a small saucepan and bring to the boil. Place the couscous in a medium heatproof bowl and pour over the boiling stock. Cover and stand for 5 minutes. Add the butter and use a fork to fluff up the couscous and separate the grains. Season to taste and keep warm.

Place the remaining 2 tablespoons coconut oil in a frying pan over high heat. Add the fish and pan-fry until golden and just cooked through (the time will vary depending on the thickness of the fillets).

Divide the fish among serving bowls. Pour the curry sauce around the fish, then scatter with coriander leaves, coconut flakes and spring onion. Serve with the warm couscous alongside.

NUTRITION 🥄 Coconut's medium-chain fatty acids provide an alternative energy source for the brain and eating coconut has many other benefits; see page 35 for more on this.

Braised oxtail with tamarind and olives

How I love this dish. It has cooked for so long and so gently that the meat just falls off the bone, and my favourite part is to pick up each piece and eat it with my fingers. It's a slow process and a pressure cooker can be used to get the meat perfectly cooked before you tackle the reduction of the sauce to achieve the desired unctuousness, but mostly I cook it in a heavy cast-iron pot with a lid. If you don't have any tamarind, orange peel may be used instead to great effect. This is definitely a dish to put in the centre of the table and share with family or friends, but make sure there are lots of finger bowls and extra serviettes handy. Things can get messy!

SERVES 6

⅓ cup (80 ml) extra virgin olive oil, plus extra for drizzling
2 large brown onions, coarsely chopped
Spelt flour, for dusting
Sea salt flakes and freshly ground black pepper
2 kg oxtail, trimmed and cut into 5 cm lengths
50 g unsalted butter, chopped
1 cup (250 ml) red wine
2 cloves garlic, finely chopped
10 sprigs thyme
2 bay leaves
3 tablespoons tamarind concentrate
1 x 400 g tin low-salt whole peeled tomatoes
1 litre beef stock
2 oranges, zest removed in wide strips using a peeler
2 tablespoons aged red wine vinegar
2 tablespoons vino cotto or balsamic vinegar
4 sticks celery, cut into 1 cm dice
160 g black olives, pitted
1½ cups (300 g) raw pearl barley
½ cup finely chopped flat-leaf parsley

Gremolata
Finely grated zest of 1 lemon
Finely grated zest of 1 orange
1 cup finely chopped flat-leaf parsley
2 cloves garlic, minced

Preheat the oven to 140°C (fan-forced).

Heat 2 tablespoons olive oil in a medium saucepan over low–medium heat. Add the onion and cook for 8–10 minutes or until translucent. Remove from the heat and set aside.

Season the flour with salt and pepper. Toss the oxtail pieces in the flour, shaking off the excess. Heat the butter and the remaining olive oil in a large frying pan over high heat. Cook the oxtail, in batches, until golden on both sides, transferring to a large heavy-based casserole as you go.

Add the wine and simmer for 1 minute, scraping the bottom of the pan to release all the caramelised bits from the base. Add the garlic, cooked onions, herbs, tamarind and tomatoes and simmer over high heat until the wine has reduced a little. Add the stock and 1 litre water and bring to the boil. Pour the liquid over the oxtail, making sure the meat is submerged. Cover and bake for 3–4 hours or until the meat is coming away from the bones. Remove from the oven, stand until cool, then refrigerate overnight.

Using a small sharp knife, remove any white pith from the back of the orange zest. Drop into a saucepan of boiling water and simmer for 1 minute to rid the zest of bitterness; repeat the process. Drain and stand until cool. Thinly sliced the zest lengthways, then cover and refrigerate until needed.

The following day, using a large shallow spoon, remove and discard the solidified fat from the top of the oxtail. Gently remove the oxtail pieces, place on a plate, cover with plastic film and refrigerate until ready to serve. Transfer the cooking liquid to a saucepan and bring to the boil, skimming off any excess fat as it rises to the surface. Add the red wine vinegar and vino cotto or balsamic and simmer over medium heat until reduced by half. Add the orange zest (reserving 1 tablespoon to serve), the celery and olives and adjust the seasoning.

Meanwhile, place the barley in a sieve and rinse under cold running water. Place in a saucepan with 4 times the amount of cold water. Bring to the boil over high heat, then reduce the heat to low and simmer for 30–40 minutes or until tender. Drain well, then stir through a drizzle of olive oil. Place in a serving bowl and cover with plastic film to keep warm, then stir through the parsley just before serving.

To make the gremolata, combine all the ingredients in a bowl.

To serve, gently reheat the oxtail in the microwave until warm, then add
to the hot sauce and stir gently to coat. Alternatively, when the sauce is half
reduced, return the oxtail to the sauce and continue heating through at
a simmer to warm the meat through while the sauce reduces a little more.
Do not do this over high heat.

Serve the braised oxtail scattered with the gremolata and reserved orange
zest, and the warm barley on the side.

Lambs fry with spinach

I grew up eating lambs fry and every other sort of offal imaginable as part of our regular diet. I do love it but it has to be cooked with care or it can be more like cardboard. I have never soaked the liver in milk before cooking it but many do. To me, the secret is to strip the sinew from the liver, dust it in seasoned flour and cook until it's only just done and still pink on the inside. The bacon, chard and caramelised onions are there to keep you interested in case you're not sure about the liver, but I would happily eat a plate of it just on its own!

SERVES 4

1 lambs fry (about 850 g)
8 slices traditionally cured belly
  bacon (I use black pig belly bacon)
½ cup (65 g) spelt flour
Sea salt flakes and freshly ground
  black pepper
30 g unsalted butter
Extra virgin olive oil, for drizzling
8 large chard leaves, coarsely
  chopped

Caramelised onion

20 g unsalted butter
1 tablespoon extra virgin olive oil
2 large brown onions, thinly sliced
2 tablespoons vino cotto

To make the caramelised onion, melt the butter in a frying pan over low heat. Add the olive oil and onion and cook, stirring regularly, for 20 minutes or until caramelised to a lovely rich golden brown. Increase the heat to high, add the vino cotto and cook for 1–2 minutes or until slightly thickened. Remove from the heat and reheat just before serving.

Meanwhile, using a small sharp knife, make a small incision in the liver, then use your fingers to peel off the membrane. Remove any sinew. Cut the liver into 2 cm thick slices. Set aside.

Place the bacon in a large frying pan over medium heat and cook until crisp. Drain on paper towel and keep warm.

Place the flour on a plate and season with salt and pepper. Place the butter and a drizzle of olive oil in a large frying pan over medium heat and cook until nut brown. While the butter is cooking, dust the liver slices in flour and shake off the excess. Add the liver to the pan and cook for about 1 minute on both sides, then remove the pan from the heat. Leave resting in the pan for a few minutes. It's important not to overcook the liver – it's best just pink in the centre.

Heat a drizzle of olive oil in another large frying pan over medium heat. Add the chard leaves and toss until just wilted. Serve the liver with the chard, caramelised onion and bacon.

Pork shoulder slow cooked in buttermilk with cavolo nero and walnut miso dressing

I am a very fussy pork eater. I only buy heritage pork and my favourite is Berkshire, or black pig; there is a totally different flavour and texture and yes, fat level and all of those things are very important to me, as is the way they have been farmed. The shoulder is my favourite cut and I use my slow cooker – and when I say slow, in this case I mean 16 hours, always on low. It is so tender and yet as long as it's not 'overcooked' it can be sliced easily (though always with a very sharp knife). I've taken the idea from a traditional Italian dish of pork cooked in milk; I use buttermilk as it offers a great counterpoint for the richness of the pork. It always curdles by the way, so don't be put off by that. The cavolo nero dish that accompanies it is so moreish that all you kale doubters out there will eat your words!

SERVES 8

3.25 kg Berkshire pork shoulder, skin on
1 tablespoon sea salt flakes
60 g walnuts
1.8 litres buttermilk
2 teaspoons fennel seeds
2 star anise
2 tablespoons unpasteurised white (shiro) miso
2 tablespoons verjuice
1 large bunch cavolo nero or curly kale, stalks discarded (about 6 cups chopped leaves), washed
2 tablespoons extra virgin olive oil

Rub the pork all over with the salt, then stand at room temperature for 1 hour.

Preheat the oven to 180°C (fan-forced). Place the walnuts on a baking tray and toast for 8–10 minutes or until golden. Pour into a clean tea towel and rub off the skins while still warm.

Place the pork in a large slow cooker. Whisk together the buttermilk and 600 ml cold water. Pour over the pork, add the spices, then cover and cook on the lowest setting for about 16 hours or until nearly falling apart.

Just before serving, grind half the walnuts in a mortar and pestle until the nuts begin to break down. Add the remaining walnuts and pound until a coarse paste forms. Transfer to a bowl, then stir in the miso and verjuice.

Bring a large saucepan of water to the boil. Add the cavolo nero or kale and cook for 3 minutes, then quickly drain into a colander. Spread out over paper towel or a clean tea towel to drain.

Heat the olive oil in a large frying pan over medium heat. Add the cavolo nero or kale and toss until heated through. Combine in a bowl with the walnut and miso paste, and serve as a side to the buttermilk pork shoulder.

Roast sweet potatoes, parsnips, purple potatoes and roasted garlic with ricotta

I love every season but root vegetables and citrus make winter a particularly special time. Fresh herbs are important to my cooking and winter isn't as kind to the herb garden, although rosemary never falters, and sage to a degree and thyme still have something to offer. Increasingly I find myself turning to lemon thyme – it does need some nurturing to keep it going but it's worth it. While flavour is my driving force, there is something about really colourful food that is immediately appealing, which is why I include a range of root vegetables here. They need to be cooked through properly so keep an eye on them and adjust the timing to suit your oven – you want them so tender they yield to the fork as you eat.

SERVES 6

1 bulb garlic
Extra virgin olive oil, for drizzling
500 g orange sweet potato, peeled
300 g purple potato, unpeeled
300 g parsnip, unpeeled
   if super fresh
2 cups (400 g) ricotta (see page 271)
1½ cups (120 g) grated parmesan
1 cup (280 g) thick natural
   probiotic yoghurt
1 free-range egg
Finely grated zest of 2 lemons
Finely grated zest of 2 oranges
Sea salt flakes and freshly ground
   black pepper
1 cup (100 g) toasted walnuts,
   coarsely chopped
3 tablespoons lemon thyme leaves
½ bunch chives, finely chopped

Preheat the oven to 180°C (fan-forced). Lightly grease a 22 cm springform tin with olive oil.

Place the garlic bulb on a piece of foil and drizzle with olive oil. Wrap up to make a parcel, then bake for 30 minutes or until soft and caramelised. Remove from the oven and set aside to cool. Increase the oven temperature to 200°C (fan-forced).

Meanwhile, using a mandolin or sharp knife, cut the potatoes and parsnip into 5 mm thick slices. Steam or microwave each vegetable separately until soft but not falling apart (3–4 minutes in the microwave as a starting point). Spread out on a tray to cool, keeping them separate.

Squeeze the garlic out of the skins into a bowl. Mash with a fork with enough olive oil to make a paste.

In a food processor, blend the ricotta, parmesan, yoghurt and egg until smooth. Transfer to a bowl, add the citrus zests and season to taste, then fold through the walnuts.

Beginning with the sweet potato, layer half the slices over the base of the tin in overlapping layers. Scatter with one third of the thyme, then pour over one third of the ricotta mixture. Layer the parsnip over the ricotta, followed by another third of the thyme and ricotta. Add the remaining sweet potato and thyme, then spread with the garlic paste. Pour over the last of the ricotta, then layer the purple potatoes over the top. Place on a baking tray and bake for 25–30 minutes or until the top layer of purple potato is lightly coloured. If time permits, stand for 1 hour before cutting. To serve, spoon onto plates, drizzle with olive oil and scatter with chives.

Chicken and chickpea tagine with turmeric, sweet potato and prunes

I have such respect for tagines as a dish and loved every one I tried on a trip to Morocco many years ago, but I have never been able to master the technique using a tagine (the cooking vessel) so I make this in a heavy cast-iron pot instead. The timing of a chicken tagine is critical as overcooked chicken is a travesty. I cook the chicken right through, then take it out while all the other flavours come together and the sauce reduces. Shortly before serving I return the chicken to the pot to warm through. The prunes, lemon and mint are all so important to the final flavour so don't leave them out.

SERVES 4

½ cup (125 ml) extra virgin olive oil

6 chicken thigh fillets, skin on, cut into 2.5 cm cubes

Sea salt flakes and freshly ground black pepper

Large pinch of saffron threads

1 large brown onion, coarsely chopped

2 cloves garlic, finely chopped

1 tablespoon finely grated fresh turmeric

3 teaspoons ground cumin

1 teaspoon ground cinnamon

1 x 400 g tin low-salt crushed tomatoes

2 cups (500 ml) chicken stock

300 g sweet potato, unpeeled, scrubbed and cut into 4 cm pieces

120 g prunes, pitted

1 x 400 g tin chickpeas, drained, rinsed

1 lemon, zest removed in wide strips with a peeler, white pith discarded

Chopped coriander and mint, to serve

⅓ cup (95 g) natural probiotic yoghurt

Lemon wedges, to serve (optional)

Couscous

1 cup (200 g) wholemeal couscous

1½ cups (375 ml) boiling water or chicken stock

30 g unsalted butter

1 tablespoon chopped mint

1 tablespoon chopped flat-leaf parsley

Heat 3 tablespoons olive oil in a large frying pan over high heat. Season the chicken with salt and cook for 6–8 minutes or until golden all over. Remove from the pan and set aside on a plate, reserving the juices.

Meanwhile, place the saffron threads in a small bowl and pour over ½ cup (125 ml) hot water. Stand for 5 minutes.

Heat the remaining olive oil in a large saucepan over medium heat. Add the onion and garlic and cook for 4–5 minutes or until soft. Add the turmeric, cumin and cinnamon and cook for 1 minute or until fragrant. Add the saffron water, tomatoes, stock, sweet potato and prunes. Season with salt and pepper and stir to combine. Place a lid on top to partially cover, then simmer for 15–20 minutes or until thickened. Stir in the chickpeas, lemon zest, chicken and reserved resting juices. Season with salt and pepper, then simmer for 2 minutes or until just heated through.

Meanwhile, to make the couscous, place the couscous in a medium heatproof bowl and pour over the boiling water or stock. Cover and stand for 5 minutes. Add the butter and use a fork to fluff up the couscous and separate the grains. Season to taste and keep warm. Just before serving, stir through the herbs.

Transfer the tagine to a serving bowl and scatter with herbs. Serve with couscous, yoghurt and lemon wedges, if desired.

NUTRITION Prunes are a rich source of antioxidant polyphenols such as chlorogenic acid.

A tagine on the table looks magical but you don't need one of these lovely clay Moroccan pots to make this dish.

Roasted root vegetables with vino cotto, Brussels sprouts and hazelnuts

Whenever possible I resist peeling vegetables, particularly when they are to be roasted, but I do realise that cooking is about detail and about what feels right. If the vegetables you buy aren't shiningly fresh then I would peel them. If you find the sweet potato too sweet for your tastes drizzle over some extra lemon juice halfway through the roasting. I don't hesitate to use my microwave to cook green vegetables, particularly Brussels sprouts (see page 102 for more on this). This dish is substantial enough to be enjoyed on its own, but also makes a lovely accompaniment to a roasted leg of lamb.

SERVES 4-6

500 g white sweet potato, peeled and cut into 2 cm thick rounds
½ cup (125 ml) extra virgin olive oil
6 sprigs thyme
Sea salt flakes
600 g Queensland Blue or Jap pumpkin, seeded and cut into wedges
6 parsnips, halved lengthways, then widthways
6 organic or heirloom carrots, halved lengthways
12 Brussels sprouts, bases trimmed and scored
½ cup (70 g) toasted hazelnuts, skins removed, coarsely chopped

Dressing

2 tablespoons vino cotto
2 tablespoons verjuice
½ cup (125 ml) hazelnut oil
Sea salt flakes and freshly ground black pepper

Preheat the oven to 220°C (fan-forced). Line 3 baking trays with baking paper.

Place the sweet potato in a bowl and toss with 2 tablespoons olive oil, the thyme sprigs and a good pinch of salt. Spread in a single layer on one of the lined trays and roast for 40 minutes, turning halfway through.

At the same time, place the pumpkin in a bowl and toss with 2 tablespoons olive oil and a good pinch of salt. Spread over another lined tray and bake for 30–40 minutes or until golden and tender.

Place the parsnip and carrot in a bowl and toss with the remaining olive oil and a good pinch of salt. Spread over the third lined tray and roast for 20–30 minutes or until caramelised. During cooking, rotate the trays to ensure even colour or roast all the vegetables separately, if needed.

Place the Brussel sprouts in a microwave-safe container with 2 tablespoons water, cover and cook on high for 2 minutes. Remove and stand with the lid on for 5 minutes to continue cooking through. Alternatively, cook the sprouts in lightly salted boiling water for 4–5 minutes or until just tender. Drain, cool slightly and cut in half.

For the dressing, place all the ingredients in a small jar, then seal and shake to combine well.

To serve, reheat the vegetables if necessary. Place in a large bowl and pour over the dressing. Gently toss, then place on a large serving plate. Scatter with the hazelnuts and season, then serve immediately.

NUTRITION ✎ Brussels sprouts are a revelation when cooked lightly and are rich in vitamins C and K, and folate.

Dessert

Coconut cream custard with oranges and caramelised walnuts

You can see that I'm keen on coconut milk and cream and find so many ways to use them as the base for a dessert. This is partly because their inherent sweetness means I don't need to add much sugar, but mainly I just love their great flavour and seductive richness. When I add honey I always suggest raw honey; I consider it the benchmark in flavour and quality as it hasn't been heated beyond the minimum required to be able to pour it into a jar, though I know it's not as readily available as commercial honey.

SERVES 6

2 tablespoons raw honey

1 cinnamon stick

½ vanilla bean, halved lengthways, seeds scraped

2 oranges, peeled, white pith removed, flesh segmented

Splash of Cointreau (optional)

Finely grated zest of 1 lime (optional)

Custard

1 x 400 ml tin coconut milk

100 ml coconut cream

1 teaspoon vanilla bean paste

2 tablespoons raw honey

1 tablespoon cornflour

2 free-range eggs

Pinch of ground cinnamon

Pinch of sea salt flakes

Caramelised walnuts

½ cup (50 g) walnuts

20 g icing sugar, sifted

To make the custard, place the coconut milk, coconut cream, vanilla and honey in a medium saucepan. Stir over medium heat until almost boiling.

In a separate bowl, whisk together the cornflour, eggs, cinnamon and salt until well combined. Whisking constantly, gradually pour the hot milk into the egg mixture, then return to the pan. Stir over medium heat with a wooden spoon until the mixture thickens enough to coat the back of the spoon. Remove from the heat, then strain through a sieve into a jug. Serve hot or cold.

For the caramelised walnuts, preheat the oven to 180°C (fan-forced). Place the walnuts on a baking tray and cook for 8 minutes or until lightly toasted. Pour into a clean tea towel and rub off the skins while still warm. Increase the oven temperature to 200°C (fan-forced). Place the walnuts in a small bowl, splash lightly with water, then dust with the icing sugar. Spread in a single layer over a baking tray lined with baking paper and cook for 8 minutes or until caramelised. Remove from the oven and set aside to cool.

Place the honey and 2 tablespoons water into a very small saucepan. Bring to the boil over low heat, then simmer for 3 minutes or until the bubbles become thick and glossy – just before they start to colour. Stir in the cinnamon stick, vanilla bean seeds and scraped bean, the orange segments and the Cointreau, if using. Shake the pan for another 2 minutes or until just combined. Remove from the heat and set aside.

To serve, divide the custard among serving bowls. Top with a generous spoonful of oranges and scatter with caramelised walnuts and zest, if using.

NUTRITION ❧ Raw honey has antioxidant and antibacterial properties but, as a sugar, is best consumed in small quantities.

Strawberry and yoghurt dessert with nut crumble

Sometimes we lose sight of when a food is in its natural season, and for strawberries it's spring.
The first strawberries of the season, when picked ripe, are so special that just a plate of these with some
mascarpone and orange zest is the definition of perfection. However, strawberry growers have the same
issue as so many other produce growers and that is, sadly, that if the fruit is picked perfectly ripe it won't
travel to market. I combat this by cutting them in half and drizzling with the smallest amount of vino cotto
or balsamic, which significantly heightens the flavour of the strawberries. The nut crumble is delicious
and can be made in advance and stored in an airtight container, but by all means make a simpler version
with just one type of nut if preferred. It will still be great eating.

SERVES 6

2 x 250 g punnets ripe, dark red
    strawberries, hulled and halved
1 tablespoon vino cotto or
    balsamic vinegar
800 g natural probiotic yoghurt
1 tablespoon thinly sliced lemon
    verbena or mint leaves

Nut crumble

¾ cup (45 g) coconut flakes
1½ tablespoons macadamia oil
1½ tablespoons raw honey
½ cup (70 g) slivered almonds
3 tablespoons hazelnuts
3 tablespoons macadamia nuts
1 tablespoon linseeds (flaxseeds)
Pinch of sea salt flakes
¼ teaspoon ground cinnamon

To make the nut crumble, preheat the oven to 180˚C (fan-forced).

Place the coconut flakes on a baking tray and toast for 5 minutes or until
light golden. Remove from the oven and set aside.

Place the macadamia oil and honey in a microwave-safe bowl and heat
until both ingredients have melted together. Alternatively, place in a small
saucepan and stir over low heat until melted.

Place the nuts in a blender and pulse until chopped, leaving some texture,
then place the chopped nuts, linseeds, macadamia oil mixture, salt and
cinnamon in a bowl and stir to combine well. Spread the crumble in an
even layer over a baking tray lined with baking paper. Bake for 20 minutes
or until golden – you may have to turn the tray after 10 minutes to ensure
even colour. Remove from the oven and place on a wire rack to cool and
crisp up. Once completely cold, stir through the toasted coconut flakes,
then store in an airtight container. There will be leftovers but it will keep
well for a week or so.

About 20 minutes before serving, drizzle the strawberries with vino cotto or
balsamic. Stand for 20 minutes to bring out the flavour in the strawberries.

To serve, divide the yoghurt among serving glasses. Top with the
strawberries, then the nut crumble and lemon verbena or mint.

Bananas on the barbecue*

These are great to serve at a barbecue, particularly if your bananas are ripening too quickly. My favourite variety is the naturally sweet Lady Finger but, unlike the more common Cavendish banana, these need to be dotted with lots of black patches to be properly ripe, otherwise they have a very drying tanniny mouthfeel which is most unappealing. I have three Tahitian lime trees in pots and they bear fruit so prolifically that I have an embarrassment of riches when they're in season and am always looking for ways to utilise them. They have a great affinity with coconut so work beautifully in this simple treat. My grandchildren aren't so keen on the ginger but I love it.

SERVES 4

2 tablespoons lime juice
1 tablespoon extra virgin coconut
    oil, melted
1 tablespoon raw honey
1 teaspoon finely grated ginger
4 large ripe bananas
Finely grated zest of 1 lime

Preheat a barbecue grill plate to high.

Combine the lime juice, coconut oil, honey and ginger in a small bowl.

Roast the bananas in their skins on the grill until blackened on all sides. While still hot (being careful not to burn yourself), peel back the skin and brush the lime and coconut mixture over the bananas. Sprinkle with the lime zest and serve immediately.

Citus and passionfruit terrine ★

This is such an elegant dish for a special occasion when you have the fabulous colours of blood oranges and pink grapefruit to work with. The terrine is infused with the unique flavour of passionfruit as the jelly is made with its juice, then extra pulp spooned on top for texture. Working with gelatine becomes second nature after a bit of practice, enabling seasonal fruit to present so beautifully. Segmenting the citrus fruit will take some time so this is one to keep for a quiet day or enlist willing helpers!

SERVES 10

20 large passionfruit
5 navel oranges
7 blood oranges
3 pink grapefruit
70 g sugar
7 x 2 g gold-strength gelatine leaves
1 cup (280 g) natural probiotic
    yoghurt

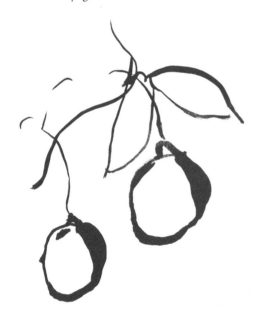

Cut 15 passionfruit in half and scrape out the pulp into a blender. Pulse briefly – this helps separate the seeds from the pulp. Strain through a fine sieve into a jug, pressing down well to extract as much juice as possible, and discard the seeds. You will need 1 cup (250 ml) strained juice. If you are short you can make it up with some of the fresh citrus juice after segmenting.

Remove the peel and white pith from the citrus fruit. Using a small sharp knife and holding the fruit over a bowl fitted with a sieve, segment all the fruit, one at a time and keeping each fruit separate. To segment, cut between the white sections running from the top to the bottom of the fruit. Squeeze the juice from the remaining flesh into the bowl. Lift up the sieve and arrange the segments in a single layer on a tray lined with a tea towel, then pat dry. Add a little of the juice to the passionfruit juice to make the quantity required if needed, or enjoy a freshly squeezed juice!

Place the sugar and 70 ml water in a small saucepan and stir over low heat until the sugar has dissolved. Bring to the boil, then simmer for 2 minutes and remove from the heat. Measure 100 ml syrup and add to the strained passionfruit juice. Place in a small saucepan and bring to the boil, then remove from the heat.

Meanwhile, soak the gelatine leaves in cold water for 5 minutes or until soft. Drain and squeeze out the excess water from the gelatine, then add to the hot juice mixture and stir until the gelatine has dissolved. Set aside to cool slightly.

Spray a rectangular mould approximately 10 cm x 18 cm (or a straight-sided loaf tin) with oil spray and line with three layers of plastic film. To do this, rub a damp cloth over a workbench, then spread the plastic film approximately 30 cm x 40 cm and cut off. Rub the plastic film with the damp cloth and place another layer on top. Repeat to make three layers – this will ensure strength when pulling the set terrine out of the mould. Press the layered plastic film into the mould, taking care to avoid creases, and leave the sides overhanging.

To build the terrine, pour over just enough jelly mixture to cover the base of the mould. Top with an even layer of the navel orange segments – they should all be touching and tightly compacted. Spoon over a little more jelly mixture, then repeat with the blood orange segments, followed by the pink grapefruit segments being sure to fill all the gaps with the fruit. Repeat until all the fruit is used, then press the fruit down gently, ensuring

not too much jelly is inside the terrine or the fruit will float to the surface — there will be some jelly left over. Refrigerate the terrine overnight or until set.

To serve, remove the terrine from the mould by lifting up the plastic film — it should come out easily. Using a large hot sharp knife, cut the terrine into 2.5 cm thick slices and serve with yoghurt and the remaining passionfruit pulp.

Orange, ginger and dark chocolate truffles

I don't know anyone who could resist these. They might be a bit fiddly to make at the last dipping stage if you've not done a lot of chocolate work before, but this is one time you really do need to double dip in order for the truffles to set quite hard. I think after one bite you'll be convinced: this really is one time you can say the whole is far greater than the sum of its parts. Yes, I just love them and one is all you need!

MAKES ABOUT 20

160 g Medjool dates, seeded
⅓ cup (80 ml) freshly squeezed
    orange juice
1 cup (80 g) toasted flaked almonds
1½ tablespoons extra virgin coconut
    oil, melted
1 teaspoon finely grated orange zest
1 teaspoon ground ginger
Pinch of sea salt flakes
2 tablespoons extra virgin
    coconut oil
200 g dark couverture chocolate
    (70% cocoa solids), chopped

Place the seeded dates and orange juice in a small bowl, cover and stand overnight.

Drain the dates, then place in a food processor with the flaked almonds, coconut oil, orange zest, ginger and salt. Blitz until well combined, making sure you keep some texture. Transfer the mixture to a small bowl, cover closely with plastic film and refrigerate for 1 hour to set.

Roll the mixture into balls about 15 g each, then place on a tray lined with baking paper and freeze for 30 minutes.

To coat the truffles, place the coconut oil and chopped chocolate in a heatproof bowl. Place over a saucepan of just-simmering water and stir occasionally until melted, smooth and well combined.

Remove the tray of truffles from the freezer. Using a skewer or gloves, dip one truffle at a time in the chocolate, then lift out and allow the excess chocolate to drain back into the bowl. Place on the tray and repeat until all the truffles have been dipped. Refrigerate until the chocolate has set, then repeat the dipping process with the remaining melted chocolate mixture. Refrigerate until set, then store in an airtight container in the refrigerator until ready to serve.

Pink grapefruit jelly with segments and almonds in honey

The first thing you need to do here is buy a lot of pink grapefruits. Unless you're at a farmers' market this might seem a bit extravagant, but it's really not if you utilise every bit of the fruit by dehydrating the skins. I have a very old tabletop dehydrator with lots of layers, which I use to dry as many citrus skins as I can. When they are totally dry I put them in the food processor and pulverise them into a powder which I add to cereals or cake batters to fantastic effect. Anyhow, back to this dish: I love the freshness and mouthfeel of jellies and would happily have this as a special dessert on any occasion, perhaps with a little almond yoghurt cream (see page 223).

SERVES 8-10

9 pink grapefruit
50 g raw honey
24 g gelatine powder
Thinly sliced mint, to serve

Almonds in honey

1 cup (80 g) flaked almonds
2 tablespoons raw honey

Peel 7 grapefruit and use a small sharp knife to remove the white pith. Roughly chop up the fruit, discarding any seeds, and place in a high-powered blender. Turn to high and blend as smooth as possible.

Place 1 litre of the blended grapefruit and the honey in a saucepan over low heat until warm. Place the gelatine powder in a small bowl with 2½ tablespoons warm water, then add to the grapefruit mixture and stir until dissolved. Pour the jelly into a 1 litre capacity mould or two 2 cup (500 ml) capacity moulds. Refrigerate for 3 hours or overnight until set.

Meanwhile, for the almonds in honey, preheat the oven to 180°C (fan-forced).

Place the almonds on a baking tray lined with baking paper and drizzle with the honey. Bake for 10 minutes, then turn the tray around and bake another 5 minutes or until evenly golden. Remove and stand the tray on a wire rack until the almonds are cool and crisp. When cold, coarsely break up and store in an airtight container until ready to serve.

To serve, unmould the jelly onto a large serving plate. Segment the remaining grapefruit (see page 208) and serve with the jelly, scattered with mint and the broken almonds in honey.

Peach Melba

I've written this recipe for baked peaches largely to compensate for the often-disappointing flavour of fresh peaches. Unless you buy them from a farmers' market, peaches are usually offered for sale before they are ripe simply, but sadly, because of the logistics of getting fruit to market. Baking will bring out their flavour and perfume, but if you have perfectly ripe fresh peaches, eliminate that step entirely. Depending on the brand of mascarpone and yoghurt you buy you may need to whip the mascarpone cream to a thickish consistency rather than until just combined.

SERVES 4

4 ripe yellow peaches
40 g unsalted butter
Finely grated zest of 1 orange
100 g mascarpone
100 g natural probiotic yoghurt
½ teaspoon ground cinnamon
15 g icing sugar, sifted
200 g raspberries
3 tablespoons flaked almonds,
   lightly toasted

Preheat the oven to 200°C (fan-forced).

Cut the peaches in half, remove the seeds and place, cut-side up, on a baking tray. Place a small piece of butter in each peach half and bake for 12–15 minutes or until golden and just soft. While still warm, slip the skins off the peaches and set aside.

In a bowl, mix the orange zest, mascarpone, yoghurt, cinnamon and icing sugar until smooth and combined.

Divide the peaches and berries among plates and serve with a generous dollop of mascarpone cream and a scattering of flaked almonds.

NUTRITION Fresh raspberries and peaches are good sources of vitamin C, beta-carotene, polyphenols and manganese.

Coconut panna cotta with raspberries and toasted almonds

While I have added a little honey here it's definitely optional as there is a real sweetness to the coconut milk and cream. Taste it as you go and see if you want to drop the honey back. Gelatine is a magic ingredient but one that budding cooks are often nervous about using. Given that the success of a panna cotta depends on it having a good 'wobble', I would recommend practising on a smaller volume first if you're worried. You want it to be silky in the mouth and not overset. Raspberries are one of summer's delights but any berry at all would be perfect here, and in fact my favourite of all is mulberries if you can get some. We have a huge tree in our chook yard, which sounds great I know, but it is so tall and the best fruit is always up so high that I'm just as likely to have purple-stained hair as purple-stained hands as I pick.

SERVES 4

1 cup (250 ml) coconut milk
1 cup (250 ml) coconut cream
½ teaspoon vanilla bean paste
50 g raw honey
5 x 2 g gold-strength gelatine leaves
200 g raspberries, blackberries
  or mulberries
½ cup (40 g) flaked almonds,
  lightly toasted

Place the coconut milk, coconut cream, vanilla and honey in a saucepan over medium heat. Bring to the boil, then remove from the heat.

Meanwhile, separate the gelatine leaves and add to a bowl of ice-cold water. Stand for 5 minutes or until soft. Drain the gelatine and squeeze out the excess liquid. Add to the hot coconut mixture and stir until dissolved. Strain through a fine sieve and pour into four ½ cup (125 ml) capacity moulds or cups. Refrigerate overnight or for at least 3 hours.

To serve, remove the panna cottas from the refrigerator and dip the bottom of the moulds briefly in hot water to loosen. Invert the panna cottas onto serving dishes and stand at room temperature for 30 minutes.

Scatter the panna cottas with the berries and flaked almonds and serve immediately.

Mango, lime and coconut sago pudding

I can't say sago was at all interesting to me until I came to live in the Barossa Valley and was taught to make 'rote grutze'. This unique dessert combines the juice and pulp of red grapes with sago, and it was only after I tried it that I understood the ability of sago to beautifully set a cold pudding without any gelatine. Light bulb moment! Mango, lime and coconut are all flavours of the tropics that I love to call on in the heat of summer.

SERVES 4–6

80 g sago
2 cups (500 ml) coconut milk
½ vanilla bean, halved lengthways and seeds scraped
Finely grated zest and juice of 2 limes
2 medium or 1 very large ripe mango
1 tablespoon very thinly sliced mint
3 tablespoons toasted coconut flakes

Place the sago, coconut milk, vanilla bean seeds and scraped bean, and ¾ cup (180 ml) water in a medium saucepan and stand for 30 minutes.

Place the pan over medium heat and bring to the boil, stirring occasionally. Reduce the heat to low and cook, stirring often, for 10–15 minutes or until the sago is tender. Remove from the heat and stir in most of the lime zest. Divide the mixture among serving glasses or dishes, then cover and refrigerate for 1 hour.

To serve, peel the mangoes and cut off the cheeks. Thinly slice into a bowl and mix with the lime juice.

In a blender, puree one third of the mango and any flesh from around the seed. Place in a bowl with the mint and stir. Spoon the mango puree over the puddings, then top with the mango slices. Scatter with the coconut flakes and remaining lime zest and serve.

Red papaya with lime and blueberries ⭐

I know, you can't really call this a recipe but I'm including it because it's a stunning way of using what's in season to finish a meal. I love pink or red papaya but it's harder to find. Any papaya for me does need that squeeze of lime over it (or lemon if you prefer) to give its richness a bit of acid balance. The blueberries could of course be a dish on their own ... preferably lots of them.

SERVES 5

1 large red papaya, beautifully ripe and in season
1 lime
125 g blueberries

Cut the papaya in half lengthways and scoop out the seeds. Cut each half lengthways into 5 thin wedges (depending on the size of the fruit).

Finely grate the lime zest over the top, then cut the lime in half and squeeze over the juice. Sprinkle with the blueberries and serve with a spoon to scoop the flesh from the skin.

Grapes in verjuice ★

While this is my idea of a refreshing summer snack it can so easily be transformed into a dessert by serving it with fresh ricotta drizzled with honey and a piece or two of almond bread. I love making jellies in a jar and dipping into them when I'm a little hungry. The grapes encased in the jelly just pop in your mouth and the freshness of the verjuice works on the hottest summer day. You could use any fruit at all in this same way.

SERVES 6
(MAKES 2 JARS AND A JELLY MOULD)

3 cups (750 ml) verjuice
20 g raw honey
16 g gelatine powder
350 g white seedless grapes

Place the verjuice and honey in a saucepan over low heat. Mix the gelatine powder and 1½ tablespoons warm water in a small bowl. Add to the warmed verjuice and stir until dissolved. The liquid needs to be just hot enough to dissolve the gelatine but if you heat it too high, the jelly will go cloudy. Remove from the heat and cool slightly.

Fill your jelly mould and 2 small jars nearly to the top with the grapes. Pour over the slightly cooled jelly mixture. Refrigerate for at least 3 hours or overnight.

To serve, if you've used a mould like I have and want to serve it turned out, dip the base of the mould into very hot water for about 20 seconds to begin. Depending on the shape, you might have to use a knife to release a vacuum around the edge and try again for an extra 10 seconds. Don't dip the jelly in hot water for too long or the jelly will melt.

NUTRITION ✎ Recent studies have shown that the regular consumption of verjuice, a gentle alternative to lemon juice or vinegar, can lower your blood pressure.

Peaches stuffed with ginger and almonds ★

Desserts are far from a constant in my life but I'm always looking for ways to use the perfectly ripe fruit from our orchard. It's also a great way to utilise less-than-ripe fruit as the roasting process softens the peaches and brings out their perfumed flavour. The warmth of the ginger counteracts the sweetness of the fruit. Depending on the ripeness of your fruit, you may need to extend the cooking time – just keep checking them and take them out when you're happy with the texture. It's very difficult to buy soft fruits that are picked when perfectly ripe, but if you buy them a few days ahead and leave them out of the refrigerator they will ripen to a degree.

SERVES 4

4 ripe yellow or white peaches
¼ cup (20 g) toasted flaked almonds
⅓ cup (25 g) finely chopped crystallised ginger
50 g unsalted butter, finely diced
2 teaspoons lemon zest
1 teaspoon ground ginger
Pouring cream, to serve (optional)

Preheat the oven to 200°C (fan-forced).

Halve the fruit and remove the seeds and any bruised flesh, then scoop out a little extra flesh, to make a bigger hollow, and chop it.

Finely chop two-thirds of the almonds. Then mix the chopped peach flesh with the chopped almonds, crystallised ginger, butter, lemon zest and ground ginger. Combine well to make a paste, then pile it into the cavities in the peach halves.

Place on a baking tray lined with baking paper. Bake for 10 minutes or until the fruit is tender but still holding its shape.

Scatter with the remaining almonds and serve hot, warm or cold with any juices and a splash of cream, if desired.

NUTRITION ✎ Peaches are full of the antioxidant polyphenols, lutein and caffeic acid, as well as some vitamin C.

The old-fashioned★ persimmon sorbet

This has to be the easiest dessert you could ever make. All you need to do is find the 'old-fashioned' variety of persimmon, which has to be diaphanous or meltingly soft before it's edible. We have a tree that bears this fruit prolifically every year and I throw the super-ripe fruit into the freezer for us to have later as a sorbet. Nothing else to be done! If you're tempted to plant a persimmon I think you would probably get more use out of the newer varieties of 'non-astringent' persimmon – they also have a great flavour but are used when firm – but if you have room, why not have both kinds?

SERVES 4

4 large ultra-ripe old-fashioned persimmons

Place the whole persimmons in the freezer overnight. When ready to consume, cut off the tops and eat the centre out with a spoon. Sheer delight!

Black sticky rice pudding with coconut and mango

This classic tropical pudding can be served simply with a good dollop of yoghurt or perhaps an ice cream made with extra virgin olive oil. In the photo we serve the rice pudding with grilled banana and a squeeze of lime but you could easily mash some ripe banana and fold it through the rice if you didn't want to bother with the grill.

SERVES 4

1 cup (200 g) black glutinous rice
½ cup (125 ml) coconut milk
½ cup (125 ml) coconut cream
2 tablespoons raw honey, or to taste
2 mangoes, peeled (you need about 230 g mango flesh)
2 tablespoons lime juice, plus extra for drizzling
4 small bananas (Lady Finger bananas with black spots on the skin if available), peeled
Thick natural probiotic yoghurt, to serve

Soak the black rice overnight in cold water.

The following day, place the coconut milk, coconut cream and 2 cups (500 ml) water in a saucepan and bring to the boil over medium heat. Drain the black rice, stir into the coconut mixture and reduce the heat to low. Cook, stirring regularly, for 40–50 minutes or until all the liquid has been absorbed. Stir in the honey to taste, then divide among serving glasses and refrigerate until cold.

Puree the mango flesh and lime juice in a blender until smooth. Pour into the glasses on top of the black rice.

To serve, preheat a barbecue grill plate or chargrill pan to high. Cook the bananas until lightly grilled on all sides, then remove from the heat and drizzle with extra lime juice. Place on top of the puddings and serve with a dollop of yoghurt.

The tropical flavours of coconut, lime and mango
are a delectable combination.

Cider poached pears *

Poaching pears with spices adds a lot more flavour than a photograph can show. They absorb the star anise and cinnamon so well and if you want extra colour you could throw a few threads of saffron into the poaching liquid (just a few though as saffron can so easily become overpowering). It's worth taking the extra step of reducing the poaching juices to create a syrup, then serve the pears as they are or with a dollop of yoghurt or a generous drizzle of cream.

MAKES 8 POACHED PEARS

½ cup (125 ml) pure apple cider vinegar
   (containing the natural mother ferment)
2 cups (500 ml) organic pure apple juice
2 cups (500 ml) apple cider
1 vanilla bean, split lengthways
1 cinnamon stick
2 star anise
3 cm piece ginger, peeled and sliced
8 medium ripe Beurre Bosc pears, peeled

Place all the ingredients except the pears in a deep 20 cm saucepan. Bring to the boil over medium heat. Add the pears and cover closely with a piece of baking paper (cartouche). Reduce the heat to low and simmer for 8–15 minutes (depending on the ripeness of the pears) – remember they will continue to cook while cooling. Remove from the heat and stand the pears in the poaching liquid until cool.

Remove the pears from the liquid. Place the pan back on the stovetop and simmer over low heat until the liquid has thickened slightly. Pour the syrup over the pears to serve.

Pear and dark chocolate almond crumble

I love a good crumble and this is the richest one of all that I make. The marriage of pear and chocolate is a blissful one, and here the chocolate buttons melt in delightful patches throughout the crumble as it bakes. While I suggest making the crumble topping in a food processor, I do find that when I have time, rubbing the butter into the mix with the tips of my fingers is very good therapy!

SERVES 8

1.2 kg semi-ripe Beurre Bosc pears, skin on and cored
50 g unsalted butter
80 g good-quality dark chocolate buttons
   (70% cocoa solids)
Finely grated zest of 1 orange
Cream, to serve

Crumble topping

3 tablespoons raw sugar
⅓ cup (50 g) wholemeal spelt flour
1¼ cups (100 g) flaked almonds, finely ground
120 g cold unsalted butter, diced
¾ cup (65 g) organic rolled oats
Pinch of sea salt flakes

To make the crumble topping, place the sugar, flour, ground almonds and butter in a food processor. Pulse until the butter starts to bring the mixture together. Add the oats and salt and pulse until a crumble consistency forms (do not overwork the mixture or it will form large clumps). Refrigerate until needed.

Preheat the oven to 200°C (fan-forced).

Cut the pears lengthways into 7–9 mm thick slices. Heat the butter in a large frying pan over medium–high heat. Add the pear slices and saute until golden (depending on the pears this might take up to 30 minutes). Place the pears in a 25 cm baking dish. Sprinkle over the chocolate buttons and orange zest. Top with the crumble mixture, then bake for 20–25 minutes or until golden. Serve warm with your choice of cream.

Macadamia crepes with figs and coconut

How sophisticated we are about pancakes these days! When I was a child, my mother would make them with just lemon and sugar and we thought they were amazing. I still love them this way, but making your own 'meal' from macadamias, almonds or pistachios certainly elevates them to dinner-party status. If your figs are super-ripe and in perfect condition serve them au natural. Actually it's fig time right now and I need a break – I think I'll go out and pick some before the birds get to them.

MAKES 10 CREPES

Extra virgin olive oil, for cooking
10 fresh figs, stalks trimmed and
    halved lengthways
2 tablespoons vino cotto or
    balsamic vinegar
1 teaspoon finely grated orange zest
½ cup (25 g) toasted coconut flakes

Crepe batter

½ cup (65 g) toasted macadamia nuts
2 tablespoons wholemeal spelt flour
4 free-range eggs
½ cup (125 ml) unsweetened almond
    milk, preferably homemade
    (see page 270)
½ teaspoon finely grated orange zest
Pinch of sea salt flakes

To make the crepe batter, place the toasted macadamia nuts in a high-powered blender and process until very finely ground. Add the remaining ingredients and blend until smooth. Pour into a jug and allow to rest for 15 minutes.

Heat a 23 cm frying pan over medium heat, add 1 teaspoon olive oil and swirl to cover the base. Lift the pan from the heat, then pour in a thin layer of batter, tilting the pan to evenly cover the base. Cook for 1–2 minutes or until light golden and the edges start to curl. Gently flip the crepe over and cook for another 30 seconds. Transfer to a plate and repeat with the remaining batter, stacking the crepes as you go.

Heat a large heavy-based frying pan over high heat. Brush the cut-side of the figs with vino cotto or balsamic and place, cut-side down, into the pan with a drizzle of olive oil. Cook just until golden, then remove from the pan. Fold the crepes into quarters and serve with the figs, orange zest and toasted coconut flakes. Drizzle with any leftover juices from the fig pan.

Roasted rhubarb and almond yoghurt cream ✦

No matter how simple the dishes are, it's all about the produce. In this case look for the reddest, plumpest rhubarb you can find, with leaves so fresh they look like they've just been pulled out of the ground. (But remember that rhubarb leaves are poisonous so don't be tempted to utilise them or even give them to the chooks.) While almond milk is easy to buy commercially, check the label to make sure it doesn't have added sugar or preservatives. Better still, have a go at making it yourself (see page 270) – the taste is truly worth it. When you are making a 'jelly' of any kind, and this almond yoghurt cream has gelatine in it, bear in mind that you'll need a few hours for it to set properly and allow yourself plenty of time.

SERVES 6

1 bunch rhubarb, leaves and ends trimmed (about 500 g after trimming)
3 tablespoons raw honey, or to taste
Finely grated zest of 2 oranges
2 tablespoons orange juice
1 teaspoon ground star anise
25 g cold unsalted butter, finely chopped

Almond yoghurt cream

½ cup (125 ml) unsweetened almond milk, preferably homemade (see page 270)
1 vanilla bean, halved lengthways, seeds scraped
2½ x 2 g gold-strength gelatine leaves
50 g raw honey
400 g thick natural probitoic yoghurt
2 tablespoons lemon juice
½ teaspoon freshly grated nutmeg

To make the almond yoghurt cream, place the almond milk, vanilla seeds and scraped bean in a small saucepan and bring to the boil over low heat.

Meanwhile, soak the gelatine leaves in cold water until soft. Squeeze out the excess liquid, then add to the hot milk and stir until dissolved. Set aside to cool slightly.

Combine the honey, yoghurt and lemon juice in a medium bowl. Whisk in the cooled milk, then strain the mixture into a serving bowl. Dust with nutmeg, then cover and refrigerate overnight or for at least 3 hours.

Preheat the oven to 220°C (fan-forced). Line a baking tray with baking paper.

Cut the rhubarb into 1.5 cm pieces. Place in a bowl with the honey, orange zest, orange juice and star anise and toss to combine well. Place the rhubarb on the lined tray in a single layer. Dot the butter over the rhubarb, then roast for 10–15 minutes or until just cooked, but not falling apart.

To serve, divide the rhubarb among plates or bowls and serve with a generous spoonful of almond yoghurt cream.

Chocolate cloud cake with nut cream and rose petals

As the name implies, this cake should be as light as air. It's a total chocolate fix, having so little else to keep it afloat ... unless you count the 10 eggs of course. And if the chocolate element isn't indulgent enough, consider the filling of nut butter and whipped cream. There are many lovely nut butters out there, but my favourite for this would have to be macadamia butter, to really push us over the edge! Luckily, life always seems to offer up plenty of reasons to celebrate.

SERVES 10-12

350 g good-quality dark chocolate
   (70% cocoa solids), broken
   into pieces
50 g unsalted butter
2 tablespoons raw honey
10 free-range eggs, at room
   temperature, separated
Pinch of sea salt flakes
Organic fresh rose petals,
   to decorate (optional)

Nut cream

200 ml whipping cream
½ cup mint leaves, finely chopped
100 g pure nut butter

Preheat the oven to 150°C fan-forced. Grease and line 2 x 20 cm springform tins.

Melt the chocolate and butter together in a heatproof bowl placed over a saucepan of just-simmering water (don't let the bottom of the bowl touch the water). Remove from the heat, stir in the honey and set aside.

In the bowl of an electric mixer, whisk the egg whites with a pinch of salt until stiff peaks form.

In a separate bowl, whisk the egg yolks until thick and pale. Slowly whisk in the chocolate mixture until just combined. Fold in one third of the egg whites, then ever so lightly, fold in the remaining whisked whites. (It is important to work quickly and not let the chocolate butter mixture get cold or it will set.)

Divide the batter between the prepared tins. Bake for 25 minutes or until a skewer withdraws clean. Remove from the oven and stand on a wire rack until completely cooled.

To make the nut cream, beat the cream in a large bowl until stiff peaks form. In a separate bowl, combine the mint, nut butter and a small amount of the whipped cream. Gently fold in the remaining cream.

To assemble, place one of the cakes on a serving plate and spread half the nut cream over the top, leaving a 2 cm border. Place the remaining cake on top and spread with the remaining cream. Scatter with rose petals, if using.

NUTRITION The good news is that dark chocolate is rich in polyphenol antioxidants, particularly catechins and procyanidins, and these have antioxidant and anti-inflammatory properties that are good for your blood vessels. Chocolate also provides some iron, manganese and magnesium.

*The very scent of quinces
cooking is enough to comfort me
and remind me that all is well
with the world.*

Quinces with blancmange and fennel almonds ★

I smile inside when I write about quinces. They are an important part of my first memories of coming to live in South Australia nearly 45 years ago. Every cottage in the Barossa – no matter how derelict – had a quince tree and it was my Barossa friend Hazel Mader who first taught me how to transform something that is inedible raw into a precious jewel.

SERVES 4

2 Smyrna quinces
½ lemon
2 tablespoons raw honey

Blancmange

140 g blanched almonds
1 cup (250 ml) full-cream milk
1 cup (250 ml) buttermilk
2 x 2 g gold-strength gelatine leaves

Fennel almonds

50 g blanched almonds
1 teaspoon fennel seeds
2 tablespoons raw honey

To make the blancmange, preheat the oven to 180°C (fan-forced). Place the almonds on a baking tray and cook for 8–10 minutes or until golden. Cool, then place in a container with the milk and buttermilk and stand at room temperature for 4 hours.

Blend the almond mixture in a high-powered blender until smooth. Strain through a fine sieve and discard the solids. Heat ½ cup (125 ml) of the almond milk in a saucepan over low heat until hot. Soak the gelatine leaves in cold water for about 3 minutes or until soft. Squeeze out the excess water, then add to the hot milk and stir until dissolved. Add the remaining almond milk and stir to combine. Strain once more through a fine sieve, then pour into a serving dish and refrigerate for 3 hours or until set.

Wash, peel and core the quinces, reserving the skins and core. Squeeze the lemon into a large bowl of cold water. Cut the quinces into quarters or eighths, depending on the size, placing them into the acidulated water as you go to prevent discolouration.

Place the reserved skins and cores in an ovenproof medium saucepan with the honey and just enough water to cover and simmer over low heat for 40 minutes or until it takes on a rosy glow.

Preheat the oven to 120°C (fan-forced).

Add the quince wedges to the skins and cores, cover closely with a piece of baking paper (cartouche), then transfer to the oven and bake for 2 hours or until tender and coloured. Remove and set aside.

To make the fennel almonds, increase the oven temperature to 180°C (fan-forced). Place the almonds on a baking tray and toast for 8–10 minutes or until golden.

Place the fennel seeds in a small dry saucepan and shake over high heat for 1–2 minutes or until fragrant. Add the honey and almonds and stir for 3 minutes or until the honey starts to caramelise. Pour onto a baking tray lined with baking paper and stand until cool. Store in an airtight container until needed.

To serve, spoon the quince and a little syrup over the blancmange and scatter with the fennel almonds.

Lime and coconut tofu cheesecake

My first experience of tasting tofu in a cheesecake was when I was a guest judge on MasterChef and I'd given tofu as one of the core ingredients the contestants had to hero. I was blown away by a chocolate and tofu cheesecake that had the most incredible silky texture so it was a simple extension to look for other flavours to marry with it while still retaining that beguiling silkiness. This one totally fits the bill, although it's important to taste the lime to be sure it has the acidity needed. This is one time I suggest looking for really green limes to give the freshness required, whereas normally I recommend picking or buying Tahitian limes when they are turning yellow for real ripeness and volume of juice. Again, it's about the detail.

SERVES 10–12

Base

⅔ cup (50 g) desiccated coconut
⅓ cup (25 g) flaked almonds
20 g coconut flour
⅓ cup (30 g) organic rolled oats
Pinch of sea salt flakes
3 Medjool dates, seeded
½ teaspoon ground ginger
3 tablespoons extra virgin coconut
   oil, melted

Filling

300 g soft silken tofu
1 cup (250 ml) coconut cream
½ cup (125 ml) strained lime juice
3 teaspoons powdered gelatine
2 tablespoons pure maple syrup
1 tablespoon finely grated lime zest

Jelly

1 tablespoon powdered gelatine
30 g strained apricot jam
200 ml strained orange juice

Preheat the oven to 180°C (fan-forced). Grease and line the base of a 24 cm springform tin with baking paper.

To make the base, place the coconut and almonds on separate baking trays lined with baking paper. Toast the coconut for 4–5 minutes and the almonds for 8 minutes or until both are golden. Remove from the oven and stand until cool.

Transfer to a food processor, along with the flour, oats, salt, dates and ginger and process until finely chopped. Using the pulse button, gradually add the melted coconut oil and process until the mixture comes together. Press the mixture evenly over the base of the prepared tin and refrigerate until needed.

To make the filling, place the tofu in a fine strainer set over a bowl and leave to drain for 1 hour. Place the coconut cream in the bowl of an electric mixer and refrigerate until chilled.

Combine the lime juice and gelatine in a small saucepan over medium heat. Stir until the gelatine has dissolved, then remove from the heat and set aside to cool slightly.

Place the drained tofu and the maple syrup in a blender and process until smooth. Add the lime zest and gelatine mixture and blend until combined.

Using an electric mixer, whisk the coconut cream in the chilled bowl on the highest setting until thick and airy. Gently fold in the tofu mixture until combined. Pour over the chilled base and refrigerate for at least 3 hours or until set.

When the cheesecake is set, make the jelly. Place the gelatine, jam and half the orange juice in a small saucepan and stir over low heat until the gelatine has dissolved. Remove from the heat and stir in the remaining juice. Gently pour over the set cheesecake. Refrigerate for another hour or until the jelly has set. Use a hot knife to cut the cheesecake into slices.

Many people find
cheesecake too heavy but do
try this one — it's just so
light and refreshing.

Baked apples

A good baked apple is such a comforting old favourite, no matter what stuffing you use (and it could well be just raisins with butter as Mum made for us as children). I thought I should go to a little more trouble here, and the addition of almonds, oats and orange zest does lift things considerably. You absolutely need to serve this with yoghurt, cream or even custard, depending on your sensibilities, to mingle with the delicious juices that escape during baking.

SERVES 6

⅓ cup (55 g) sultanas
⅔ cup (160 ml) verjuice
1 cup (80 g) flaked almonds
½ cup (50 g) organic rolled oats
1 teaspoon ground cinnamon
Pinch of freshly grated nutmeg
Pinch of sea salt flakes
1 teaspoon finely grated orange zest
50 g extra virgin coconut oil
   or unsalted butter, at room
   temperature
6 small Granny Smith apples
   (or if you prefer a sweeter apple,
   Pink Lady)
½ cup (125 ml) pure apple juice
300 ml pouring cream or natural
   probiotic yoghurt

Place the sultanas and 2 tablespoons verjuice in a small bowl and leave to stand overnight.

Preheat the oven to 180°C (fan-forced).

Place the almonds and rolled oats on a baking tray lined with baking paper. Bake for 6–8 minutes or until golden, stirring halfway through. Set aside to cool, then place in a food processor. Using the pulse button, process until broken down, but still with texture. Transfer to a bowl and stir through the cinnamon, nutmeg, salt and orange zest. Rub in the coconut oil or butter and mix well to combine.

Using a melon baller, scoop out the centre of the apples, starting from the top of the fruit and leaving them connected at the bottom. Use a sharp paring knife to score a line all the way around the centre of the apples – this helps the moisture to escape and prevents the apples from exploding during cooking.

Fill the apples with the almond mixture, then place in a small baking dish. Pour in the apple juice and the remaining verjuice (this should come about 1 cm up the sides of the apple). Bake for 45–60 minutes until golden, soft to touch and wrinkled. Remove from the oven and cool slightly, then serve with cream or yoghurt.

DESSERT

Silky choc orange jaffa mousse

Ah memories. I'm going to show my age here and tell you that it was such a treat to buy a box of Jaffas when we went to the 'pictures' on a Saturday afternoon, when all that was showing were westerns. And it wasn't just the crunch of the orangey red coating into the chocolate (even then an addictive combination). I couldn't resist the temptation to roll a few Jaffas down the aisle during the quieter moments in the film. I can still hear the noise they used to make, and the love of the flavour lives on today, though perhaps in a slightly more sophisticated form.

SERVES 4

300 g soft silken tofu
125 g good-quality dark couverture
    chocolate (70% cocoa solids)
3 tablespoons pure cocoa powder
3 tablespoons full-cream milk
    (or almond or coconut milk)
1 tablespoon extra virgin coconut oil
3 tablespoons soft brown sugar
1 teaspoon finely grated orange zest
1 tablespoon vino cotto

To serve

2 oranges, segmented
⅓ cup (80 g) creme fraiche
2 tablespoons coarsely grated
    dark couverture chocolate
    (70% cocoa solids)

Place the tofu in a fine sieve set over a bowl and drain for 15 minutes.

Meanwhile, place the chocolate, cocoa powder, milk, coconut oil and sugar in a heatproof bowl over a saucepan of barely simmering water (making sure the base of the bowl doesn't touch the water). Stir occasionally until melted and smooth.

Place the drained tofu into a blender and process until smooth. Add the warm chocolate mixture, orange zest and vino cotto and blend until well combined. Working quickly (as the mix starts to set once cold) spoon the mousse into glasses, cover and refrigerate for at least 3 hours or until set.

To serve, top each glass with 3 orange segments, then a spoonful of creme fraiche and a sprinkling of grated dark chocolate.

Coconut crepes with citrus compote

I've never managed to keep a crepe pan exclusively for cooking crepes, as you often read is so desirable, but I wonder if this was before non-stick pans came into our daily lives. Of course I'm aware that as soon as a non-stick pan has its seal broken it becomes a negative, but if you limit these pans to lower-temperature cooking they work so well with just the smallest amount of oil or butter. Perhaps more important than a specific pan is a specific size; it has to be just the right size for the crepe but allow you to ease a spatula under the edge to flip it over. Anyway, whatever pan you use, the crepes can be cooked in advance, stacked between sheets of baking paper and warmed to serve.

SERVES 4

1 ruby grapefruit, peeled and
    white pith removed
1 regular grapefruit, peeled
    and white pith removed
1 orange, peeled and white
    pith removed
2 blood oranges, peeled and
    white pith removed
2 tablespoons pure maple syrup
Finely grated zest of 1 lime
2 tablespoons extra virgin
    coconut oil
240 g coconut yoghurt
Toasted coconut flakes, to serve

Crepe batter

4 free-range eggs
⅔ cup (160 ml) coconut milk
3 tablespoons coconut flour

To make the crepe batter, whisk the eggs, coconut milk and coconut flour in a large bowl until a smooth batter forms. Pour into a jug, cover and allow to rest for 15 minutes.

Meanwhile, using a small sharp knife and holding the fruit over a bowl fitted with a sieve, segment all the fruit, one at a time and keeping each fruit separate. To segment, cut between the white sections running from the top to the bottom of the fruit. Squeeze the juice from the remaining flesh into the bowl. Place the citrus juices, maple syrup and lime zest in a small saucepan and simmer over low heat until thick and syrupy. Add the citrus segments and gently stir for 1–2 minutes, being careful not to break up the segments, then remove from the heat.

Heat a 23 cm frying pan over medium heat. Add 1 teaspoon coconut oil and swirl to cover the base. Lift the pan from the heat, then pour in a thin layer of the batter, tilting the pan to evenly cover the base. Cook for about 1–2 minutes or until light golden and the edges start to curl. Flip the crepe over gently and cook for another 30 seconds. Transfer to a plate and repeat with the remaining batter and coconut oil, stacking the crepes as you go. Makes 8 crepes.

To serve, place a large spoonful of citrus compote and a generous tablespoon of coconut yoghurt on one side of each crepe. Fold over, scatter with toasted coconut flakes and serve warm.

NUTRITION Citrus fruits and zest are good sources of vitamin C as well as a few anthocyanins and other flavonoid antioxidants.

DESSERT

The secret to winter food is definitely citrus,
and the mix of different colours and flavours
in this compote is just perfect with the coconut.

Roast pear halves with prunes and walnuts

I have a newfound respect for pears. It started when we bought our neighbour's orchard of several thousand apricot, peach, apple and pear trees – a totally emotional buy, but we couldn't risk one of the last orchards of the Barossa being pulled out. We have been farming for over 40 years, mostly vines, olives and quinces, but nothing prepared us for just how much attention an orchard needs. This is a real labour of love, it has to be said, but it soon became clear that pears have much to offer. For a start, there are so many different varieties, all with their individual flavours. The trees are tall and majestic, and when flooded they soak up the extra water without complaint; and their fruit is picked when it works for us as they ripen off the tree. Ripe pears are wonderful to eat fresh, they're beautifully plump and succulent when cut for drying, and are great for making cider. And last but not least, they can so easily be turned into a great dessert. As I said: respect.

SERVES 4

40 g walnuts
2 large pears
2 tablespoons raw honey,
    plus extra for drizzling
2 tablespoons linseeds (flaxseeds)
⅓ cup (55 g) pitted prunes
2 tablespoons finely grated
    orange zest
1 teaspoon ground cinnamon
2 teaspoons finely grated ginger
Pinch of sea salt flakes
45 g cold unsalted butter, diced
200 g creme fraiche

Preheat the oven to 180°C (fan-forced).

Place the walnuts on a baking tray and cook for 8 minutes or until lightly toasted. Pour the warm nuts into a clean tea towel and rub off the skins while still warm.

Cut the pears in half and use a melon baller to scoop out the centres, leaving a 1.5 cm thick border. Place, cut-side up, on a baking tray lined with baking paper.

Place the honey, linseeds, walnuts, prunes, orange zest, cinnamon, ginger and salt in a food processor and pulse just until the mixture comes together. Fill each scooped-out pear half with one quarter of the filling, then top with one quarter of the butter. Bake for 30 minutes or until the pears are tender. The cooking time will vary depending on the ripeness of the pears. Remove from the oven and stand for 10 minutes. Serve the warm pears with creme fraiche, drizzled with a little extra honey.

Almond and ginger cake with roasted rhubarb

The thing I like so much about this cake is that it rises up like a souffle, is a little crisp around the edges and then falls a bit to give a crater in which to nestle the roasted rhubarb and yoghurt (or creme fraiche if you prefer). In other words, no one will question the success of the cake because the last thing you want is a perfectly flat surface. Generously and deliciously, this cake gives you absolute license to 'fail'.

SERVES 12

2 cups (320 g) blanched almonds
1½ teaspoons baking powder
Pinch of sea salt flakes
½ teaspoon freshly grated nutmeg
1 teaspoon ground ginger
3 free-range eggs, at room
    temperature
½ cup (125 ml) pure maple syrup
3 tablespoons extra virgin olive oil
1 tablespoon finely grated orange
    zest, plus extra to serve
1 cup (280 g) natural probiotic
    yoghurt

Roasted rhubarb

6 rhubarb stalks (about 500 g),
    trimmed and washed, cut into
    2.5 cm lengths
Finely grated zest of ½ orange
2 tablespoons soft brown sugar
40 g cold unsalted butter, chopped

Preheat the oven to 160˚C (fan-forced). Grease and line a 23 cm springform tin with baking paper.

Place the almonds on a baking tray and cook for 8–10 minutes or until golden. Remove from the oven and allow to cool completely, then process in a food processor until finely ground.

In a large bowl, mix together the ground almonds, baking powder, salt, nutmeg and ginger.

In the bowl of an electric mixer fitted with the whisk attachment, whisk the eggs and maple syrup on high speed for about 10 minutes or until light and fluffy, and doubled in size. With the motor running, add the olive oil in a thin steady stream. Using a spatula, gently fold the orange zest and dry ingredients into the egg mixture, then pour into the prepared tin. Bake for 40–50 minutes or until golden and a skewer withdraws clean. Do not open the oven during the cooking time. Remove from the oven and allow to cool in tin. Increase the oven temperature to 200˚C (fan-forced).

To make the roasted rhubarb, place the rhubarb on a baking tray lined with baking paper. Scatter with the orange zest, sugar and butter and bake for 12–15 minutes or until just tender. Remove from the oven and allow to cool.

Place the cooled cake on a serving plate. Top with the yoghurt, then the cooled rhubarb and finish with a little extra orange zest.

Chocolate, prune and hazelnut ganache in spelt and cinnamon pastry

Isn't it wonderful that darker, higher-percentage chocolate is good for us? This super-rich, super-simple dessert would satisfy the most entrenched sweet tooth yet it is not actually super sweet. A lot of this comes down to the prunes. I love prunes, but somehow in all the years of having the Pheasant Farm Restaurant it was hard to 'sell' a prune dessert (though I've observed that if the name is tweaked to 'dried plums' and paired with chocolate it races out the door). Well I am firmly committed to the prune and will not disguise them here. And oh my goodness, this pastry: it's moreish just on its own and so forgiving it can be pressed into a tart mould rather than rolled, if you prefer. This beautiful tart is best served straight from the refrigerator.

SERVES 12

1⅓ cups (225 g) pitted prunes
1 cup (250 ml) verjuice
½ cup (70 g) hazelnuts
100 g extra virgin coconut paste
 or coconut butter
1 tablespoon extra virgin coconut
 oil (optional)
200 g good-quality dark couverture
 chocolate (70% cocoa solids),
 coarsely chopped
Creme fraiche, to serve (optional)

Pastry

185 g wholemeal spelt flour
1 teaspoon ground cinnamon
60 g runny honey
125 g cold unsalted butter, chopped
Pinch of sea salt flakes
45 g creme fraiche
2 tablespoons verjuice

Place the prunes and verjuice in a small bowl and set aside to rehydrate for 45 minutes (if they are already soft and plump); soak drier prunes overnight. Drain and cut the prunes in half.

To make the pastry, place all the ingredients, except the verjuice, in a food processor and pulse to combine. Using the pulse action, gradually add the verjuice and process until the pastry just comes together. Turn out and shape into a disc, then wrap in plastic film and refrigerate for 30 minutes.

Preheat the oven to 180°C (fan-forced). Lightly grease a 24 cm fluted tart tin with a removable base.

Roll out the pastry on a lightly floured surface or between 2 sheets baking paper, until about 2 mm thick. Place the pastry in the tin and carefully press into the sides. Using a small sharp knife, trim the sides to neaten. Refrigerate for 20 minutes.

To blind bake the tart shell, cover the inside of the tin with a piece of baking paper or foil, leaving the sides overhanging. Fill with dried beans or rice. Bake for 15 minutes, then remove from the oven and carefully remove the paper or foil and the beans or rice. Return the tart shell to the oven and bake for another 8–10 minutes or until the base and sides are golden and dry. Remove from the oven and stand until cool.

Meanwhile, place the hazelnuts on a baking tray and cook for 5–8 minutes or until lightly toasted. Pour into a clean tea towel and rub off the skins while still warm. Coarsely chop the nuts and set aside.

Heat the coconut paste or butter in a small saucepan until smooth and melted; if it isn't melting readily, add the coconut oil. Remove the pan from the heat, then quickly add the chocolate and stir until melted.

To assemble the tart, scatter the chopped toasted hazelnuts over the cooled pastry base. Place the prunes evenly around the base of the tart. Pour the chocolate ganache over the top, then refrigerate the tart for 2 hours or until set. Serve with creme fraiche, if you like.

Snacks

Wattle seed, hazelnut and chocolate biscuits

Let me say there is wattle seed and there is wattle seed, and it all comes down to freshness and the way it is roasted. Until I tasted fresh wattle seed at a wild food cooking competition in Alice Springs many years ago I thought it tasted like stale coffee and wasn't attracted to it at all. Then I experienced the cooking of Raylene Brown of Kungkas Can Cook, who taught me so much about indigenous ingredients. I love to use wattle seed now and, yes, there is a scent of coffee but it's nutty and fresh when bought from a good supplier such as Outback Pride. These biscuits really show the flavour off.

MAKES ABOUT 22

95 g hazelnuts (see note)
110 g unsalted butter, softened
½ cup lightly packed (95 g) soft
 brown sugar
1 tablespoon wattle seed,
 toasted, cooled and ground
 (see page 279)
1 teaspoon vanilla extract
1 large free-range egg
115 g white spelt flour
½ teaspoon baking powder
¼ teaspoon sea salt flakes, crushed
80 g good-quality dark couverture
 chocolate (70% cocoa solids),
 coarsely chopped
10–12 chocolate buttons, to decorate

Preheat the oven to 180°C (fan forced). Grease and line 2 baking trays with baking paper.

Place the hazelnuts on one of the baking trays and cook for 8–10 minutes or until golden. Pour into a tea towel and rub off the skins while still warm. Set aside to cool. Reserve 12 of the hazelnuts to decorate the biscuits, then finely chop the remainder.

Reduce the oven temperature to 160°C (fan-forced).

Using an electric mixer fitted with the paddle attachment, beat the butter, sugar, ground wattle seed and vanilla for 3–4 minutes, scraping down the sides occasionally, until light and fluffy. Add the egg and combine well.

In a separate bowl, whisk together the flour, baking powder and salt. Add to the butter mixture and beat on low speed just until the dough comes together. Stir in the chopped hazelnuts and chopped chocolate until well combined. Roll tablespoons of mixture into balls, place onto the prepared trays and press down slightly. Top with a hazelnut or a chocolate button. Bake for 15 minutes or until golden around the edges.

Remove from the oven and stand on the trays for 5 minutes before transferring to a wire rack to cool completely. Store in an airtight container.

Note: If you don't have hazelnuts on hand, macadamias would be a delicious, and fittingly indigenous, alternative.

NUTRITION Wattle seed provides protein, calcium, iron, selenium and zinc.

Chocolate, gubinge and seed slab

This is the treat to end all treats: the dark chocolate, the crunch of the seeds, the sweetness of the raisins, the zest of the orange, the nuttiness of the almonds and, wait for it, the gubinge powder! Also known as Kakadu plum, this native ingredient is so full of vitamin C it's off the charts (look for it in health food stores) but for me it's the intense, tart flavour that's the icing on the cake here. Spread the slab mixture as thin or as thick as you like and let it set, then sit back and listen to everyone waxing lyrical about how good it is.

SERVES 10

1½ tablespoons pepitas (pumpkin seeds)
1½ tablespoons sunflower seeds
150 g dark chocolate (70 % cocoa solids), chopped
1 tablespoon extra virgin coconut oil
1 teaspoon gubinge powder (see page 278)
Pinch of sea salt flakes
3 tablespoons sultanas or raisins
3 tablespoons almonds, toasted
1 teaspoon thinly sliced orange zest

Place the pepitas in a frying pan and shake over medium heat until lightly toasted. Remove from the pan and repeat with the sunflower seeds.

Place the chocolate and coconut oil in a heatproof bowl over a saucepan of just simmering water until melted and smooth (making sure the base of the bowl doesn't touch the water). Remove from the heat and stir in the gubinge powder and salt. Add the toasted seeds and sultanas or raisins and combine well.

Pour the mixture onto a tray lined with baking paper and spread out to about 5 mm thick. Scatter with the almonds and orange zest, then refrigerate for 1 hour or until set. Break into pieces and store in an airtight container in the refrigerator.

NUTRITION 🌿 Gubinge powder has high levels of vitamin C, as well as phenolic antioxidants.

Nut and fruit bar

Everything you need in a satisfying snack, these bars are full of good things, and quick and easy to make. Lovely with a cup of tea or packed into a lunchbox to take to school or work.

MAKES 10 BARS

1¼ cups (150 g) ground almonds
Pinch of sea salt flakes
¼ teaspoon baking powder
1 teaspoon ground cinnamon
½ cup (80 g) blanched almonds
½ cup (50 g) walnuts
3 tablespoons linseeds (flaxseeds)
½ cup (75 g) raisins
100 g extra virgin coconut oil
75 g raw honey
1 teaspoon vanilla extract
70 g almond butter
1 teaspoon finely grated orange zest

Preheat the oven to 175˚C (fan-forced). Grease and line an 11 cm x 34 cm tart tin with removable base or similar.

Place the ground almonds, salt, baking powder and cinnamon in a large bowl and whisk to combine well. Stir in the nuts, seeds and raisins.

Place the coconut oil, honey, vanilla and almond butter into a small saucepan and stir over low heat until just warmed through. Alternatively, place in a microwave-safe bowl and heat for 30 seconds. Pour into the dry ingredients, add the orange zest and stir to combine well.

Press the mixture into the prepared tin and bake for 15–20 minutes or until golden. Stand until cool, then cut into 10 bars.

Dee's banana bread ★

Extra-ripe bananas have always had a place in our food life. I wouldn't use preservatives when my children were young so buying ice cream was difficult – the only preservative-free ice cream I knew of then was Golden North honey ice cream and, as good as it was, I needed an alternative. The solution was to freeze super-ripe bananas, which offered an even more natural ice cream so no one felt they were missing out. I don't need to do this any more but when you have a stash of extra-ripe bananas or see them on sale, don't let them go to waste. Make this amazing banana bread instead. It's best eaten warm from the oven, although it's also delicious the next day toasted and served with fresh banana and yoghurt.

MAKES 1 LOAF

¾ cup (75 g) walnuts
½ cup (70 g) coconut flour
1 teaspoon ground cinnamon
2 teaspoons baking powder
20 g chia seeds
300 g extra-ripe banana flesh
   (about 3 medium bananas)
6 free-range eggs
8 Medjool dates, seeded
3 tablespoons macadamia oil
1 teaspoon vanilla bean paste

Preheat the oven to 180°C (fan-forced). Grease a 10 cm x 20 cm loaf tin or similar (you can use a variety of tin sizes as long as the height of the tin allows you to bake the loaf to 7 cm high). Line the base and sides with baking paper, leaving the sides overhanging.

Place the walnuts on a baking tray and cook for 8–10 minutes or until golden. Pour into a clean tea towel and rub off the skins while still warm. Stand until cool, then chop. Reduce the oven temperature to 160°C (fan-forced).

Combine the coconut flour, cinnamon, baking powder and chia seeds in a bowl and set aside.

Place the banana, eggs, dates, macadamia oil and vanilla in a food processor and blend until smooth. Add the coconut flour mixture and pulse until just combined. Stir in half the walnuts, then pour the batter into the prepared tin. Scatter the remaining walnuts over the top, then bake for 35–45 minutes or until a skewer withdraws clean. Remove from the oven and stand to cool slightly.

NUTRITION 🍃 Dates are a good source of fibre, polyphenol antioxidants such as flavonoids, as well as copper, lutein and beta-carotene.

Coffee, date and walnut balls★

I had my first taste of these 'ball' snacks at Gwinganna Lifestyle Retreat in the hills of Coolangatta, a place where health and indulgence sit comfortably side by side, offering a particularly special experience. These were always served with a mid-morning drink of some kind after a good physical workout. I should say these particular balls would seldom be offered at Gwinganna as coffee is not usually on the menu, but the idea of it comes from there. They are definitely a pick-me-up and not something I'd have after dinner or I'd never get to sleep

MAKES ABOUT 20 BALLS

150 g Medjool dates, seeded
2 tablespoons hot espresso
½ cup (50 g) walnuts, plus extra
to decorate (optional)
½ cup (70 g) hazelnuts
1 teaspoon vanilla bean paste
1 teaspoon ground cinnamon
Pinch of sea salt flakes
¾ cup (60 g) desiccated coconut

Place the dates in a bowl and pour over the hot espresso. Stand for 30 minutes or overnight if time permits.

Preheat the oven to 180°C (fan-forced).

Place the walnuts and hazelnuts together on a baking tray lined with baking paper. Cook for 8–10 minutes or until golden. Pour into a clean tea towel and rub off the skins while still warm.

Drain the dates and reserve the coffee. Place the dates in a food processor with the nuts, vanilla, cinnamon and salt and pulse until a slightly textured dough forms. You may need to add some of the reserved coffee if the mixture appears dry – the soaking time will influence this. Roll heaped teaspoons of th emixture into balls (about 15 g each), then roll in the desiccated coconut. Top with extra toasted nuts, if desired. Store in an airtight container in the refrigerator or freezer.

NUTRITION 🍃 Coffee is a rich source of antioxidants such as polyphenols and hydrocinnamic acid.

Turmeric and lemongrass chicken skewers ★

These could easily be a snack to enjoy with drinks but I usually serve them at a barbecue. They take so little time to cook, making them a very handy starter while the rest of the serious barbecuing goes on. They can also be made with chicken wings rather than cutting up chicken thighs, but whatever you decide they are definitely finger food so serviettes are essential.

SERVES 4

½ teaspoon black peppercorns
3 cloves garlic
3 coriander roots, well rinsed
30 g fresh bright turmeric, peeled and coarsely chopped
2 lemongrass stalks, pale ends only, coarsely chopped
1 tablespoon fish sauce
10 g palm sugar, grated
4 x 200 g chicken thigh fillets, cut into 2–3 cm wide strips
Sea salt flakes

Yoghurt dip

150 g natural probiotic yoghurt
2 tablespoons hulled tahini
1 tablespoon lemon juice, or to taste

Using a mortar and pestle or small blender, grind the peppercorns, garlic, coriander roots, turmeric and lemongrass until a paste forms. Add the fish sauce and palm sugar and stir until well combined. Place the chicken and spice paste in an airtight container, toss to coat well, then cover and refrigerate overnight.

Soak 16 bamboo skewers in water for 30 minutes so they don't burn during cooking.

Preheat a barbecue flat plate to high.

Thread the chicken onto the soaked skewers. Place the skewers on the lightly oiled barbecue and season with salt. Cook for about 4 minutes on each side or until cooked through.

Meanwhile, to make the yoghurt dip, whisk all the ingredients together until smooth and well combined.

Serve the chicken skewers with the yoghurt dip on the side.

Trail mix ★

I like to take a handful or two of this mix when I'm travelling to town for meetings and won't have the chance to eat a proper meal. It's true, a simple pile of fresh nuts would do the job perfectly well, but the addition of sultanas and dark chocolate make it more indulgent, and I'm all for that! It will keep in the refrigerator for up to 2 weeks if you're very strong willed.

MAKES 3 CUPS

1½ cups (240 g) mixed raw nuts (hazelnuts, Brazil nuts, walnuts, almonds, pecans, macadamias etc.)
3 tablespoons pepitas (pumpkin seeds)
3 tablespoons coconut flakes
½ cup (80 g) sultanas
½ cup (95 g) good-quality dark chocolate (70%) chips

Preheat the oven to 180°C (fan-forced).

Place the mixed nuts on a baking tray and cook for 8–10 minutes or until golden. Pour into a clean tea towel and rub off the skins while still warm. Set aside to cool.

Place the pepitas and coconut flakes on separate baking trays and toast for 5 minutes or until golden. Remove from the oven and set aside to cool.

Place the nuts, pepitas and coconut flakes in a bowl. Stir through the sultanas and chocolate chips. Store in a zip-lock bag or airtight container in the refrigerator for up to 2 weeks.

NUTRITION ✎ This mix is a healthy alternative to the processed foods we often grab on the run. It contains protein, selenium, manganese, and polyunsaturated and monounsaturated fatty acids.

Olive oil Anzacs

I declare myself to be very much a coffee drinker, although I only have two short espressos in the morning, so there are times when a cup of tea is the only thing to keep me going. I love a biscuit with tea as a treat and these beauties remind me of a much earlier time: as a child I would dunk that last bit of an Anzac biscuit into very hot tea, just as my mother did. This is a more grown-up version of a traditional Anzac and the addition of the gubinge powder (also known as Kakadu plum) gives a great zing to cut through the sweetness.

MAKES 12

1 cup (130 g) wholemeal spelt flour
¾ cup (60 g) desiccated coconut
2 g salt, iodine added
½ teaspoon bicarbonate of soda
10 g gubinge powder (see page 278)
½ cup firmly packed (110 g) dark brown sugar
¾ cup (65 g) organic rolled oats
3 tablespoons pepitas (pumpkin seeds)
3 tablespoons seeded Medjool dates
¾ cup (180 ml) extra virgin olive oil
45 g raw honey
1 teaspoon finely grated orange zest

Preheat the oven to 180°C (fan-forced).

In a large bowl, combine the flour, coconut, salt, bicarbonate of soda, gubinge powder and sugar.

Place the rolled oats and pepitas in a food processor and blitz until fine. Add to the bowl with the flour.

Place the dates in the food processor and blend into a puree. Add the olive oil, honey, orange zest and flour mixture and pulse until the mixture comes together. Roll the mixture into 12 balls (about 50 g each). Place on a baking tray lined with baking paper, allowing room to spread, and bake for 15–20 minutes or until light golden. Stand on the tray to cool completely, then store in an airtight container.

Cocoa and banana balls

One of these balls is the perfect little something to enjoy after dinner. They are quick and simple to make, and you can use pitted prunes instead of dates if you prefer. They may look small but they are rich and totally delicious.

MAKES ABOUT 28

½ cup (80 g) blanched almonds
75 g (1 cup) shredded coconut
¾ cup (60 g) desiccated coconut
180 g banana flesh (about 2 medium bananas)
Pinch of sea salt flakes
100 g Medjool dates, seeded
1¼ tablespoons extra virgin coconut oil, melted
1 tablespoon vino cotto or balsamic vinegar
2 tablespoons pure cocoa powder

Preheat the oven to 180°C (fan-forced).

Place the almonds on a baking tray and cook for 8–10 minutes or until golden. Remove and set aside to cool, then toast the shredded coconut and desiccated coconut on separate trays for 5 minutes or until light golden. Remove from the oven and allow to cool.

Place the almonds, banana, salt and dates in a food processor and blend until smooth. Add the coconut oil, vino cotto or balsamic, cocoa powder and shredded coconut and pulse until the mixture comes together into a nice smooth paste. Transfer to a bowl, then cover and refrigerate for 1 hour or until firm.

Roll the mixture into small balls (about 3 teaspoons each). Roll in the desiccated coconut, then store in the refrigerator in an airtight container.

Gluten-free biscotti

It goes without saying that you can replace the gluten-free flour with wholemeal flour if you like – no need to make any other changes. I love using pistachios as much for their colour as their flavour but use whatever nuts you like, and don't leave out the chocolate or dried apricots. I urge you to search out Australian dried apricots and support our local farmers or they won't continue to produce them – definitely a great loss as their flavour is incredibly different and wonderful. On my soapbox again!

MAKES ABOUT 35 PIECES

120 g pistachio nuts
1⅓ cups (200 g) gluten-free
    plain flour
1 teaspoon baking powder
½ teaspoon sea salt flakes
⅓ cup firmly packed (75 g) soft
    brown sugar
50 g dark chocolate (70% cocoa
    solids), chopped
⅓ cup (50 g) dried Australian
    apricots (preferably Barossa
    of course), chopped
Finely grated zest and juice of
    1 orange
1 teaspoon finely chopped rosemary
2 large free-range eggs
2 tablespoons raw honey

Preheat the oven to 180°C (fan-forced).

Place the pistachios on a baking tray and cook for 6–8 minutes or until light golden. Remove from the oven and stand until cool.

In a large bowl, combine the flour, baking powder, salt, sugar, chocolate, apricots, orange zest and rosemary.

In the bowl of an electric mixer, whisk the eggs until light and foamy. Fold in the honey, the dry ingredients and enough orange juice to make a smooth but not too wet dough. Shape into a log about 30 cm long and 6 cm wide and place on a baking tray lined with baking paper. Bake for 20–25 minutes or until lightly golden. Remove from the oven and stand on the tray until cool. Reduce the oven temperature to 150°C (fan-forced).

Once cool, use a large serrated knife to cut the log into 5 mm thick slices. Place on the baking tray, cut-side up, in a single layer and bake for another 10–15 minutes or until golden, crisp and dry. Remove from the oven and cool, then store in an airtight container.

Lentil keftedes with yoghurt and lemon ★

These are another great idea to serve with drinks when you're not offering a whole meal. Make the mixture in advance and cook the little patties after your guests arrive if, like us, everyone congregates in the kitchen. Serve hot from the pan with a squeeze of lemon.

MAKES ABOUT 20

¾ cup (160 g) green lentils
½ cup (125 ml) extra virgin olive oil,
   plus extra to serve
Sea salt flakes and freshly ground
   black pepper
200 g picked spinach leaves
1 free-range egg
½ cup dill sprigs, chopped
100 g Persian feta, crumbled
¾ cup (65 g) organic rolled oats
25 g LSA
Lemon wedges and natural probiotic
   yoghurt or hummus,
   to serve

Rinse the lentils, then place in a saucepan with 4 times the amount of cold water. Bring to the boil, then reduce the heat to low and simmer for 20 minutes or until tender. Drain, then return to the pan and stir through 1 tablespoon olive oil and a good pinch of salt. Stand until cool.

Meanwhile, heat 1 tablespoon olive oil in a large frying pan over high heat. Add the spinach and saute for 1–2 minutes or just until wilted. Pour into a colander and stand until cool, then squeeze out the excess liquid and finely chop.

Pulse the cooled lentils in a food processor until chopped but keep some texture – you don't want to blend to mush. Add the egg and pulse until combined. Transfer to a large bowl, stir in the dill, feta, oats and LSA and adjust the seasoning.

Heat the remaining olive oil in a large frying pan over low heat. Add heaped tablespoons of the keftede mixture and flatten slightly. Cook for 2–3 minutes on each side or until golden. Drain on paper towel, then repeat with the remaining mixture. Transfer to a serving plate, drizzle with a little olive oil and serve with lemon wedges and yoghurt or hummus.

NUTRITION 🌿 Lentils are a good source of fibre, protein, folate, copper, manganese and vitamins B1 and B6.

Chickpea pancake with caramelised onion, currants, pine nuts and yoghurt

Made with chickpea flour, these pancakes are really delicious. The onion in this recipe is cooked quite quickly, but I've recently decided that, as I add caramelised onion to so many dishes, it's worth making a big batch to always have on hand. If I'm doing so, I just cook sliced onion very slowly and gently in a heavy-based pan until the natural sugars in the onion caramelise, then spoon it into sterilised jars. It keeps in the refrigerator for months, and I'm grateful I took the trouble every time I use it.

SERVES 4-6
(MAKES 4 FLATBREADS)

3 tablespoons currants
2 tablespoons verjuice
2 tablespoons extra virgin olive oil, plus extra for drizzling
2 red onions, thinly sliced
Sea salt flakes and freshly ground black pepper
20 g unsalted butter
3 tablespoons toasted pine nuts
⅓ cup (95 g) natural probiotic yoghurt
1 cup coriander leaves

Flatbread

1 teaspoon ground turmeric
1½ cups (225 g) chickpea flour (besan)
2 teaspoons sea salt flakes
1 tablespoon extra virgin coconut oil, melted
2 tablespoons extra virgin olive oil
60 g unsalted butter

To make the pancake batter, heat a small frying pan over medium–high heat. Add the turmeric and shake for 30 seconds or until aromatic. Remove from the heat and put into a small bowl.

Place the flour and salt in a large bowl. Whisk in 1½ cups (375 ml) warm water until a completely smooth batter forms. Whisk in the melted coconut oil and turmeric, then cover the bowl with a tea towel and set aside for 1 hour or overnight if possible.

Meanwhile, soak the currants in the verjuice for at least 1 hour or overnight if possible.

Heat the olive oil in a small saucepan over medium heat. Add the onion and a pinch of salt and cook, stirring occasionally, for 10 minutes or until soft and translucent. Add the butter and cook for another 5 minutes. Stir in the pine nuts, currants and verjuice, season to taste and remove from the heat.

To cook the pancake, preheat the grill to high.

Heat a 20 cm frying pan over medium heat. Add 2 teaspoons olive oil and 15 g butter. When melted, add one quarter of the batter (about ¾ cup), tilting the pan to coat the base evenly. Cook for 2–3 minutes or until golden. Spread over one quarter of the onion mixture, then place under the grill for 3–4 minutes or until set and golden, being careful not to burn the currants. Repeat with the remaining mixture. Serve the pancakes immediately, topped with yoghurt, coriander leaves and a drizzle of olive oil.

NUTRITION 🌿 Chickpea flour will provide you with protein and fibre, manganese, folate and copper.

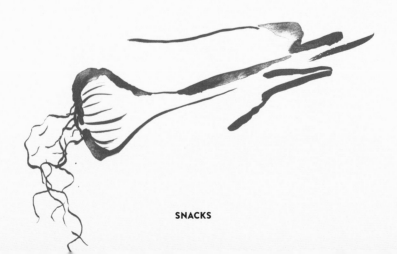

You could make tiny versions of
this sweet and earthy pancake to
serve as a nibble with drinks.

Roasted almonds with anchovies

Let me warn you these nuts are not everyone's cup of tea, but if you love anchovies they will probably be yours. You make a garlicky anchovy paste with the egg white, toss through the almonds and bake until crisp. Serve them with a glass of wine before dinner.

SERVES 12

1 x 45 g tin best-quality anchovies in extra virgin olive oil, drained
1 clove garlic
1 tablespoon extra virgin olive oil
3 teaspoons sea salt flakes
1 free-range egg white
1 tablespoon finely grated lime zest
1½ cups (240 g) almonds

Preheat the oven to 200˚C (fan-forced). Line a baking tray with baking paper.

In a small blender, process the anchovies, garlic, olive oil, salt and egg white until a fine paste forms. Transfer to a large bowl. Stir through the lime zest, then add the nuts and combine well.

Spread the nuts over on the lined tray and roast for 15 minutes. Stir, then roast for another 10 minutes or until golden. Remove from the oven and stand until cool. Store in an airtight container.

Pickled baby carrots

MAKES ABOUT 1 KG

1 kg baby carrots, scrubbed and green tops trimmed to about 1 cm

Pickling solution

150 ml white vinegar
150 ml verjuice
½ cup (110 g) sugar
1 tablespoon sea salt flakes
1 teaspoon caraway seeds
1 teaspoon fennel seeds
1½ teaspoons coriander seeds
4 cloves
1 cinnamon stick
10 sprigs thyme

To make the pickling solution, place all the ingredients in a large heavy-based saucepan, add 2 cups (500 ml) cold water and bring to the boil. Reduce the heat and simmer for 10 minutes to infuse all the flavours.

Place the carrots in a heatproof container with a lid.

Strain the pickling solution, discarding the solids, then pour the hot liquid over the carrots. Allow to cool to room temperature, then cover with the lid and store in the refrigerator. The pickled carrots will keep for up to 3 months.

SNACKS

Baba ganoush with barbecued broccoli dippers ⭐

I know you can buy a tub of baba ganoush from almost any delicatessen but can I tell you the flavour of one you make from an eggplant picked from your own garden will astound you. I'm so obsessive that even when making it commercially, as we sometimes do, I will only do so when the grower picks them for us and we make it next day, using a robust extra virgin olive oil. As with all simple recipes, it's the details that make the difference.

SERVES 6–8

1 small head broccoli
2 tablespoons extra virgin olive oil

Baba ganoush
2 large eggplants (about 600–800 g)
⅓ cup (90 g) unhulled tahini
1 clove garlic, crushed
1 tablespoon pomegranate molasses
½ teaspoon ground cumin
1–2 tablespoons lemon juice
Sea salt flakes and freshly ground
    black pepper
⅓ cup (80 ml) extra virgin olive oil
2 tablespoons chopped
    flat-leaf parsley
2 tablespoons chopped mint
Seeds of ½ pomegranate

To make the baba ganoush, preheat the oven to 250°C (fan-forced).

Place the eggplants on a baking tray and roast for 15–20 minutes or until the skin has blackened and blistered and the flesh is soft. Remove from the oven and set aside to cool. Peel off and discard the skin and scoop the flesh into a colander. Leave to drain for 10–15 minutes.

Process the tahini, garlic, molasses, cumin, lemon juice, salt, pepper and olive oil in a food processor until smooth. Add eggplant and chopped herbs and pulse until just combined. Check the seasoning, then transfer to a serving bowl.

Preheat a barbecue grill plate to high.

Peel the broccoli stalks and trim a little off the base. Cut into large florets with the stalk attached. Place in a bowl, drizzle with olive oil and season with salt, then toss to coat well. Barbecue the broccoli for about 5 minutes or until golden and cooked through. Remove and cut into bite-sized pieces, keeping some stalk on each piece.

To serve, scatter the pomegranate seeds over the baba ganoush and serve with the barbecued broccoli alongside for dipping.

Grilled haloumi with olive tapenade ⭐

I've tried and rejected some varieties of haloumi that are so 'squeaky' and bouncy they have no flavour. And while I understand that of course there are traditional ways of making it in Cyprus and other countries of the Mediterranean, I love that many local cheese makers are taking the tradition and putting an Australian slant on it. A great example is the Barossa Valley Cheese Company. Their haloumi is actually a staple in our refrigerator and Colin is the master at cooking it as friends stand around with a glass of wine in hand. The flavour and texture of just-cooked good haloumi is something else entirely.

SERVES 8

225 g good-quality haloumi,
  cut crossways into 8 slices
Extra virgin olive oil, for pan-frying
Lemon thyme leaves, to serve

Tapenade

250 g pitted Kalamata olives
1 clove garlic, chopped
1 tablespoon baby capers
  in brine, rinsed
1 tablespoon lemon thyme leaves
1 teaspoon chopped marjoram
1 teaspoon chopped rosemary
1 tablespoon finely grated
  orange zest
2 tablespoons red wine vinegar
⅓ cup (80 ml) extra virgin olive oil

To make the tapenade, place all the ingredients in a food processor and pulse until combined but not too smooth. Makes about 350 g.

Pat dry the haloumi slices with paper towel. Heat a good drizzle of olive oil in a large non-stick frying pan over medium heat, add the haloumi and cook until golden on both sides. Place the hot haloumi on a serving plate and dollop with some of the tapenade. Scatter with lemon thyme leaves and serve immediately.

Note: The tapenade will make more than you need for this recipe, but will keep refrigerated in an airtight container for up to 4 weeks. Just make sure you cover it with a thin film of olive oil to prevent it from oxidising.

NUTRITION 🌿 Olives provide copper, iron and fibre, and mono-unsaturated fatty acids as well as some polyphenolic antioxidants.

Frozen halva treat

I'm often almost apologising for not having a sweet tooth but there are some 'sweet' flavours I can't resist. And halva is right at the top of the list; indeed I should admit I find it positively addictive. The great thing about this being a frozen treat is that the only freezer we own is in the garage at the bottom of the garden, which saves me from eating them all at once!

MAKES 12 SMALL BARS

3 tablespoons hazelnuts
1½ tablespoons extra virgin coconut oil
3 tablespoons pure maple syrup
1 teaspoon vanilla bean paste
¼ teaspoon sea salt flakes
⅔ cup (180 g) unhulled tahini
⅓ cup (50 g) Australian dried pears, finely chopped
2 tablespoons black or white toasted sesame seeds (or a mixture of both)

Preheat the oven to 180°C (fan-forced).

Place the hazelnuts on a baking tray and cook for 8 minutes or until lightly toasted. Pour into a clean tea towel and rub off the skins while still warm. Finely chop and set aside.

Grease and line a 10 cm x 18 cm baking tin with baking paper, leaving the sides overhanging.

Place the coconut oil in a small saucepan over low heat until just melted. Remove from the heat and stir in the maple syrup, vanilla and salt. Using a fork, mix through the tahini, chopped nuts and dried pear. Pour the halva mixture into the prepared tin and smooth the top. Scatter with the toasted sesame seeds, then freeze for 5 hours or until firm.

Remove from the freezer and cut into 2.5 cm x 4.5 cm bars. Wrap each one in baking paper and twist the ends like bon bons, then store in an airtight container in the freezer until ready to consume.

NUTRITION 🌿 Tahini (especially if unhulled) and the sesame seeds are rich in calcium, copper and iron. They also provide protein, vitamin E, magnesium and manganese.

Gluten-free carrot cake

If you are avoiding gluten, you don't want to miss out on lusciousness and you don't have to. This is a beautifully moist carrot cake and, although there is none of the traditional icing on top, you could easily add it if you like. Don't skip the step of roasting the walnuts – of all nuts they are the ones most likely to become rancid in storage, and the process of roasting them and off rubbing the skins takes that flavour away.

SERVES 8–10

½ cup (50 g) walnuts
1½ cups (225 g) gluten-free
 self-raising flour
1 teaspoon ground cinnamon
1 teaspoon finely grated ginger
1 red apple, grated with skin on
200 g carrot (about 1 large), grated
 with skin on if fresh
Finely grated zest of 1 lemon
⅓ cup (55 g) sultanas
2 free-range eggs
⅓ cup firmly packed (75 g) soft
 brown sugar
⅓ cup (80 ml) extra virgin olive oil
2½ tablespoons macadamia oil
Raw honey, for drizzling
Thick natural probiotic yoghurt,
 to serve (optional)

Preheat the oven to 180°C (fan-forced). Grease and line a 13 cm x 23 cm loaf tin with baking paper.

Place the walnuts on a baking tray and cook for 8 minutes or until lightly toasted. Pour into a clean tea towel and rub off the skins while still warm. Coarsely chop and set aside.

Sift the flour and cinnamon into a bowl.

In a separate bowl, combine the ginger, apple, carrot, lemon zest and sultanas.

Place the eggs and sugar into the bowl of an electric mixer fitted with the whisk attachment and whisk on high speed until thick and pale. Reduce the speed to medium. Combine the oils in a jug and, with the motor running, add to the egg mixture in a steady stream. Fold the flour and carrot mixtures into the egg mixture until just combined.

Pour the batter into the prepared tin and scatter the walnuts over the top. Bake for 45 minutes until golden and a skewer withdraws clean. Remove from the oven, drizzle with honey and stand until cool. Slice and serve with yoghurt, if desired.

Pumpkin, zucchini and olive loaf ⭐

It's easy to think that pumpkin doesn't have a season as it's available all year round but autumn is its time, and zucchini insists on producing no matter how hard you try to ignore its upkeep in the garden. Buying a good pumpkin is easier said than done and for this reason it's best to buy one already cut to show its colour (assuming it's not from your own garden of course). As a rough guide, the deeper the colour, the riper it is likely to be. Be fussy!

SERVES 8-10

80 g black olives, pitted

3 cups (375 g) coarsely
  grated pumpkin

1 cup (135 g) coarsely
  grated zucchini

3 tablespoons unhulled tahini

5 free-range eggs

70 ml extra virgin olive oil

2 cups (240 g) ground almonds

1 cup (90 g) organic rolled oats

2 teaspoons baking powder

¼ teaspoon freshly grated nutmeg

3 tablespoons pepitas
  (pumpkin seeds)

Preheat the oven to 165˚C (fan-forced). Grease and line a 13 cm x 23 cm loaf tin with baking paper.

Place the olives in a food processor and pulse until coarsely chopped. Transfer to a large bowl. Add the pumpkin, zucchini, tahini, eggs and olive oil. Whisk to combine well.

In a separate bowl, combine the ground almonds, rolled oats, baking powder and nutmeg.

Combine the wet and dry ingredients, then pour into the prepared tin. Scatter the pepitas over the top and bake for 45 minutes or until a skewer withdraws clean. Remove from the oven and allow to cool for 20 minutes before removing from the tin.

Serve warm or leave to cool completely. To freeze, cut into 1.5 cm thick slices and freeze in portions in zip-lock bags. It tastes great toasted.

To serve, be creative with your toppings. You could try toasting slices, then top with avocado and cooked eggs (poached, fried, scrambled), or ricotta and sliced tomato. It is also delicious with hummus and rocket leaves, or simply serve it warm with butter.

Dill omelettes with carpaccio of salmon and capers

Life wouldn't be the same without nibbles to offer friends with a lovely glass of wine, and these tiny morsels are so quick to make that you can virtually leave everything to the last moment. Just have all the ingredients ready and let your guests be involved in putting them together. Well, it works for me …. I love asking my friends to help!

MAKES 16

1 tablespoon extra virgin olive oil, plus extra for drizzling
3 tablespoons baby capers in brine, rinsed
240 g super-fresh skinless salmon, bones removed, sliced as thinly as possible
Sea salt flakes and freshly ground black pepper
160 g ricotta (see page 271), crumbled
Dill sprigs and lemon wedges, to serve

Dill omelettes

1 cup (200 g) ricotta (see page 271)
4 free-range eggs
2 tablespoons dill sprigs, chopped
Sea salt flakes and freshly ground black pepper
40 g unsalted butter
2 tablespoons extra virgin olive oil

Heat the olive oil in a small saucepan over medium heat. Add the capers and cook, shaking the pan regularly for 4–5 minutes or until crisp. Drain on paper towel and set aside.

To make the omelettes, place the ricotta and eggs in a mixing bowl and whisk together. Stir in the chopped dill and season with salt and pepper.

Heat half the butter and half the olive oil in a large, non-stick frying pan over medium heat. Add tablespoons of the mixture and cook until golden on both sides. Repeat with the remaining olive oil, butter and ricotta mixture.

Shortly before serving, toss the salmon in a small bowl with a drizzle of olive oil and season to taste. Top the warm omelettes with the dressed salmon, crumbled ricotta, fried capers and dill sprigs, and serve with lemon wedges to the side.

Caper and liver crostini

What an unbeatable combination: creamy chicken livers, caramelised onion and salty capers. Again, it's the liver that's my first love here. I've cooked a lot of these in my time and I find that cooking them whole first, then trimming the connective tissue and cutting them makes all the difference to the texture and flavour. This would have to be my all-time favourite pre-dinner snack with drinks.

MAKES 8 PIECES

3 tablespoons extra virgin olive oil, plus extra for drizzling
1 large red onion, halved and very thinly sliced
Sea salt flakes
1 teaspoon vino cotto or balsamic vinegar
3–4 large slices wholemeal sourdough bread, about 1 cm thick
30 g unsalted butter
125 g chicken livers, untrimmed
2 tablespoons salted capers, rinsed
2 tablespoons chopped flat-leaf parsley

Heat 2 tablespoons olive oil in a small saucepan over medium heat. Add the onion and a pinch of salt and cook, stirring regularly, for 10–12 minutes or until translucent. Add the vino cotto or balsamic, then reduce the heat to low and cook for another 10 minutes or until soft and caramelised.

Toast the bread, then drizzle with olive oil. Cut into 8 large triangles and keep warm.

Heat the butter in a heavy-based frying pan over medium heat. Cook until nut brown, then add the remaining 1 tablespoon olive oil to stop the butter from burning. Add the chicken livers (be careful as they spit) and cook for 1 minute on each side. Remove from the heat and stand the livers in the pan for 1 minute. Remove the livers from the pan and quickly trim off any connective tissue, then cut into 2 cm pieces. Return to the pan. Add the capers, 2 tablespoons caramelised onion and the parsley and toss to combine. Spoon onto the toasted bread and finish with a sprinkle of sea salt flakes.

Nut and seed snack bars

My friend Simon Bryant made these when we were filming The Cook and the Chef. Simon and I agreed on so many things about food – freshness, seasonality and sustainability – but usually cooked from a very different place and flavour profile. With these, however, we met exactly in the middle. I played with his original recipe and tried incorporating the chocolate into the bars but decided the decadent ganache topping is what makes them so hard to resist.

MAKES 24 BARS

1 cup (80 g) desiccated coconut
3 tablespoons sesame seeds
½ cup (80 g) pepitas
    (pumpkin seeds)
½ cup (75 g) sunflower seeds
½ cup (80 g) blanched almonds,
    finely chopped
½ cup (70 g) macadamia nuts,
    finely chopped
1 cup (200 g) buckinis (see page 278)
80 g seeded Medjool dates,
    cut into 4 mm thick pieces
80 g dried peaches, cut into
    1 cm pieces
Pinch of sea salt flakes
2 teaspoons finely grated lemon zest
190 g unhulled tahini
150 g raw honey
3 tablespoons extra virgin
    coconut oil

Chocolate ganache

300 g dark chocolate (70% cocoa
    solids), chopped
1 tablespoon extra virgin coconut oil

Preheat the oven to 180°C (fan-forced). Grease and line a 24 cm x 32 cm baking tin with baking paper.

Spread out the coconut, seeds and nuts on a baking tray and cook for 8–10 minutes or until golden. Transfer to a large bowl. Add the buckinis, dates, peaches, salt and lemon zest and combine well.

Heat the tahini, honey and coconut oil in a small saucepan over low heat until melted. Pour over the dry ingredients and, working quickly, mix well. Press into the prepared tin, then refrigerate for 30 minutes or until cold.

To make the ganache, place the chocolate and coconut oil in a heatproof bowl over a saucepan of just-simmering water (don't let the bottom of the bowl touch the water). Stir until melted and smooth, then pour over the base and refrigerate for another 2–3 hours or until set.

Cut into bars and store in an airtight container in the refrigerator. The bars also freeze well.

NUTRITION This bar might seem indulgent but all of its ingredients are rich in minerals and good fats. Buckwheat seeds (buckinis) provide good-quality protein, fibre, manganese and antioxidant flavonoids, particularly rutin.

Hot chocolate with homemade almond milk

I specify almond milk here but it's also lovely with cow's milk – just ensure it's full fat as it needs to be luscious enough to carry the cocoa powder and melted chocolate. If you're buying almond milk I recommend the unsweetened one without preservatives. The cinnamon and vanilla paste add their own special identity and are ingredients I usually have to hand, but if you don't it's still beautiful without them.

SERVES 3

1½ cups (375 ml) almond milk, preferably homemade (see page 270)
1 tablespoon pure cocoa powder
50 g dark chocolate (70% cocoa solids), finely chopped
½ teaspoon vanilla bean paste
Pinch of ground cinnamon
Pinch of sea salt flakes
1 tablespoon raw honey (optional)
6 sprigs mint, leaves picked

Place the almond milk and 1 cup (250 ml) water in a medium saucepan. Add the cocoa, chocolate, vanilla, cinnamon, salt and honey, if using. Bring to just below the boil, stirring regularly. Tear the mint leaves and divide half of them among 3 mugs. Pour over the hot chocolate, scatter with the remaining mint and serve.

NUTRITION Almond milk provides vitamin E as well as some manganese and copper.

Spelt and sultana pancakes with creme fraiche

A sweet but not too sweet snack, which is just perfect for me. I've used spelt for these tiny pancakes because I like the flavour but you could use any flour you want to. I always reconstitute my dried fruit in verjuice as it gives a special tang that suits my palate (and I make it myself so it's always available!) but if you don't have any just soak the fruit in just enough water to rehydrate, without any extra liquid to diminish the flavour.

MAKES 25–30 PANCAKES

⅓ cup (55 g) sultanas
1½ tablespoons verjuice
1 cup (130 g) wholemeal spelt plain flour
2 teaspoons baking powder
Pinch of sea salt flakes
150 ml almond milk, preferably homemade (see page 270)
3 free-range eggs, separated
1 teaspoon finely grated lemon zest
1 tablespoon runny honey, plus extra to serve
20 g unsalted butter, melted
Extra virgin olive oil, for cooking
1 cup (240 g) creme fraiche

Place the sultanas and verjuice in a container and soak overnight.

Place the flour, baking powder and salt in a large bowl and stir to combine.

In a separate bowl, whisk together the milk, egg yolks, lemon zest and honey. Combine the wet and dry ingredients.

Place the egg whites in the bowl of an electric mixer fitted with the whisk attachment. Whisk on medium speed until soft peaks form, then fold the egg whites, sultanas and melted butter into the batter until combined.

Heat a drizzle of olive oil in a large frying pan over low–medium heat. Add tablespoons of batter and cook for 2–3 minutes on each side or until golden and cooked through. Serve warm with the creme fraiche and extra honey.

Carrot, silverbeet and couscous fritters ★

While I have included these in the snack chapter they work just as well in a larger size for breakfast or lunch. Couscous is a magic ingredient as it only needs to soak in boiling water for 5 minutes, then it's ready. The carrot could be replaced with any vegetable you have in your crisper, you could use rocket instead of silverbeet, and as long as you have eggs to pull it together, the fritters will still taste great if you leave out the ricotta or curd. Serve them hot from the pan if you can – it makes a difference.

MAKES 10 FRITTERS

1 tablespoon extra virgin olive oil
½ cup (100 g) ricotta (see page 271)
  or fresh curd
100 g cold- or hot-smoked salmon
  or raw salmon

Fritters

3 tablespoons wholemeal couscous
3 tablespoons boiling water
Sea salt flakes and freshly ground
  black pepper
2 free-range eggs, lightly beaten
1 cup (155 g) coarsely grated carrot
2 silverbeet leaves, washed and cut
  into 5 mm pieces (about 1 cup)
1 teaspoon finely grated ginger
½ teaspoon ground turmeric or
  1 teaspoon finely grated
  fresh turmeric
1 tablespoon chopped flat-leaf parsley
1 tablespoon chopped coriander
½ cup (45 g) organic rolled oats
80 g feta, crumbled

To make the fritters, place the couscous in a small heatproof bowl and pour over the boiling water. Cover and stand for 5 minutes. Using a fork, fluff up the couscous to separate the grains. Season and set aside.

Place all the remaining ingredients in a large bowl and stir to combine well. Stir in the couscous and check the seasoning. Form the mixture into 10 small rounds about 1.5 cm thick.

Heat the olive oil in a large non-stick frying pan over medium heat. Cook the fritters, in batches, for 3 minutes on each side or until golden and cooked through. Drain on paper towel.

To serve, top the warm fritters with a dollop of ricotta or curd and a piece of salmon.

NUTRITION Silverbeet is rich in vitamins A, C and K, many polyphenol antioxidants, magnesium and copper.

Olive, lentil and lemon dip on crispbread★

As soon as I had the chance to cook with fresh lentils (and chickpeas) of the season I realised what a difference it makes, both in flavour and cooking time. I know that they are not easily accessible for everyone but I am beavering away with growers in South Australia to declare the year of harvest, just like we did with extra virgin olive oil. So just file that piece of information away and know that change is on the way. While this recipe needs pitted olives, it's important to the flavour that you don't buy them already pitted. Trust me on this.

SERVES 6-8

⅓ cup (70 g) black lentils,
    Puy lentils or similar
⅓ cup (80 ml) extra virgin olive oil
1 small brown onion, finely chopped
2 cloves garlic, finely chopped
2 tablespoons lemon thyme leaves
3 tablespoons salted capers, rinsed
200 g pitted black olives
2 tablespoons finely grated
    lemon zest
2 tablespoons lemon juice
Freshly ground black pepper
1 quantity crispbread (see page 273)
Thinly sliced flat-leaf parsley,
    to serve

Rinse the lentils and place in a medium saucepan with 4 times the amount of water. Bring to the boil over high heat, then reduce the heat to low and simmer for 30–40 minutes or until tender. Drain and set aside to cool.

Heat 2 tablespoons olive oil in a small saucepan over medium heat. Add the onion and cook for 10 minutes or until translucent. Add the garlic and cook for another 2 minutes, then remove from the heat.

Place the drained lentils, onion mixture, thyme, capers, olives, lemon zest, half the lemon juice and remaining 2 tablespoons olive oil in a food processor and blend until well combined. Season with a little pepper, then taste and add the remaining lemon juice if necessary.

To serve, place a small spoonful of olive dip on top of each crispbread, sprinkle with parsley and serve immediately.

Basics

Almond milk

MAKES ABOUT 1 LITRE

1 cup (160 g) blanched almonds
2 Medjool dates, seeded
1 litre cold filtered water
1 teaspoon unhulled tahini (optional)

Soak the almonds and dates together in cold water overnight.

Drain and rinse the almonds and dates, then place in a blender with the filtered water and tahini, if using. Blend until smooth and creamy. Strain through a nut bag or a sieve lined with a double layer of muslin into a jug and allow to drain. Discard the solids. Pour the milk into a glass bottle or large jar and refrigerate. It will separate as it sits, so shake before using. The almond milk will keep refrigerated for 4–5 days.

Almond kefir with kefir starter

I love to drink kefir at any time of the day because it's good for the gut and I love its sour flavour.

MAKES ABOUT 2 CUPS (500 ML)

15 g kefir starter grains for milk (see page 279)
2 cups (500 ml) almond milk, preferably homemade (see above)
1 large Medjool date, seeded

Place the kefir grains, almond milk and date in a 1 litre capacity glass jar with a tight-fitting lid. Cover the mouth of the jar with a piece of muslin or similar and seal with string or a rubber band.

Leave on the workbench at approximately 24°C for 7–10 hours. In the cooler months, it might help to find somewhere warm like the cupboard under the stove.

Remove the muslin cloth, then place a lid on the jar and ferment in the refrigerator for another 48 hours. Strain the milk through a fine sieve into a sterilised jar or bottle and discard the date. Refrigerate until chilled, then consume within 3–4 days.

Coconut kefir water

MAKES ABOUT 2 CUPS (500 ML)

15 g kefir starter grains for water (see page 279)
2 cups (500 ml) organic pure coconut water
8 sultanas

Place the kefir grains, coconut water and sultanas in a 1 litre capacity glass jar with a tight-fitting lid. Cover the mouth of the jar with a piece of muslin cloth or similar and seal with string or a rubber band.

Leave on the work bench at approximately 24°C for 24–48 hours. In the cooler months, it might help to find somewhere warm like the cupboard under the stove.

Strain through a fine sieve into a sterilised jar or bottle. Refrigerate until chilled. Kefir water will keep refrigerated for up to 2 weeks, but the longer you leave it, the stronger the fermentation flavour will be.

Oat milk

MAKES ABOUT 1 LITRE

1 litre cold filtered water
3 small Medjool dates, seeded and chopped
Pinch of sea salt flakes
25 g organic rolled oats
⅓ teaspoon ground cinnamon
¼ teaspoon vanilla extract
¾ teaspoon raw honey

Place all the ingredients in a medium bowl, cover and stand at room temperature overnight.

The following day, pour into a blender and process for 1–2 minutes or until smooth. Leave the milk to rest for 1 hour.

Strain the milk through a fine sieve into a sterilised glass jar or bottle. The oat milk will keep refrigerated for 4–5 days. It will separate as it sits, so give it a good shake before using.

Homemade ricotta

I'm only adding this in case you are as nutty as I am about making things from scratch. I've made this one with verjuice because we make it so I don't quite count the cost in the same way that I would if I was buying it, but it does give a beautiful tang to the finished ricotta that I love.

You can of course make it without the verjuice. Just leave it out and increase the quantity of lemon juice to 100 ml. It will be lovely and fresh, just not as acidic.

MAKES ABOUT 450 G

2 litres full-cream milk
1 cup (250 ml) verjuice
1 tablespoon lemon juice
2 teaspoons sea salt flakes

Place the milk in a very clean heavy-based stainless steel saucepan. Place over very low heat and stir every 5 minutes for 30–45 minutes or until the temperature of the milk reaches 83°C. This process is important as you do not want to break the proteins in the milk so it needs to be done very slowly and accurately.

Once the milk has reached 83°C, turn off the heat, then gently stir in the verjuice, lemon juice and salt and stir for 30 seconds – you will start to see the curds form. Remove the pan from the heat and set aside for at least 15 minutes or up to 30 minutes. Line a sieve with muslin and place over a bowl. Gently ladle the curds into the cloth. Allow to drain, then serve while warm.

Note: I prefer my ricotta to be quite loose, so I add ½ cup (125 ml) of the drained whey back to the strained curds and fold it through gently. Any leftover whey can be used in a soup or as the liquid component of a bread dough.

Labneh

MAKES ABOUT 225 G

500 g Greek yoghurt

Line a sieve with a piece of muslin, leaving the sides overhanging. Place the sieve on top of a bowl, making sure the bottom does not touch the base of the bowl to allow for easy drainage. Place the yoghurt in the muslin and twist the top of the cloth, then refrigerate in the sieve over the bowl overnight. Drain the whey and reserve for another use.

If you are not eating it straight away, place the labneh in an airtight container and cover the surface closely with plastic film. Alternatively, roll it into balls and store it immersed in olive oil. The labneh will keep for up to 14 days.

Spelt and rye sourdough-style bread

Although sourdough is my favourite bread of all, there is a lot of extra work in making a 'sourdough mother' and looking after it. There are so many wonderful sourdough recipes out there that if you have the time and love the flavour then it's great to do. This is a much simpler process and the natural yoghurt gives a great 'sour' effect that adds so much to the combination of flours. Like all breads, it's lovely straight out of the oven but after that this makes wonderful toast. We made this bread in a Le Creuset (a heavy cast-iron pan with a lid) which lightly steamed the bread, resulting in a beautifully soft texture, but you can use a regular loaf tin if you prefer.

MAKES 1 LOAF

½ cup (60 g) rye flour
1 cup (130 g) wholemeal spelt flour
1½ cups (240 g) white bread flour, plus extra for dusting
1 teaspoon sea salt flakes
8 g dried yeast
2 tablespoons extra virgin olive oil, plus extra for greasing
500 g natural probiotic yoghurt

Place all the ingredients into the bowl of an electric mixer fitted with the dough hook. Add 2 tablespoons warm water, then knead for 8–10 minutes or until smooth, elastic and slightly sticky. Transfer to a lightly oiled bowl, cover and leave in a warm, draught-free place for 6 hours or until doubled in size.

Turn out onto a lightly floured surface and knead lightly to create a smooth ball. Place on a baking tray lined with baking paper, seam-side down. Cover with a piece of lightly oiled plastic film and stand in a warm draught-free place for 2 hours or until risen by half.

Preheat the oven to 200°C (fan-forced).

Place a Le Creuset or similar heavy-based pan with a lid in the oven to warm for 30 minutes. Carefully remove the lid and lift the risen dough on the baking paper into the hot pan. Place the lid on top and bake for 30 minutes. Remove the lid and bake for another 8–10 minutes or until golden. Remove from the pan and stand on a wire rack to cool.

Buttermilk rye

MAKES 2 X 400 G ROUND LOAVES

140 g rye flour
145 g wholemeal flour
7 g dried yeast
10 g rye flakes, plus extra for sprinkling
7 g caraway seeds
6 g sea salt flakes
1 cup (250 ml) buttermilk, plus extra for brushing
80 g molasses
1 cup (160 g) white bread flour, approximately
extra virgin olive oil, for greasing

Place the rye and wholemeal flours in the bowl of an electric mixer fitted with the dough hook. Add the yeast, rye flakes, caraway seeds and salt and mix on low speed until well combined.

Meanwhile, place the buttermilk and molasses in a small saucepan and stir over low heat until the mixture reaches 37°C. Add to the flour mixture and mix until just combined. Add three-quarters of the bread flour, then mix on low speed for 3 minutes or until the dough is smooth and comes away from the side of the bowl – you may need to add the remaining 3 tablespoons flour. Once you have a nice smooth dough, mix on medium speed for 2 minutes.

Place the dough in a lightly oiled bowl, cover the surface of the dough with plastic film, then cover the bowl with a tea towel. Place in a warm place for 1½ hours or until doubled in size.

Punch down the dough with your fist, then divide in half. Shape each half into a smooth ball. Place on a large baking tray lined with baking paper, leaving space around each ball, then press down to 3 cm thick. Brush the top and sides with the extra buttermilk and sprinkle with the extra rye flakes. Cover with plastic film and stand in a warm place for 1½ hours or until doubled in size again.

Preheat the oven to 200°C (fan-forced).

Place the loaves in the centre of the oven and bake for 16–20 minutes or until golden and the bread sounds hollow when tapped on the base. Remove from the oven and stand on a wire rack to cool.

Seeded Laucke rye bread mix

How many times have I heard people say it is impossible to buy good bread where they live, but that making it at home is too hard to contemplate? This recipe will change your mind.

Laucke's bread mixes are designed for bread machines and make the process so simple. I have added extra grains here for even more flavour, crunch and goodness, which means you'll need more yeast than the quantity specified in the original mix. if you have a bread machine, just follow the instructions; if not, mix the ingredients in a bowl and allow the dough to rise in the traditional way. Never let it be said again that you can't get your hands on a good loaf of bread!

MAKES 1 LOAF

1 x 600 g packet rye bread mix
9 g dried yeast
430 ml water
2 tablespoons sunflower seeds
1 tablespoon chai seeds
2 tablespoons linseeds (flaxseeds)
2 tablespoons pepitas (pumpkin seeds)

Simply follow the packet instructions, adding the extra yeast because of the weight of the extra seeds.

Crispbread

SERVES 6

40 g organic rolled oats
60 g LSA
100 g white spelt flour
½ teaspoon sea salt flakes
1 teaspoon baking powder
1½ tablespoons extra virgin olive oil

Place the oats in a food processor and blend until fine. Add the LSA, flour, salt and baking powder and pulse to combine.

In a jug, whisk together the olive oil and ⅓ cup (80 ml) cold water. Add to the dry ingredients and pulse until a smooth dough is formed. Transfer to a bowl, cover with plastic film and stand at room temperature for 40 minutes.

Preheat the oven to 180°C (fan-forced). Line 3 baking trays with baking paper.

Divide the dough into 3 portions. Keeping the rest of the dough covered while you work, roll out one piece of dough between 2 double layers of plastic film to as thinly as possible (about 2 mm). I find plastic film is best for this dough as it doesn't stick and it allows you to roll it thinly. Remove the top layer of plastic film and invert onto one of the lined trays. Remove the other piece of plastic film and repeat with the remaining dough.

Bake for 15–20 minutes or until crisp and golden. Allow to cool on a wire rack before snapping into smaller crisps.

Chickpea crackers

I think my first-ever taste of chickpeas in anything was in Italy 20 years ago when, out of a wood-fired oven, appeared the thinnest 'farinata' (known as 'socca' in France). I completely fell in love with the flavour. This is a crispbread rather than a 'pizza style' dough but the nutty flavour of the chickpeas comes through. It's great with any kind of dip made from fresh ingredients. Try my baba ganoush on page 255.

SERVES 6

½ cup (100 g) dried chickpeas, soaked overnight in cold water
⅓ cup (50 g) cornflour, plus extra for dusting
3 tablespoons toasted sesame seeds
½ teaspoon sea salt flakes
½ teaspoon freshly ground black pepper
2 tablespoons extra virgin olive oil

Drain the chickpeas, then place in a saucepan with 4 times the amount of cold water. Bring to the boil over high heat, then reduce the heat to low and simmer for 40 minutes or until tender. Drain and stand until cool. Blend the chickpeas in a food processor until finely ground. Add the remaining ingredients and pulse to a soft dough. Wrap in plastic film, press into a large flat disc and refrigerate for 30 minutes.

Preheat the oven to 180°C (fan-forced).

Roll out the dough between 2 sheets of baking paper that have been lightly dusted with cornflour until 3 mm thick. Remove the top sheet of paper, then pick up the pastry on the baking paper and place on a baking tray. Bake for 18–20 minutes or until crisp and golden, then remove from the oven and cool on the tray. Once cold, snap into random pieces. Store in an airtight container.

Fermented beetroot sauerkraut

MAKES ABOUT 1 LITRE

4 medium beetroots (about 800 g in total), scrubbed and coarsely grated
2 tablespoons sea salt flakes
1 teaspoon toasted caraway seeds

Place the grated beetroot in a large bowl and add the salt. Using clean hands (you may want to wear kitchen gloves or cover your hands in plastic bags) knead the beetroot for about 10 minutes or until a good amount of liquid has been created. Stir in the caraway seeds.

Press the mixture into a sterilised 1 litre capacity jar with a tight-fitting lid, leaving a 2 cm gap at the top of the jar for expansion. Ensure that all the beetroot is submerged in its own liquid (you may need to add a little water).

Seal the jar and store at room temperature (about 24°C) for at least 3 days or up to 3 weeks until the desired flavour is achieved. During this time, undo the lid every day to release the pressure, then re-seal.

When ready, if you wish you can remove any discoloured, oxidised beetroot from the top. Once opened, the sauerkraut will keep refrigerated for up to 4 weeks. The longer you leave it, the stronger the fermented flavour will be. Once refrigerated, remember to open the cap once a week to release any gases.

Homemade sauerkraut

MAKES ABOUT 1 LITRE

1 head green cabbage, quartered, core removed,
  shredded or chopped
2 tablespoons sea salt flakes
1 tablespoon toasted caraway seeds (optional)

Place the cabbage in a large bowl with the salt. Using clean hands, knead the mixture for about 10 minutes or until a good amount of liquid has been created. Mix in the caraway seeds, if using (to me they make a huge difference).

Press the mixture into a sterilised 1 litre capacity glass jar with a tight-fitting lid, leaving a 2 cm gap at the top of the jar for expansion. Ensure that all the cabbage is submerged in its own liquid (you may need to add a little water).

Seal the jar and store at room temperature (about 24°C) for 4 weeks until the desired flavour is achieved. During this time, undo the lid every day to release the pressure, then re-seal. Once opened, the sauerkraut will keep refrigerated for up to 4 weeks. The longer you leave it, the stronger the fermented flavour will be. Once refrigerated, remember to open the cap once a week to release any gases.

Mandarin skin powder

During the mandarin season I simply take the skins off mandarins and place in my very old, very reliable bench dehydrator. It only has low or high settings on it so I start the first 8 hours on high and then turn it down to low overnight. The timing will depend on the thickness of the skins but it's important that they are completely dry. Blend the dried skin in a dry high-powered blender until a fine powder forms, then store in an airtight container. A sprinkle of this on cereal, in cakes or over dessert is magic!

Dukkah

MAKES 750 G

500 g flaked or slivered almonds
⅔ cup (100 g) sesame seeds
75 g fennel seeds
50 g coriander seeds
25 g whole anise seeds
Pinch of sea salt flakes

Preheat the oven to 180°C (fan-forced). Spread the almonds over a baking tray and toast for 6–8 minutes or until golden.

Meanwhile, place the sesame seeds in a large dry frying pan and shake over medium heat until golden. Pour into a bowl, then add the fennel seeds to the pan and shake for 2–3 minutes or until fragrant. Repeat with the coriander and anise seeds. Stand until cool.

Combine the toasted almonds, seeds and salt in a large bowl. Working in small batches, pulse the mixture in a food processor until broken down but still coarse in texture. Transfer to jars or airtight containers and store in the refrigerator for up to 3 months.

Golden chicken stock

My stockpot is an important piece of equipment in my kitchen, although if you have a really large one it's not always easy to find a home for it in your cupboards (even with the large country kitchen that I have, I need to keep mine in the shed!). There is something very satisfying about making your own stock; first taking the trouble to roast the bones and the vegetables, and then smelling it simmering away for hours. I use verjuice rather than white wine when deglazing the bones, which gives a gentle acidity to the stock; otherwise I find it can be a little 'flat'. I like to make a large batch of stock and freeze it in 1 litre containers to keep me going for the next 3 months. It will keep for up to 4 days in the refrigerator.

MAKES ABOUT 3.5 LITRES

1 × 2.2 kg boiling chicken, cut into pieces
  (if you are using bones only, you will need 3 kg)
2 large brown onions, halved
1 large carrot, coarsely chopped
extra virgin olive oil, for cooking
100 ml verjuice
1 large leek, trimmed, washed well and coarsely chopped
1 stick celery, coarsely chopped
1 bay leaf
6 sprigs thyme
6 stalks flat-leaf parsley
1 bulb garlic, halved widthways

Preheat the oven to 200°C (fan-forced).

Combine the chicken, onion and carrot in a roasting tin and drizzle with a little olive oil. Roast for 20–25 minutes or until golden brown.

Transfer the chicken and vegetables to a large stockpot and place the roasting tin on the stove over high heat. Add the verjuice and simmer for 30 seconds, stirring and scraping the bottom of the pan, then tip the pan juices into the stockpot. Add the leek, celery, bay leaf, thyme, parsley and garlic to the stockpot, along with about 4 litres water; the chicken and vegetables should be covered. Bring to a simmer over high heat, then reduce the heat to low and simmer gently for 3 hours. During cooking, skim any impurities from the top.

Strain the stock through a fine-meshed sieve into a bowl, then cool quickly by placing the bowl in a sink of cold water. Refrigerate or freeze until needed. Remove any solidified fat from the top before using.

Green banana flour lavosh

SERVES 6

200 g green banana flour
1 tsp sea salt flakes
10 g sugar
1 teaspoon xanthan gum
10 g white sesame seeds
10 g black sesame seeds
50 g unsalted butter
2 free-range eggs
35 ml milk
Cornflour, for dusting

Preheat the oven to 175°C (fan-forced).

Mix all of the dry ingredients in a large bowl, add the butter and rub in until you have the texture of fine breadcrumbs. Whisk together the eggs and milk and add to the dry ingredients, then bring together to form a smooth dough. Wrap in plastic film and rest in the refrigerator for 20 minutes.

Cut the dough into 6 pieces, dust with cornflour and then roll each piece between 2 sheets of baking paper until 3 mm thick. Remove the top sheet of paper, then pick up the dough on the baking paper and place on a baking tray. If you find the dough is too crumbly, place it back in the bowl with a touch of milk and bring it together as a dough, then try rolling it again.

Bake for 6 minutes, then carefully turn the dough over and bake for a further 2 minutes or until golden and crisp. Cool on a wire rack before breaking into shards to serve with dips or cheeses.

Note: Green banana flour is available at health food shops. It is high in potassium and natural vitamins and minerals. It also contains resistant starch RS2, found in few foods. Resistant starch is not digested by the body; it is food for the good bacteria in our gut and results in many health benefits.

Pantry

I would never be without a well-stocked pantry – not only because I live in the country, which can make shopping opportunities more limited, but because I like to have plenty of ingredients to hand that I can quickly turn into a beautiful meal, either just for the two of us or for unexpected guests.

extra virgin olive oil
extra virgin coconut oil, cold-pressed
verjuice (from the juice of unripe grapes)
vino cotto (or balsamic)
apple cider vinegar
pomegranate molasses
raw honey
pure maple syrup
dark chocolate (70%)
pure cocoa powder
gelatine leaves
pitted prunes
dates
currants
sultanas
raisins
dried apricots (Australian)
dried pears
unhulled tahini
unpasteurised white (shiro) miso
nori sheets
dried shiitake mushrooms
dried porcini mushrooms
chia seeds, black and white
pepitas (pumpkin seeds)
sesame seeds
linseeds (flaxseeds)
LSA (linseed, sunflower, almond mix)
sunflower seeds
dukkah
quinoa
organic rolled oats
buckwheat flour
buckinis (toasted buckwheat)
brown rice flour
spelt flour
wholemeal or wholewheat flour
black rice

brown rice
pearl barley
black barley
freekeh
lentils
chickpeas
wholemeal couscous
wholewheat pasta (I use Pangkarra)
spelt pasta
soba (buckwheat) noodles
tins of peeled roma tomatoes
    (both whole and chopped)
tins of sardines
tins of anchovies (45 g)
tins of tuna
tins of coconut milk
tins of coconut cream
turmeric
ras el hanout
ground ginger
cinnamon, ground and sticks
star anise
fennel seeds

The Fridge

almonds
Brazil nuts
macadamia nuts
free-range eggs
full-cream milk
natural probiotic yoghurt
parmesan
ricotta
silken tofu
tempeh
walnuts

Glossary

Brown rice flakes
Short-grain brown rice is roasted and then rolled flat into flakes, preserving all the nutrients of the whole grain. The flakes make a delicious and quick gluten-free porridge and can also be used in cereals and baking. It can be found in the cereal aisle in major supermarkets.

Brown rice flour
This nutritious and gluten-free flour has a richer, nuttier flavour than wheat flour and is rich in protein, manganese, iron, magnesium and other minerals. It is available at supermarkets and health food shops.

Buckinis
'Activated' buckwheat are buckwheat groats or kernels that have been soaked. It looks like wheat but it's actually the seed of a plant like rhubarb and sorrel so it's gluten free, and has loads of flavour and nutritional benefits. The little triangular seeds are 'activated' (soaked) to increase vitamin and minerals availability. The Loving Earth brand is very good and available in good health food shops or online.

Buckwheat kernels
Also known as buckwheat groats, these seeds are unsoaked. Buy buckinis (see above) if you don't have time for soaking.

Black barley
This is an heirloom grain variety that is rich in nutritional value and flavour. Sometimes called purple barley, it has a nuttier taste than white barley and provides protein, fibre, manganese, selenium, anthocyanin antioxidants and some B-vitamins. Contains gluten.

Chia seeds
These small black or white gluten-free seeds can be eaten raw or cooked. They are an excellent source of omega-3 fatty acids, fibre, protein and calcium. They are a useful ingredient in many recipes because they swell in liquid and become gelatinous. One of the world's biggest chia producers, The Chia Company, is based in the Kimberley's Ord Valley in northern Western Australia. Chia seeds can be found in major supermarkets.

Coconut amino sauce
Made from coconut sap and sea salt, this sauce has a similar flavour to a light soy sauce or tamari but is less salty. Containing 17 amino acids, this is a nutritious alternative to soy sauce and it's also gluten free.

Extra virgin coconut oil
Recent studies show that coconut oil can contribute to brain health – for more on this see page 40. Cold-pressed extra virgin coconut oil will be minimally processed, ensuring the maximum retention of nutrients and flavour. The oil should be light in colour, solid at room temperature and subtle in coconut scent and taste. Most importantly, it should be ethically produced and should support the community in which it is made.

Extra virgin coconut paste (butter)
To make this paste the whole coconut (flesh and oil) is ground into a creamy spread. Also called coconut butter in some countries.

Extra virgin olive oil
My first tip for choosing a good olive oil is to make sure that the date of harvest (not bottling) is clearly stated on the label, as the younger the oil, the better it will be. Extra virgin olive oil is never better than when it has just been crushed, which for the Barossa is in early May. It does not 'settle' enough to bottle until August or early September, but producers can store the bulk oil and bottle it at any time during the year.

The test of a good extra virgin olive oil is its freshness on both the nose and palate; after all, it is the juice of the olive and should smell as such. There should not be any sign of rancidity (think of the smell of uncovered butter left at the back of the refrigerator, or of dirty socks). Everyone has their own flavour preference so after these vital criteria are met, allow personal taste to take over. The key to a good olive oil lies in the balance of freshness of aroma, acidity and pungency – a bland oil is not my style! Do not refrigerate.

Gubinge powder
Also known as Kakadu plum, this small green fruit grows in the top end of Australia and contains about 50 times more vitamin C than an orange. See more on its nutritional properties on page 28. Milled into a powder, it can be added to juices, smoothies, baked goods or cereals. Available from health food stores or try the Loving Earth brand online.

Kefir grains

Kefir grains are made up of cultures of various strains of healthy bacteria and yeast, held together in a polysaccharide matrix created by the bacteria. There are two types of kefir grains: milk and water. Both grains have a similar function which is to ferment the liquid, making it rich in probiotic goodness.

Milk kefir grains are cultured from a symbiotic collection of bacteria and yeasts, which feed on the lactose in milk. The grains look like cottage cheese and have a slimy feel.

Water kefir grains are clear, clumpy and break apart when pressed. Water grains feed on sucrose. As they feed on the sugars in the liquid, the kefir grains multiply so this allows them to be reused. Once you've used your kefir grains, you can rinse them under filtered water and use again or store them in a zip-lock bag for up to 2 weeks if not fermenting.

Kefir grains are available from good health food shops or they can be easily purchased online.

LSA

This is a ground mix of linseeds, sunflower seeds and almonds. Adding a spoonful or two of LSA to your cereal, smoothie or baking is a convenient way to get a dose of omega-3 fatty acids, copper and zinc. It's widely available in supermarkets and once opened is best stored in your freezer to preserve the life of the seed and nut oils.

Natural coconut water

This is the clear liquid in the fruit's centre that is tapped from young, green coconuts. You can crack open a coconut if you want the freshest water possible but it's also available packaged or bottled. Be sure to look for organic unpasteurised coconut water without added flavours or sweeteners, and one that is fresh juice rather than reconstituted from a concentrate.

Puffed millet

This small ancient whole grain is gluten free and high in protein. It provides a nice crunchy texture in cereals or crumbles. Available from health food stores.

Raw honey

Most commercial honeys have been heated or pasteurised for easier packaging, a cleaner look and better storage but heating destroys much of its unique nutritional qualities. Raw honey has not been heated above the natural temperature of the hive and is the benchmark in flavour and quality. It will crystallise after a few months – just put your jar in warm water to make it liquid again.

Tofu

There are two main types of tofu, which is a curd made by coagulating soy milk. My tofu of choice is the silken tofu. Even though it can fall apart if super fresh (and fresh is best), it is the silkiness that I love rather than the firm or cotton tofu where the curds are pressed and firmer. Most people choose the firm tofu for cooking but I think the texture of silken tofu makes up for any difficulty in handling. Silken tofu can be bought 'soft' or 'firm' but will still be more delicate than firm tofu.

Umeboshi

The Japanese believe these pickled plums are good for the digestion and also combat fatigue but I love them for their salty sour flavour. A little goes a long way! Look for them in Asian grocers or health food stores.

Unhulled tahini

Tahini is a creamy paste made from ground sesame seeds. It's used to make hummus, baba ganoush and halva, or as a salad dressing. The unhulled version has been ground with the outer shell of the sesame seed which preserves more of its minerals and fibre. As you'd expect, it's darker and has a stronger flavour than the hulled version.

Unpasteurised white (shiro) miso

Miso is a fermented soybean paste made by steaming soybeans and a grain, usually rice or barley. In Japan it's traditionally fermented in cedarwood kegs for several months or as long as 3 years. White or shiro miso is fermented for just 2–8 weeks and is creamy, rich and slightly sweet compared to darker varieties. Buy unpasteurised miso as it preserves the enzymes and probiotics.

Wattle seed

These crunchy fragrant seeds come from a few edible species of our iconic Australian *Acacia* trees. They were traditionally roasted and then ground into flour between stones, to be made into a cake or damper. Rich in protein, calcium, iron, selenium and zinc, wattle seed adds a nutty roasted coffee flavour in baking. It's usually sold as ground powder, try Outback Pride or Herbie's Spices.

Index

INDEX

Acknowledgements

Maggie

I have been writing books for 20 years with my indomitable publisher Julie Gibbs, as her incredible style and her understanding of who I am has always meant so much to me. Yet this book would never have happened if I hadn't met Ralph Martins and learnt of his dedication to Alzheimer's research. I'd like to say it was a meeting of minds but given his academic background and my lack of one, I think it was really a meeting of stomachs! I strongly believe that good food truly is medicine and I feel so lucky this collaboration has happened.

This book has been such a journey. It's come about because The Maggie Beer Foundation is so important to me and I had the idea of writing a book to raise funds for the foundation. But the niggle that sits with me as I age is a fear of dementia and this was also a driving force. I wanted to do everything I could to protect my brain and then share my knowledge with everyone, no matter their age. I learnt from Ralph and his research which foods have been proven to be beneficial for brain health and then I thought carefully about how to maximise the nutrition but never ever compromise the flavour. Pleasure is as important to me as 'goodness' and my thanks go to him on so many levels.

A huge vote of thanks to Rosemary Stanton, a friend of so many years. In asking her to write the foreword for this book I underestimated the huge amount of work that she would want to undertake to critically examine it to feel comfortable to do so. Rosemary, I am indebted to you.

Thank you to Katrina O'Brien, the editor everyone would love to work with, so exacting but generous. And thank you to Daniel New. I'm so thrilled to be working again with a designer of such talent that I can recognise his work from afar. Thanks too to Christine Osmond and Rachel Carter for their detailed recipe editing – always such a big task.

I'm grateful to our very talented local photographer Dragan Radovic who took the images over a period of 18 months so we could capture each season in the Barossa - for all but one shoot where Joshua Miels, who has been our graphic designer in the business for years and is an artist himself, stepped in, with Cherie Hausler styling. Photoshoots don't happen without hard work and the need for a small tight team. A huge vote of thanks to Tracey Collins who both styled the food for all but one of the shoots and styled me when I had to be photographed too.

As ever, it's taken a team of very special people to help me pull the recipes together. The vital part of the puzzle has been Eliza Taylor, an extraordinary chef herself, who has been part of the Foundation from day one. Even though she lives in Western Australia, she did so much work for this book to make it possible for me to manage the workload. We tossed ideas around, cooked and photographed together for most of the book and never stopped learning from each other. Others helping along the way and making my life sane; Steph Busch, Cathy Radke, Adrian Walker and just at the last hurdle, Annabelle Mather.

My thanks to Mick Smith of Splitting Image for his generosity in providing the colour separation pro bono for the benefit of my Foundation.

A very special thank you to Dan Ruffino for leading such an enthusiastic and inclusive team at Simon & Schuster, particularly Anabel Pandiella and Kirsty Noffke. You have made this a great process so a huge thank you.

A final vote of thanks is to my Colin, who coped with me working solidly on the book for six months of holidays and weekends – with just the minimum of chiding from him. I'm a very lucky woman.

Ralph

I am honoured to collaborate with Maggie Beer on this book. She has taken our current knowledge on foods that are good for our bodies and translated them into delicious and nutritious meals that will benefit many. I am most grateful to Dr Stephanie Fuller for her tremendous work in the preparation and editing of the scientific background presented in this book. I'd also like to thank Miriam Cannell for her very thorough and skilled copy editing of this section.

I am privileged to have been introduced into the Alzheimer's field in 1984 by Professor Colin Masters AO a world leading pioneer. We have worked together for the last 33 years to get a better understanding of Alzheimer's disease so that we can diagnose it early for effective prevention and treatment.

I am indebted to my research team, several collaborators and researchers worldwide who have contributed to much of the research outcomes mentioned in this book. I particularly wish to thank the founding members of my team who have painstakingly put the building blocks in place which has led to our current research programs namely: Athena Paton, Georgia Martins and Kevin Taddei.

My research has been funded by Edith Cowan University, Macquarie University, McCusker Alzheimer's Research Foundatiion, Hollywood Research Foundation, and the Lion's Alzheimer's Research Foundation. Malcolm McCusker AC, CVO, QC and his family are particularly acknowledged for their seminal funding in establishing my team and their longstanding support for over 20 years.

This book is dedicated to all families and their loved ones with Alzheimer's disease or related dementias.

Maggie's Recipe for Life: 200 delicious recipes to help reduce your chances of
Alzheimer's and other lifestyle diseases
First published in Australia in 2017

A JULIE GIBBS BOOK

for

SIMON & SCHUSTER
AUSTRALIA
A CBS COMPANY

Simon & Schuster (Australia) Pty Limited
Suite 19A, Level 1, Building C, 450 Miller Street, Cammeray, NSW 2062

10 9 8 7 6 5 4 3 2 1

A CBS Company
Sydney New York London Toronto New Delhi
Visit our website at www.simonandschuster.com.au

National Library of Australia Cataloguing-in-Publication entry

Beer, Maggie, author.
Maggie's recipe for life : 200 delicious recipes to help
reduce your chances of alzheimer's and
other lifestyle diseases / Maggie Beer,
Professor Ralph Martins ; Dragan
Radocaj, photographer.

ISBN: 9781925596953 (paperback)
ISBN: 9781925596960 (Ebook)

Includes index.

Subjects: Cooking.
Health.
Longevity.
Mental health–Nutritional aspects.
Brain–Diseases–Prevention.

Other Creators/Contributors:
Martins, Ralph, author.
Radocaj, Dragan, photographer.

Publisher: Julie Gibbs
Design and illustration: Daniel New / OetomoNew
Project manager: Katrina O'Brien
Editors: Miriam Cannell, Christine Osmond and Rachel Carter
Cover image: by Dragan Radocaj
Colour separation by Splitting Image
Printed and bound in China by 1010 Printing International Ltd

The paper used to produce this book is a natural, recyclable product made from
wood grown in sustainable plantation forests. The manufacturing processes conform
to the environmental regulations in the country of origin.